P9-BJW-263

THE CHILD

Other Books by Drs. Freedman and Kaplan

COMPREHENSIVE TEXTBOOK OF PSYCHIATRY
Alfred M. Freedman and Harold I. Kaplan, EDITORS   1967

PSYCHOPATHOLOGY OF ADOLESCENCE
Alfred M. Freedman (with Joseph Zubin), EDITOR   1970

COMPREHENSIVE GROUP PSYCHOTHERAPY
Harold I. Kaplan (with Benjamin J. Sadock), EDITOR   1971

STUDIES IN HUMAN BEHAVIOR
Alfred M. Freedman and Harold I. Kaplan, GENERAL EDITORS
DIAGNOSING MENTAL ILLNESS: EVALUATION IN
PSYCHIATRY AND PSYCHOLOGY   1972
INTERPRETING PERSONALITY: A SURVEY OF
TWENTIETH-CENTURY VIEWS   1972
HUMAN BEHAVIOR: BIOLOGICAL, PSYCHOLOGICAL,
AND SOCIOLOGICAL   1972
TREATING MENTAL ILLNESS: ASPECTS OF
MODERN THERAPY   1972
THE CHILD: HIS PSYCHOLOGICAL AND
CULTURAL DEVELOPMENT   1972
VOL. 1: NORMAL DEVELOPMENT AND
PSYCHOLOGICAL ASSESSMENT
VOL. 2: THE MAJOR PSYCHOLOGICAL DISORDERS
AND THEIR TREATMENT

THE CHILD
His Psychological and Cultural Development

VOLUME TWO

The Major Psychological Disorders and Their Treatment

ALFRED M. FREEDMAN, M.D.

*Professor and Chairman, Department of Psychiatry,
New York Medical College*

AND

HAROLD I. KAPLAN, M.D.

Professor, Department of Psychiatry, New York Medical College

EDITORS

Studies in Human Behavior

New York   ATHENEUM   1 9 7 2

The editors express their appreciation to the following publishers and publications for permission to reprint portions of the works cited.

Abelard-Schuman, Ltd.: J. Needham, *A History of Embryology*, © Joseph Needham 1959.

Alfred A. Knopf, Inc.: P. Aries, *Centuries of Childhood*, New York, 1962.

American Journal of Orthopsychiatry: T. Schneirla and J. Rosenblatt; Behavioral organization and genesis of the social bond in insects and mammals, New York, 1961. Copyright, the American Orthopsychiatric Association, Inc.

Harvard University Press (Loeb Classical Library): Aristotle, *Aristotle's Generation of Animals*, A. L. Peck, translator, Cambridge, 1943.

International Universities Press, Inc.: E. Bleuler, *Dementia Praecoi or The Schizophrenias*, New York, 1950; H. Hartmann, *Problems of Infantile Neurosis: A Discussion*, New York, 1954.

Penguin Books Ltd.: B. Farrington, *Greek Science*. Copyright © Benjamin Farrington, 1944, 1949.

Copyright © 1971 by Alfred M. Freedman and Harold I. Kaplan
Excerpted and adapted in whole or in part from
Comprehensive Textbook of Psychiatry, © 1967 by
the Williams and Wilkins Company
All rights reserved
Library of Congress catalog card number 74-178070
Published simultaneously in Canada by McClelland and Stewart Ltd.
Manufactured in the United States of America
Composition by H. Wolff, New York
Printed and bound by The Murray Printing Company,
Forge Village, Massachusetts
Designed by Kathleen Carey
First edition

Preface

This book is one of a series of volumes based on the First Edition of the *Comprehensive Textbook of Psychiatry*, which we edited for use in medical schools. Dr. Helen S. Kaplan served as Assistant to the Editors of that edition. The *Comprehensive Textbook* resulted from our part in setting up the undergraduate and graduate programs in psychiatry at New York Medical College. New articles have been written for these volumes, and certain subjects have been updated or eliminated, in an effort to reach a wider audience.

The responsibility for teaching psychiatry has made us acutely aware of the whole spectrum of current progress in the continuing search for the causes of mental disorders. Recent scientific research has placed at the disposal of the clinical practitioner new knowledge that must be incorporated into existing theoretical and therapeutic methods. Our aim is to include in these volumes all such major contributions in the basic and social sciences that have an influence on the teaching and practice of psychiatry. We have attempted to derive a balanced and current summary of psychiatric thinking in a variety of fields.

The interaction with distinguished and creative colleagues in the preparation of the material contained in these volumes has been most gratifying. We have had a unique opportunity to engage in a stimulating exchange of ideas and to establish rewarding personal relationships as well.

Many people have given us dedicated and valuable help, and we wish to express our deep appreciation to them. We would mention in particular Lois A. Baken, Elaine Cohen, Pauline DeMarco, and Marian Hailey. And we give special thanks to Joan Welsh for her invaluable help in editing and styling this series.

A. M. F.
H. I. K.

Contents

A R E A   D

Psychiatric Treatment of Children

Introduction

A book on child psychiatry presents in microcosm the main elements in the entire field of psychiatry. Within the structure of the whole personality, the development of the child plays a central role, and the study of child development must be prominent in the study of all psychiatry as well as in the specific field of child psychiatry. The psychiatric disorders of children bear, for the most part, much similarity to those of adults, and people usually carry over into their adult years the disorders they developed in childhood. The history of the child, for good or ill, determines the history of the adult. The child is indeed "father of the man," as Wordsworth said. This becomes increasingly evident from a comparison of this book with the others in the Studies in Human Behavior series. Certain disorders do appear in children and not in adults; and certain adult disorders, by their very nature, are unlikely in childhood. Nevertheless, the correlation between the disorders of the early stage of life and those of later periods is extremely high. And, in a great many cases, prompt diagnosis and treatment in childhood can resolve problems that might otherwise continue to assert themselves in an adult context.

There is one significant way, however, in which the parallel between child psychiatry and the psychiatric treatment of adults ceases to be valid. Any disorder in a child who needs treatment is probably also disturbing the majority of the normal population in roughly his same age group. Both the normal child population and the population that responds maladaptively have problems of establishing identity, evolving a proper psychosexual role, resolving dependency problems, and so on. This is not the case with neurotic adults. Their disorders may better be depicted as being somewhere on a spectrum of all adult behavior rather than labeled merely as "sick" instead of "healthy." Neurotic adults are usually still dealing with conflicts that other adults long since resolved, even if imperfectly. Disturbed children, on the other hand, have much in common with the rest of their age-level population in that they are all wrestling with the same sort of problems.

The Child, volumes I and II, provides a survey of the entire range of problems child psychiatry deals with. The field is a relatively new and growing one, although every aspect of Western culture has, even if negatively, paid some attention to the question of child development. It is a field that holds tremendous promise for all psychiatry and for every discipline in which the evaluation of normal child development plays a part. Its ramifications reach far beyond psychiatry into education, religion, and those vexed areas of racial, economic, ethnic, and sexual discrimination to which, of late, so much attention has been paid by society at large.

Volume II is divided into four areas, each covering one aspect of the field with which the child psychiatrist is concerned. A general introduction to child psychiatry is followed by an area on assessment. The central portion of the volume is concerned with the major psychiatric disorders of childhood, including such special problems as dyssocial behavior and retardation. The final area deals with the psychiatric treatment of children.

Because awareness of the criteria of healthy development is a *sine qua non* of child psychiatry, a chapter on normal child development precedes consideration of clinical descriptions and treatment. Thereafter, in keeping with the eclectic approach of this book, attention is turned to the three basic levels of organization in the child—the psychological, the social or interpersonal, and the physiological. In childhood, more than in any other stage of development, all three levels mesh and intertwine. Of equal importance in the consideration of childhood is the awareness of the constant change taking place within the matrix of the child's relationship to his family and society. Both the child and his external world are in a continual state of flux. It follows, then, that the psychiatric evaluation of the child should include an assessment of his total functioning, including his level of physical and psychological development and the degree to which his functioning reflects the impact of his environment.

Particular attention is paid to nosological problems, which are frequently more acute in this subspecialty than in the field of psychiatry as a whole. Idiosyncratic problems arise from the fact that here, more than in any other area of psychiatry, the diagnostician must continually refer to what is generally considered normal behavior. And so the Group for the Advancement of Psychiatry has developed a classificatory scheme of child psychiatric disorders that includes the highly significant major category, Healthy Responses, incorporating behavior that might be considered normal in dealing with situational or developmental crises or with other challenges, whether relatively normal or idiosyncratic.

It has long been recognized that the classification of psychiatric disorders in childhood and adolescence as provided in the American Psychiatric Association's first edition of *Diagnostic and Statistical Manual: Mental Disorders* (DSM-I) and in its revision, DSM-II, is unsatisfactory. This fact was officially noted by the Committee on Child Psychiatry of the Group for the Advancement of Psychiatry (GAP) in Report No. 62,

Vol. 6. The committee pointed out that the American Medical Association's *Standard Nomenclature of Diseases and Operations*, which is identical to DSM-I, "leaves untouched many of the developmental gradients of psychopathology in childhood and adolescence. The need remains for a separate classification dealing with childhood and adolescence . . . despite some overlap between the problems of the latter age group and those of adults." Accordingly, the GAP proposed a new classification of childhood psychopathological disorders in 1966.

This classification forms a theoretical framework based on three basic propositions: (1) the psychosomatic concept of the unity of mind and body and the interrelatedness of psychological and somatic processes; (2) the developmental dimension central to the study of the child; and (3) the psychosocial aspects of the child's existence in his family and in society. These propositions support the concept of multiple causative factors of a predisposing, contributory, precipitating, and perpetuating nature. Portions of the GAP monograph are summarized in this book.

Although the GAP classification uses many of the nosological definitions included in the AMA's standard nomenclature, it has introduced a number of new concepts. For instance:

1. The category Healthy Responses permits "the identification of healthy patterns of response" and reduces "the traditional tendency to magnify minor problems and fit the child into a pathological category or diagnose the absence of disease." This category emphasizes "the need for the assessment of positive strengths in the child wherever possible and [avoids] so far as possible the diagnosis of healthy states by the exclusion of pathology." Criteria covering intellectual, social, emotional, personal, and adaptive functioning as well as age-appropriate psychosocial functioning are given. Included in this category are developmental crises, such as the identity crisis in adolescence, and transient situational crises, such as the role of mourning in the healthy grief reaction.

2. "Developmental deviations pertain to overall deviations in maturational rate or sequence or to different aspects of personality development." This category "delineates those deviations in personality development which may be considered beyond the range of normal variation in that they occur at a time, in a sequence, or in a degree not expected for a given age level or stage of development." These deviations may involve maturational patterns or specific areas of development, such as motor, sensory, speech, cognition, social, psychosexual, affective, and integrative development. Such deviations may either be resolved with the passage of time or lead to a more structured disorder.

3. Another innovation in the GAP classification is the detailed symptom list, which is specifically applicable to children. The GAP list is similar to the symptom list designed primarily for adults in the AMA's standard nomenclature.

The editors of this book have retained the standard nomenclature

wherever applicable and have used some of the newer headings included
in the GAP report as supplementary data. A table setting forth and explaining the GAP classificatory system for child psychiatry is included.
Another table lists the various disorders as defined in DSM-I and in
DSM-II, which was published in 1968. One article sheds further light
on nosology in child psychiatry by comparing the nomenclature of DSM-I
with that of DSM-II and with the GAP classificatory system.

The problem of nosology is but one of the problems faced by this
subspecialty in the area of assessment. The psychiatric examination of the
child presents problems radically different from those encountered in the
examination of adult patients. For one thing, the examination almost
always involves not only the patient but also the patient's family. Another
variation results from the fact that the young child communicates through
play and other actions. Several chapters give an overview of psychiatric
evaluation, both neurological and psychological.

In the area of psychiatric treatment, the subspecialty again presents
unique aspects. The therapeutic approach to the child is generally through
free play, which is analogous to free association in the adult. For the child,
nonverbal communication generally plays the primary role, although the
importance of verbal communication should not be ignored. The area
concerned with the psychiatric treatment of children discusses these
problems and provides a survey of the history, techniques, and theoretical
assumptions underlying the individual therapy of children. A discussion of
group therapy for children presents the variations that make this form of
treatment different in accordance with the age of the group being treated.
Subsequent chapters survey other modalities of treatment—the organic
and the residential. The use of any one of these modalities does not, of
course, exclude the use of the others; indeed, two or even more of these
treatment modalities can be used effectively together.

Another aspect of child psychiatry surveyed here is the relationship
between psychiatry and the school. Learning disabilities are one of the
most common disorders in child psychiatry, and it is of course in the
school that these disorders become manifest. Many children are referred
to child psychiatrists because of learning disabilities. The chapter that
covers the subject surveys the psychogenic learning disabilities and describes treatment both for learning disabilities and for other school-related
psychiatric manifestations, such as school phobia. An extensive discussion
of mental retardation presents a history of the attitudes toward retardation
and of the knowledge and classification of it, plus a discussion of its
causes, epidemiology, symptoms, and diagnosis. Steps toward the treatment
of both the child and his family are set forth, and a discussion of the
nature and development of normal intelligence can be read with profit
in context with the article on child psychiatry and the school.

As mentioned above, the central portion of this volume provides a comprehensive discussion of psychoneurotic, psychophysiological, and person-

ality disorders in childhood. Some psychoneurotic reactions—such as animal phobias, nocturnal anxiety attacks, and the death phobia that is often seen around the age of 8 years—are most common in children; but for the most part the childhood neuroses parallel those of adulthood, and the chapters on psychoneurotic disorders and personality disorders can be read as an introduction to the entire field of neurosis and personality disorders. The chapter on psychophysiological disorders is somewhat more specific for children, describing the disorders, such as bronchial asthma, that are particularly prevalent in childhood. Some childhood disorders are of social as well as individual importance; among these are juvenile delinquency and addiction to alcohol and drugs.

On a number of levels, this book provides a comprehensive introduction to the various fields in which the child psychiatrist is called on to operate. This introduction, the survey of both normal and disordered development in the child, and the up-to-date discussion of classification problems make it particularly useful as a general overview of the entire field of child psychiatry.

AREA A

Introduction to Child Psychiatry

CHAPTER ONE

History of Child Psychiatry

LEO KANNER, M.D.

INTRODUCTION

THE CONCEPT of child psychiatry as a distinct specialty did not arise —and could not have arisen—before the twentieth century. The story until then is not a narrative of a practiced discipline but rather an account of the building stones that eventually formed the foundations of the present-day structure. The time is not too far in the past when children were a part of the household chattel, when Dickens' *Oliver Twist* was fiction based on stark reality, when unrestricted child labor sucked health and spirit out of impecunious youngsters, when the Prussian police denounced the first kindergartens as hotbeds of socialism.

EIGHTEENTH CENTURY

There is no evidence of any organized concern with child development and child behavior in antiquity or in the Middle Ages. It was not until the era immediately preceding the French and American revolutions that the new gospel of the rights of man had in its wake a spurt of reforms extended to the hitherto neglected or oppressed. Shackles began to be removed from psychotic persons. Voices were raised *against* slave trade and *for* humane treatment of prison inmates. Handicapped children became the recipients of constructive attention. Pereire proved that it was possible to teach deaf-mutes to communicate with those around them. In 1784 Haüy founded in Paris the first school for the education of the blind.

NINETEENTH CENTURY

Itard, while trying to civilize the "savage boy of Aveyron," introduced methods designed to help severely retarded children. In 1841 Guggenbühl opened, on the Abendberg in Switzerland, the first residential center for young mental defectives. This was so startling an innovation that princes, physicians, and clergymen came to admire and to learn. Within a short time, similar institutions were set up in several European countries and, as a result of the efforts of Samuel Gridley Howe, have been set up in this country as well since 1848.

Meanwhile, inspired especially by Rousseau's *Emile*, published in 1762, and the writings of Locke, a few scientists became curious about the stages of infantile development. They observed their own offspring and recorded the day-by-day unfolding of their functions. They followed the example of the Swiss educator Pestalozzi, whose diary of his son, however, still carried a ballast of mysticism and pious idealism. Darwin, Preyer, and others were subsequently able to strip their observations of unwarranted generalizations. In the 1880's, Stanley Hall analyzed the responses obtained from questionnaires sent out to thousands of parents and presented data in terms of percentage calculations. A new body of research emerged that, as developmental psychology, made up in the span of one generation for much that had been neglected throughout the ages.

Sporadic contributions to the knowledge of children's deviant behavior began to come from the fields of neurology, pediatrics, and psychiatry. These interests existed alongside each other, with only tenuously maintained areas of mutual contact. Toward the end of the nineteenth century, several texts were published on psychic disorders, mental diseases, or insanity of children. Behavioral deviations interested Emminghaus, Moreau de Tours, Ireland, and Manheimer, chiefly as they seemed to fit diagnoses according to classifications devised for adults. These treatises represented a first step toward the unified consideration of early life neuroses and psychoses. But, on the whole, psychiatrists still kept themselves aloof—children were neither heard nor seen by most of them professionally.

TWENTIETH CENTURY

FIRST DECADE

In 1900 the Swedish sociologist Key, having waged a successful battle for the emancipation of women, predicted that the twentieth century was destined to be "the century of the child." A number of things happened that tended to confirm her prophecy.

In 1899 Illinois and Colorado had passed statutes establishing juvenile courts, in which delinquent children were to be handled separately and differently from adult violators of the law. As juvenile courts began to spring up all over the country, some of the judges, eager to learn *why* the young offenders had been driven to their transgressions, consulted psychiatrists, who thus were obliged to occupy themselves with children's behavior and its motivations. As a result, Healy founded the Juvenile Psychopathic Institute in 1909 in connection with the Chicago Juvenile Court and published his book, *The Individual Delinquent*, in 1915, a report based on case studies instead of diffuse speculations on delinquency in the abstract.

In 1905 Binet and Simon made public their intelligence scale, introduced by Goddard in this country in 1910 and adapted in 1916 by Terman to its geographic and ethnic area. These tests afforded a concrete means of helping teachers evaluate a child's ability to grasp classroom instruction. This was the first reliable attempt to prevent educational mismanagement.

Simultaneously, adult psychiatry underwent major changes. Kraepelin's work served as a stepping stone toward the humanization of the specialty. His clear descriptions of symptoms, the *what* of mental illness, aroused curiosity about the *whence* and *why*. Freud and Meyer advocated a dynamic attitude that saw the origins of present trouble in experiences of the past. Biographic exploration became an obligatory part of history-taking. Biography, if pursued consistently, leads always back to the time when each patient was a child. This search for the meaning of childhood events as precursors of later illness created an appetite for immediate acquaintance with troubled children themselves and ripened the thought of prophylactic intervention at the time of the earliest onset. This thought was taken up vigorously by Beers, who in 1909 founded the National Committee for Mental Hygiene.

Thus between 1899 and 1909 the decks were cleared for individual work with problem children. Juvenile courts, psychometry, dynamic psychiatry, and the mental hygiene movement served as the main incentives. Educators, psychologists, and psychiatrists began to *think about* children in a practical, individually helpful manner. Previous indifference and supercilious disdain were replaced by an attitude of sympathy and a desire to understand and to be of service.

SECOND DECADE

The following decade was mainly one of legislative implementation of some of these insights, a transition from unorganized philanthropy to systematic communal endeavor. The emphasis lay on environmental cushioning of the decidedly delinquent, the noticeably retarded, and the woefully neglected. Probation officers were added to the juvenile courts. Foster home organizations were authorized to remove children from homes in which they suffered from proved parental mistreatment. Special classes in public schools helped retarded and otherwise handicapped students to get an education commensurate with their abilities. The principal goal was protection from brutality, bad examples, malnutrition, gangdom, and scholastic competition against overwhelming odds. People no longer merely *thought about* children but were prepared to *do something to* them with the aid of adequate community facilities.

THIRD DECADE

In 1921 Thom opened the Boston Habit Clinic for the guidance of problem children; in 1922 child guidance clinics were set up in a few communities; in 1930 there were about five hundred such clinics, and more than fifty countries sent delegates to the First International Congress of Mental Hygiene in Washington, D. C. These clinics were tridisciplinary teams of psychiatrists, psychologists, and social workers. They added a new dimension to the study of personality development. Until then, most theories had centered around innate, constitutional, instinctive propensities of the individual. The clinics broadened the scope beyond what was going on within a child to include the external, attitudinal forces that impinge on him. This was a departure of major importance, which saw emerging behavior as the consequence of a fusion of centrifugal and centripetal influences. Treatment therefore embraced efforts to do something *for* children by working constructively with the family and the school. The mutuality of parent-child relationship became a new topic of investigation.

In 1926 Homburger published his book on the psychopathology of childhood. This was a pioneering enterprise encompassing all that was then known about the subject and carrying together all the building stones to make them available for an integrated edifice. Anna Freud began to apply psychoanalytic principles to the treatment of disturbed children and, through the introduction of play therapy, formulated a method for including the child patient himself in the remedial arrangement by doing things *with* him as well as *to* and *for* him.

MORE RECENT EVENTS

In 1930 a children's psychiatric service was inaugurated at the pediatric department of The Johns Hopkins Hospital. Thus, it became possible to reach children, from the beginning of life to and beyond pubescence, with any kind of developmental and behavioral anomaly, with any kind of single and combined organic, intellectual, psychogenic, attitudinal, and sociological implication. The different clusters of building stones found themselves in one place and could be assembled under one roof.

On May 19, 1933, at a meeting of the Swiss Psychiatric Association, Tramer suggested for this new branch of medicine the name *Kinderpsychiatrie*, to which he gave added currency in the title of the first journal of the specialty founded by him in 1934. In 1935 Kanner used the equivalent term "child psychiatry" in the first textbook of the discipline in the English language. In 1937, at the initiative of Heuyer, a congress met in Paris under the heading of *psychiatrie infantile*. Child psychiatry acquired an acknowledged identity, a name of its own, and a vigorous representation.

This recognition has led in the last three decades to the establishment of training centers and professorships in leading universities, specialized periodicals, national and international societies and conventions, the creation of outpatient clinics and residential units for emotionally disturbed children, and intensive research activities.

In the 1930's and 1940's fundamental contributions were made to the study of childhood psychoses by Lutz in Switzerland, Ssucharewa in Russia, Creak in England, and Despert, Bender, Kanner (infantile autism), and Mahler (symbiotic psychosis) in this country. Goldfarb's work triggered interest in the effects of early maternal deprivation. Levy and Allen gave new directions to psychotherapeutic endeavor. A field of primary prevention has begun to include epidemiology and prenatal and paranatal factors in the scope of child psychiatry.

Child psychiatry has come of age and is here to stay. It has its roots in many areas: education, pediatrics, neurology, general psychiatry, psychology, sociology, jurisprudence, genetics, and biochemistry. It has been able to integrate all these considerations into one unified though widely ramified discipline within a short time.

REFERENCES

Kanner, L. *Child Psychiatry*, ed. 3. Charles C Thomas, Springfield, Ill., 1957.

Kanner, L. Trends in child psychiatry. J. Ment. Sci., 105: 581, 1959.

Kanner, L. American contributions to the development of child psychiatry. Psychiat. Quart. Suppl., 35: 1, 1961.

Kanner, L. A *History of the Care and Study of the Mentally Retarded*. Charles C. Thomas, Springfield, Ill., 1964.

Mora, G. Child psychiatry in the United States: its development and present status. Z. Kinderpsychiat., 22: 15, 1954.

Tramer, M. Historisches. In *Lehrbuch der allgemeinen Kinderpsychiatrie*, ed. 4, p. 561. Schwabe, Basel, 1964.

Walk, A. The pre-history of child psychiatry. Brit. J. Psychiat., 110: 754, 1964.

CHAPTER TWO

Normal Child Development

LEON EISENBERG, M.D.

INTRODUCTION

THIS CHAPTER attempts to define the concept of development and to indicate its implications for the understanding of human personality. Personality is used here to mean a set of attitudes and action tendencies— probabilities for given patterns of overt behavior in specified social fields —that characterize an individual at a particular period; it includes both affective and cognitive elements. Personality is viewed as an emergent from the interaction between individual physiological traits, personal experiential history, and social field forces. The apparent constancies of personality in an individual are commonly taken to indicate a crystallized set of mental structures that it is difficult to alter once maturity has been reached; this view pays insufficient attention to the consequences of uniformity of social role in serving to maintain the manifest regularities of behavior.

Although this discussion concludes at the stage of adolescence, developmental changes continue through senescence; personality is constantly in the making.

HISTORY OF DEVELOPMENTAL CONCEPTS

If a historic perspective requires justification, Needham reminds us:

The history of science is the guarantee of its freedom. The mistakes of our predecessors remind us that we may be mistaken; their wisdom prevents us from assuming that wisdom was born with us; and by studying the processes of their thought, we may hope to have a better understanding, and hence a better organization, of our own.

FORCES BEHIND DEVELOPMENT

Preformationist concept. A fragment surviving from the Ionian philosopher Anaxagoras, who lived in the fifth century B.C., comments on the origin of things: "Hair cannot come out of not-hair, nor flesh out of not-flesh." This notion is echoed in the Hippocratic writings on embryology:

> Everything in the embryo is formed simultaneously. All the limbs separate themselves at the same time and so grow, none comes before or after the other, but those which are naturally bigger appear before the smaller, without being formed earlier.

This quotation is of particular interest because of its appeal to reason rather than experience. Other passages make it clear that embryos had been examined. The observed was explained by a preformationist doctrine that coerced and restricted the observations that at face value would have suggested unequal times of beginnings for the different parts of the embryo. This doctrine was given poetic expression by Seneca:

> In the seed are enclosed all the parts of the body of the man that shall be formed. The infant that is borne in his mother's wombe hath the rootes of the beard and hair that he shall weare one day. In this little masse likewise are all the lineaments of the body and all that which posterity shall discover in him.

For all the naiveté—by present-day standards—embodied in these quotations, they are no mere exercise in antiquarianism. The same notions implicit in classic genetic theory are still adhered to, in modified form, by many biological and behavioral scientists.

Epigenetic concept. An alternate theoretical conception was first formulated by Aristotle in the fourth century B.C. The ovum being unknown and not to be discovered for another two millennia, he concluded that the semen, as the active shaping force or soul, acted on the catamenia (menstrual fluid) as the base material to form the fetus. Aristotle grappled with the perplexing question of the order of formation of the parts. Having opened eggs at various stages in development, he commented:

> All the parts, as heart, lung, liver, eye and all the rest, come into being either together or in succession. . . . That the former is not the fact is plain even to the senses, for some of the parts are clearly visible as already existing in the embryo while others are not. That it is not because of their being too small that they are not visible is clear for the lung is of greater size than the heart and yet appears later than the heart in the original development.

In trying to account for the coming into being of that which was not evident at an earlier stage, he advanced an idea alternative to the preformationist view that the earlier stage was already present but simply invisible.

For if in a certain sense [the parts cannot be made by what is external to the semen], yet in another sense they can. It is possible, then, that A should move B and B should move C, that, in fact, the case should be the same as with the automatic machines shown as curiosities. For the parts of such machines while at rest have a sort of potentiality of motion in them, and when any external force puts the first of them into motion immediately the next is moved in actuality. As, then, in these automatic machines the external force moves the parts in a certain sense (not by touching any part at the moment but by having touched one previously), in like manner also that from which the semen comes, or in other words that which made the semen, sets up the movement in the embryo and makes the parts of it by having touched first something though not continuing to touch it. In a way it is innate motion that does this, as the act of building builds a house. Plainly, then, while there is something which makes the parts, this does not exist as a definite object, nor does it exist in the semen at the first as a complete part.

Aristotle's analogy of the automatic machine in which A moves B and B in turn moves C constitutes the first statement of the doctrine of epigenesis: successive differentiations in the course of embryogenesis. This is the essence of modern developmental theory.

Predeterminist concept. Preformationism, nonetheless, continued to be the prevailing doctrine, so much so that with the invention of the microscope the early microscopists described a homunculus with all the features of a man in the head of the sperm. Certain difficulties, however, troubled those of a theoretical bent. Hartsoeker, assuming divine creation to have occurred six thousand years earlier and calculating the number of generations of rabbits during that interval, came to the conclusion that $10^{100,000}$ rabbits would have had to exist in the first rabbit. Bonnet replied to this calculation with the rejoinder that it was always possible by adding zeros to crush the imagination under the weight of numbers. Bonnet hailed preformationism as a victory of understanding over the senses.

However, the accumulating force of new data necessitated the abandonment of preformationism in its original form. With the development of better microscopes, the expected structures were not seen in early embryonic stages. Observation of the regeneration of limbs in adult organisms and the formation of embryonic monsters made the earlier position untenable. For preformationism, there was now substituted the doctrine of predeterminism. Stemming from the theological doctrine of predestination, it offered biologists a convenient fusion of science and religion. Swammerdam commented, "Thus original sin is explained, for all men were contained in the organs of Adam and Eve."

Predeterminism became the prevailing biological theory. It was implicit in Haeckel's aphorism: ontogeny recapitulates phylogeny, a slogan still quoted in current textbooks of biology. This notion was transplanted into psychology by writers as divergent as Jung and Gesell. Jung wrote: "Ontogenesis corresponds in psychology to phylogenesis. Consequently, . . . the state of infantile thinking in the child's psychic life, as well as in dreams, is nothing but a reecho of the prehistoric and the ancient." Gesell stated: "Infancy is the period in which the individual realizes his racial inheritance. This inheritance is the end product of evolutionary processes which trace back to an extremely remote antiquity." This concept of a set of psychic forces evolved in time long past but persisting as active and *unmodifiable* in the present is implicit in Freud's concept of the unconscious. He pointed out that the very emphasis of the commandment, "Thou shalt not kill," demonstrates that men are descended from an endless chain of murderers with a love of murder in their blood. He held that, since our attitude toward death is similar to that of primitive man, primitive man lives on in our unconscious, and the primitive psyche is thus indestructible.

Scientific developments in embryology and in genetics called the predeterminist position into question. Direct intervention in embryogenesis led to the concept of the embryonic organizer or inducing substance— that is, a product of one group of cells that influences a contiguous or remote group of cells—an idea that bears a remarkable formal similarity to Aristotle's B, which, when produced by A, causes C. In genetics, Johannsen distinguished the phenotype from the genotype, the phenotype resulting from genotypic processes modified by environmental interaction in a sequential fashion. Just as the inducer is effective only within certain time limits, given environmental contingencies lead to specific consequences only when stage-related. The conflict between predeterministic and epigenetic viewpoints is still alive in embryology as well as in psychology, in instinct theory, ethology, and theories of intelligence.

PROCESS OF DEVELOPMENT

There are two contrasting models: continuous and discontinuous. The continuous view is concerned with a linear accession of events, the prototype of which is simple growth—that is, increase in the number and the size of cells. In a sense, this viewpoint is represented in psychology by associationist or stimulus-response theories in which sequential chaining of behavior is the essential principle and the learning of complex behavior is reducible to the forming of connections.

In a discontinuous model, the central assumption is a segmentation into stages or levels of development. What characterizes a stage or level is an internal structure or set of laws or, to use computer language, a stage-specific program governing the response of the organism to a given stimulus configuration. Lehrman's studies of the ring dove provide elegant illustrations of the differential effects of external stimuli at different stages of the reproductive cycle. A female ring dove, prior to courting by a male, ignores eggs and nests if they are placed in her cage; after courting, she broods if they are made available. Courting, to be effective, must occur after sexual maturity. Courting leads to nest-building if materials are available; nest-building activity itself increases the likelihood of subsequent brooding. The reproductive cycle does not occur in the absence of a mate and is abortive if nesting materials are not available or if the eggs are removed once they are laid.

It is appropriate to distinguish between *growth*, increase in the number and size of cells; *experience*, summation of all previous internal and external stimulation; and *maturation*, altered function resulting from interaction between growth and experience. Maturation, according to the viewpoint adopted here, is not linear but discontinuous, one might almost say quantized. Stages of development follow an age sequence, but stages and ages are not equivalent terms, though they are often incorrectly used as synonyms. The sequence of stages is not automatic but dependent on both central nervous system growth and life experience; chronological change can proceed while psychological maturation lags. There is some evidence that particularly favorable environmental stimulation can accelerate progression from one stage to another, and there is clear evidence that unfavorable environments can markedly delay some aspects of development.

There appear to be lower limits of age for the appearance of each stage, limits determined by central nervous system maturation; thus, no amount of verbal stimulation will lead to speech within the first half year of life. On the other hand, verbal stimulation during this period does play an important role in preparing the ground for the later acquisition of language. What is not known is whether there are upper time bounds for the acquisition of a given cognitive stage—that is, are there critical periods for the development of certain abilities, such that, if the appropriate stimulus conditions are not provided within a given interval, the ability will never appear? Despite the common assumption that this is true, compelling evidence has not yet been provided in *human* development. It is more useful to assume that recoverability is possible, at least until thorough and exhaustive efforts at rehabilitation fail to bring results.

DEVELOPMENT OF THE HUMAN SPECIES

Fossil Evidence

For all his pride of place, man is a relative newcomer to the earth. If life on earth dates back some 2 billion years, the life span of modern man has occupied less than one hundredth of 1 per cent of that total. In orders of magnitude, Primates have been in existence for some 60 million years, Hominidae for 1 million years, and *Homo sapiens sapiens* (modern man) for some 50,000 years.

The Cercopithecidae (the catarrhine or Old World monkeys) and the Hominoidea superfamilies diverged from common ancestral forms. Of the

Hominoidea—Proconsul, Dryopithecus, Sivapithecus, Oreopithecus, and Ramapithecus—the last appears as the most likely candidate for the form on the path to the Hominidae and the first to the Pongidae (the anthropoid apes). The family Hominidae, which includes both apelike men and man, has, as its oldest identified fossil precursors, the australopithecines discovered by Dart in South Africa. These animals possessed a brain case of 435 to 600 cc.—the same magnitude as that of the great apes, which ranged from 275 to 750 cc.—but a pelvis much like that of man; they have been found in association with pebble tools. It is still argued by some that the tools may have been made by a more advanced species preying on this more primitive precursor. Whether or not the fossil with a cranial capacity of 640 to 725 cc. and given the species name *Homo habilis* is to be differentiated from other australopithecines (*Australopithecus boisei*, *Australopithecus robustus*, *Australopithecus africanus*), these Hominidae were either derivatives of the form or forms directly ancestral to *Homo erectus* on the line to man. *Homo erectus*, represented by Pithecanthropus and Sinanthropus with brain cases in the range of 775 to 900 cc. and 915 to 1,225 cc., respectively, are immediate or collateral fossil remains of the next step in the evolutionary radiation. Intermediate between *Homo erectus* and *Homo sapiens sapiens* is *Homo sapiens neanderthalensis* with a brain case, at least in some specimens, fully as large as that of modern man. Neanderthal man is generally thought to represent an offshoot that became extinct, perhaps destroyed by Cro-Magnon man in internecine warfare (See Figure 1.)

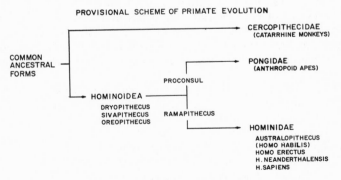

PROVISIONAL SCHEME OF PRIMATE EVOLUTION

FIGURE 1. An outline, based on contemporary anthropological evidence, of the probable evolutionary pathways en route to man. Proconsul appears to be the ancestral prototype for the pongids and Ramapithecus for the hominids. Australopithecus is the earliest form identifiable as hominid and has been estimated, in the most recent finds (1967), to be two million years old. The sequence, while probably correct in general, undoubtedly is incomplete and subject to modification on the basis of future study and discovery.

This ordering is at best approximate and subject to modification by subsequent study and by the discovery of new fossils. Moreover, differences in definition of the characteristics for species differentiation and for the category of man continue to produce dispute among anthropologists. Distinctions cannot be based on single traits but must take into account the complex or pattern of traits, as Clark emphasized. Whatever the argument as to detail, it is clear that the direction of primate evolution has been toward greater adaptability rather than greater adaptation.

The point to be emphasized is that the essential step in the differentiation of the hominids occurred well before any substantial increase in brain size had occurred. Indeed, if the pebble tools found in association with the australopithecines are, in fact, products of their manufacture, toolmaking occurred at a brain size only slightly larger than that of the chimpanzee or orangutan and was *followed* by a three- to four-fold expansion of the brain.

The role of bipedal locomotion.   The most important single factor in the evolutionary emergence of hominids as a separate and independent line is the development of erect bipedal locomotion. The pongids, on the other hand, developed a markedly different specialization toward the brachiating mode of locomotion. In the hominids, the lower limb increased in length in relation to trunk and upper limb; in the pongids, it was the upper limb that increased in relative length. In the hominids, the bones of the foot and the knee joint were modified for structural stability; in the pongids, mobility at these joints was enhanced for prehensile function. Far-reaching changes occurred in the hominid pelvic girdle because of the demands of erect posture; the pelvis of the pongid retained the general shape and proportions found in lower primates. Although muscle structure can only be inferred from fossil remains, studies on contemporary species show marked differences in muscular anatomy between ape and man.

In a recent article, Hewes has suggested that habitual food-carrying may have made bipedalism advantageous. He bases his thesis on observations of troops of Japanese monkeys, in whom a new locomotor habit could be observed to emerge as part of a chain of behaviors initiated by a new food supply. The monkeys had to walk some distance from the forest edge and return, carrying the food in their forelimbs, in order to eat in safety. In any event, Leakey's finds in the Olduvai Gorge suggest that the australopithecine was a "habitually bipedal plantigrade primate"—that is, an animal that walked on two legs and put its feet flat on the ground. Fossil fragments indicate that the hind limbs are more sapienslike than the forelimbs. The development of a prehensile hand includes elements that are both peripheral (form and proportion of bone and muscle) and central (cortical sensorimotor mechanisms with increased cerebral representation of thumb and forefinger).

The roles of the hand and the brain.   The question of whether hand or brain took the lead concerned Aristotle. On teleological grounds, Aristotle concluded:

> Now Anaxagoras has said that it is the possession of hands that made man the most intelligent of animals. The probability is that it was because he was the most intelligent that he got hands . . . if it is best that it be so, and if nature, out of what is possible, always does what is best, it is not because he has hands that man is wise, but because he is the wisest of animals that he has hands.

Recent evidence, not available to Aristotle, appears to have settled the question in quite the opposite direction.

Tool-making has been regarded as an essential characteristic of man, so much so that Benjamin Franklin suggested the name *Homo faber* for the human species. How unique are tools? Animals other than primates use tools; the sea otter smashes clams on rocks held against itself. In Napier's classification, this constitutes ad hoc tool-using—that is, the use of an object available at the time. Goodall has recently provided evidence of purposeful tool-using in the chimpanzee. These animals will soak up water in a clump of leaves, which are then brought to the mouth and squeezed. Moreover, she has photographic evidence of ad hoc tool-modifying: for termite fishing, the chimpanzee will walk some distance from the termite hill, pick a slender stalk and strip off side branches, return and thrust the stalk into the flight hole of the termite hill. When withdrawn, it is covered with termites and passed against the lips to deliver an avidly swallowed mouthful. There is as yet no evidence in animals other than man of tool-modifying for future eventuality, of ad hoc tool-making, or of the final stage, cultural tool-making. Both ad hoc tool-making and cultural tool-making are evident from the eoliths found in association with *Homo erectus*.

The crucial step in the evolutionary sequence to man was the assumption of the erect bipedal posture, which freed the hands for the manufacture of tools and weapons. Tools have important consequences for the further development of the teeth, the jaws, and the powerful temporal and masseter muscles, which in pongids are essential for the mastication of unprocessed and tough natural foods. Dental and mandibular changes occurred early in the evolutionary sequence to hominids. These structural and muscular changes, it has been suggested, may have permitted expansion of the cranium, which in the ape is confined by the massive attachment of the temporal muscles. Whatever the role of this intervening step, the manufacture of tools and weapons enhanced the survival value of central nervous system mutations, which permitted enhanced brain function, resulting in the manufacture of more effective tools, leading to a more elaborate social structure, and increasing the value of brain mutations, which permitted language development, etc. This lag of the brain behind other structural changes is also evident in the paleontology of the horse and may be a general principle in evolution.

Implications of an evolutionary view. Viewing the genesis of *Homo sapiens* from the evolutionary standpoint has important implications for the psychiatric study of modern man. By definition, the present characteristics of man are those that led to relative reproductive superiority. Modern man has existed for no more than 50,000 years after an evolution from primitive hominids over the preceding 1 million years or more; it is only the last 10,000 years, trivial from the standpoint of biological time, that have been characterized by an enormous technological and cultural efflorescence.

Man may have been left with biological traits that, though of positive survival value for conditions 50,000 years ago, may now be maladaptive for contemporary cultural conditions, at a time when man modifies his environment rather than himself. One example will illustrate this point. Stress responses, integrated through hypothalamic and limbic systems, initiate adrenal cortical and medullary activity, which leads to protein catabolism, enhanced blood coagulability, a differential shift of circulation, and enhanced carbohydrate mobilization. These anticipatory metabolic responses improve the capacity for muscular response to crisis. It has clear adaptive value in primates and in primitive man for fight or flight. But contemporary man continues to exhibit the same anticipatory mechanisms to culturally defined stress, to which an effective response is intellectual rather than physical. May not these physiological stress responses, repeatedly evoked by the complexities of urban civilization, play a role in the generation of arteriosclerosis and hypertension?

POSTNATAL BRAIN DEVELOPMENT

The development of the human brain occurs predominately during postnatal life. This would appear to be a consequence of the size of the pelvic outlet that limits permissible brain size at birth. Man differs markedly from other primates in the proportion of brain development that occurs prenatally. Whereas the ratio of adult to neonatal brain weight is about 2.2 for the chimpanzee and about 2.5 for the orangutan, the ratio for man is in the order of 3.5 to 4.0. The brain weight of the human infant is about 350 gm., about twice that of the infant chimpanzee, whose brain weight is about 170 gm.; but the adult brains are 1,450 and 375 gm., respectively. The difference is qualitative as well as quantitative. There is a four-fold increase in the neocortex, a marked elaboration of the receiving areas for the teloreceptors, a disproportionate expansion of the motor area for the hand in relationship to representation for other parts, a manifold greater representation of tongue and larynx, and a great increase in the association areas. There is no homologue in other primates for the *speech* area found in man in the cortex; in contrast, *vocalization* can be produced by stimulation of the mesencephalic system in both species.

Although the gestation period is of the same order in higher apes and man, the postnatal maturation in man is greatly prolonged. Immaturity, and with it the disadvantage of dependency, is the purchase price for the greater adult adaptability attained through the increase in learning made possible by evolution of brain size and complexity.

Conel's histological studies of cerebral cortex in infants and young children have demonstrated the enormous growth in the number and branching of dendrites and the multiplication of synaptic junctions, all occurring while the organism is subject to shaping by the environment. The denseness of the feltwork of the cortex has made it impossible to detect structural changes in relation to experience, even if these do occur. Some recent experiments by Rose et al. indicated that growth of dendrites is a continuous process throughout life. They produced laminar lesions in the cortex of rabbits by monoenergetic heavy ionizing particles. By grading the radiation dose properly, they were able to produce a laminar zone of cortical tissue destruction without inducing cysts or scarring. Several weeks after radiation, sacrificed animals displayed a translucent zone without recognizable cellular structures. Companion animals allowed to survive a month longer and then sacrificed gave clear evidence of new fibers growing through the previously acellular zone. These studies provide the first evidence of structural growth in the central nervous system of adult mammals.

EVOLUTION OF SOCIAL BEHAVIOR

Among the adaptive mechanisms with biological significance for survival are behavior sequences. Behaviors that have a reproductive advantage lead to the selective multiplication of the organisms gifted with them. The basic mechanisms must be genic, but the genes concerned do not determine the behavior; rather, they determine the readiness with which it is learned. Part of this process is a selection for emotional states that make more likely the exhibition of adaptive behavior—that is, pleasure associated with the patterns evolution demands and fear toward maladaptive sequences. Perhaps the best example is the supreme pleasure associated with the sexual act, an association that guarantees that all animals will seek to consummate the act on which the continuity of life itself depends.

What can be reasonably surmised about behavior mechanisms from the study of primate social behavior and from the study of Stone Age food-gathering and hunting societies? Primates live in groups with a surprisingly complex social order and division of labor, based on sex and age. The ubiquity of group behavior makes it clear that there must be genetic antecedents for the social learning that ties the individual to the group. Primates both young and old demonstrate marked differences in state when with and when separated from the tribe. Ethological observations of primate colonies in the wild have made clear the infrequency of full-fledged aggressive behavior within the group. Although there are differences by species and by colony, the overall picture is one in which an elaborate social hierarchy is maintained by gestures and vocal threat so that destructive attacks within the colony occur rarely. Even the traditional image of the fearsome gorilla has to be abandoned after the observations of Schaller, who found him to be a remarkably pacific and gentle creature. The social bond is fashioned initially out of the dependence of the infant on his mother and then from peer interaction. What Harlow has called "contact comfort" takes precedence in monkeys over the attachment to a nursing surrogate. But that this is based on the primacy of the grasp reflex in this species and that the grasp reflex is essential to survival are apparent when the mode of locomotion of arboreal primates is recalled. As the mother swings rapidly through the branches with the alternating use of her arms, the infant must have a genetic mechanism for clinging or be dashed to the ground.

Among the langur monkeys, the birth of an infant is an event of great attractive significance to other females, who will await a turn to handle the neonate under the watchful eye of his mother. The new mother, whatever her position in the general social hierarchy, takes precedence in governing accessibility to the infant. De Vore's field observations demonstrated that the adult male baboon is alert to distress cries by infants and young juveniles and defends them from attack; the dominant male, from whose proximity other adults flee, tolerates with surprising equanimity aggressive play and teasing by the young of the colony. Grooming behavior, reciprocated between mother and infant and between peers, is a major factor in fashioning the primate social matrix. Out of grooming, play, and the exchange of threats and gestures, strong social ties are fashioned, which maintain structured colony behavior. Although variations in the amount of aggression displayed, attributable to species differences and even to differences between colonies of a single species, are evident from field studies, the most striking overall characteristic of primate social behavior in the wild is the infrequency of intracolony physical attacks severe enough to produce injury, except under conditions of severe stress.

Among primitive peoples, all food-gathering and hunting societies exhibit the following characteristics: relatively open groups of twenty to fifty members, among whom relations are usually friendly; a kinship ethic that prescribes mutual aid (food-sharing appears to be a *sine qua non* of the human condition); division of labor by sex and by domestic (family) units; rules to regulate patterns of mating and of competition; common language; a craving for response by each individual from his human environment, a craving that appears to be as fundamental as that for food. Although the modalities of interpersonal exchange become more and more complex with social evolution, the basic needs for recognition and acceptance by peers is everywhere evident.

The most remarkable trait of human social behavior is its *variability*. Aggression is no more fundamental or ubiquitous than is generosity. Freud's formulation—"The tendency to aggression is an innate independent instinctual disposition in man"—has no more scientific evidence to justify it than the misanthropic statement by Thomas Hobbes: "I put for . . . a general inclination of mankind a perpetuall and restlesse desire of Power after Power, that ceaseth only in death. . . . [This leads] to a time of Warre, where every man is Enemy to every man . . . no Arts, no Letters, no Society, and which is worst of all, a continuall feare and danger of violent death; and the life of man, solitary, poore, nasty, brutish and short." Both are statements of political philosophies. Freud, like Herbert Spencer before him, projected onto biology the socially derived characteristics of the civilization of his time (and ours). But that civilization is no more an immediate derivative of man's nature than the culture of the Pueblo Indian or the Alaskan Eskimo, to whom aggressive competition was unknown.

DEVELOPMENT OF THE INDIVIDUAL

With the appearance of the human species, biological evolution has been superseded by cultural evolution. Man is the only animal capable of changing his environment in a planned—that is, future-oriented—fashion, though he does not always do it wisely or with a sufficiently long-range view. All organisms change their environment—bacteria in consuming food and producing wastes, beavers in building dams—but most without the ability to anticipate or to plan for consequences. Man is the only animal capable of symbol use. Other animals communicate by signs and signals, but man alone possesses *symbols* that bind time. Language permits cognitive rehearsal, thinking through the consequences of action before attempting it. Language permits the abstraction of the general from the concrete and the realignment of relationships between elements without dependence on actual or possible manipulation of the elements. By language, man can transmit the experience of the past generation to the young of the next and build continuously on his cultural heritage; this has led to the exponential growth of knowledge. Man's capacity to learn is of a different magnitude from that for any other species. Man surrenders built-in preadaptations (and hence is more vulnerable in infancy) for the capacity to adapt through learned responses in a wide variety of possible environments. This can be viewed as a choice of evolutionary strategies. These, then, are some of the issues to be faced in considering the development of the individual as the focus shifts from phylogeny to ontogeny.

Kessen's splendid collection of readings demonstrate that interest in the child as child has a cultural history. Until very recently, the child was viewed as an ill-formed or incomplete adult. The concept of childhood as a phenomenon unto itself, requiring special institutions for its preservation, is an invention of modern times. To quote Aries:

In medieval society, the idea of childhood did not exist; this is not to suggest that children were neglected, forsaken or despised. The idea of childhood is not to be confused with affection for children: it corresponds to an awareness of the particular nature of childhood. . . . Language did not give the word child the restricted meaning we give it today.

Through the eighteenth century, the conditions of childhood were extremely precarious. Children born in London had by the end of that century only a 50–50 chance of reaching their fifth birthday; infantile death rates were on the order of 400 per 1,000. The factory system of the industrial revolution demanded cheap labor, and children were, in effect, sold into slavery. An "enlightened" law of 1833, passed over savage opposition, provided that children from 9 to 13 were not to work more than 48 hours a week and those from 13 to 18 not more than 68 hours. Even these minimal regulations did not apply to children working in mines until the Earl of Shaftesbury's crusade. Only with the writings of Locke and Rousseau did childhood begin to be thought of as an epoch important in itself. Rousseau's *Emile or On Education*, published in 1762, proposed revolutionary ideas: successive stages of development, the necessity for exercise of mental functions, adaptation to age-appropriate circumstances, and individuality in development. The first baby diaries were those of Tiedemann in 1787 and of Darwin on his first-born son, William Erasmus, in 1840.

Darwinism revolutionized the concepts of psychology. The theory of evolution provided a mechanism for the doctrines of perfectibility heralded by the Encyclopedists of the French Revolution. As homologies were sought between the phylogenetic progression of species and the development of individual man in society, comparative psychology was founded, and sociology and anthropology were profoundly influenced. Man was to be understood, not by an analysis of his adult functions, but by a study of his origins—in the scale of nature and in the child.

PRENATAL FACTORS

The analysis of individual development customarily begins with birth. However, significant experiential factors influence intrauterine development. It has been shown that intrauterine curare will lead to ankylosed joints in the sheep; movements of the limbs in utero are important factors in maintaining joint mobility. The administration of androgenic hormones in the effort to prevent miscarriage alters sex differentiation in the infant. Maternal stress, through the production of adrenal hormones, may influence the behavioral characteristics of the newborn. These few examples point to the wide range of potentially significant findings from a still uncharted area of investigation.

Complications of pregnancy and parturition are precursors of prenatal and paranatal injury to the central nervous system of the infant. Pasamanick and Knobloch have introduced the important concept of a continuum of reproductive casualty extending from miscarriage and stillbirth through cerebral palsy, mental retardation, and epilepsy to learning and behavior disorders—that is, extending from lethal injury to the central nervous system to minimal brain damage without obvious neurological impairment. The prevalence of these disorders (both the pregnancy complications and the clinical psychiatric manifestations) displays a distribution that is differential by social class and related to the relative adequacy of nutritional, medical, and general hygienic factors associated with class status. In no area of psychiatry are there clearer implications for preventive measures. The decision to apply what is known and the social action to make it available without distinction of class and race could result in a significant reduction in neuropsychiatric morbidity.

Infant Stage

Once normal birth has occurred, to quote William James, "the baby, assailed by eyes, ears, nose, skin and entrails, all at once, feels it all as one blooming, buzzing confusion." How does this essentially brain stem preparation—the anencephalic infant behaves much like the normal newborn for the first four to six weeks of life—progress to the highly encephalized adult? Brain stem organization itself is different at birth from what comes into being with progressive differentiation of superordinate structures. The survival systems—breathing, sucking, swallowing, and circulatory and temperature homeostasis—are relatively functional at birth. But sensory systems are only incompletely developed; sensory impulses register at thalamic levels with no evidence of specific cortical responses. Further differentiation of neurophysiological functions depends on stimulatory reinforcement and is not an automatic consequence of the genomic structure.

Stimulus deprivation. The experiments of Riesen on chimpanzees reared in total darkness demonstrated atrophy and up to 90 per cent loss of retinal cells if the animal is maintained in the dark for 2 years. The possibility of reversibility is lost after 5 to 7 months of total darkness. Rearing in diffuse light, by placing ground glass goggles over the eyes, results in poor eye movement control and poor fixation, consequences that become irreversible with the passage of time. In children with strabismus severe enough that images fall on nonequivalent parts of the two retinas, the image from one eye is suppressed; if left uncorrected to the age of 6, there is an irreversible loss of sight in the suppressed eye, amblyopia ex anopsia.

Hubel and Wiesel have carried out a series of studies with microelectrode recordings from single cortical cells in the occipital lobes of kittens. At the earliest age, the investigators were able to identify cells responsive to the orientation of stationary linear light fronts—horizontal, vertical, or oblique—and to light fronts moving either from left to right *or* from right to left. That this organization is intrinsic is evident from the demonstration of these properties in newborn kittens with no visual experience. However, after three months of light deprivation in one eye, with the other eye maintained as a control, the kittens display functional blindness in the deprived eye, with no visual fixation, despite normal pupillary response and normal electroretinogram. At the level of the lateral geniculate, there is a 40 per cent shrinkage in cell mass. In the occipital lobes, there is an almost total absence of response in cells driven by the monocularly deprived eye. Here is an instance of the loss of functional interrelationships already present at birth but dependent on patterned stimulation for their maintenance. More recent unpublished work by these investigators indicated that the loss of functional representation in the cortex for the deprived eye is determined by the locking in of these units to the effective field of the normal eye; that is, if both eyes are deprived of visual experience, *neither* demonstrates much loss in its subtendant cortex, but *binocularly* driven cells are no longer evident. Moreover, if amblyopia is produced by severing the lateral rectus muscle in the eye of the newborn kitten, it sees well with either eye and shows corresponding occipital electrical activity but shows neither binocular vision nor occipital cells driven binocularly.

Simple passive visual experience is not enough for the acquisition of visual-motor coordination. Held and Hein have demonstrated that the development of visual placing responses and the ability to discriminate moving from stationary objects is a function of active exercise. In their studies, paired experimental kittens were exposed to a lighted environment for brief periods each day. One member of the pair is allowed to walk freely through the lighted environment; the second member is yoked to the first in such a fashion that he experiences the same translation through space but without the possibility of controlling his own movement. Only the kitten who does the active exploring develops normal visual responses. The development of intersensory integration is an active, not an automatic, process. The organism begins with its initial given capacities, and these are differentiated and interrelated via exercise so that higher-order capabilities emerge.

In the terminology of Piaget, there are two fundamental processes at work: assimilation and accommodation. Assimilation is the process of utilizing and incorporating stimulus aliments in the environment, just as the organism utilizes foods. Although Piaget used the term "aliment" in a figurative sense, it is remarkably descriptive of the visual experiments in which maintenance of the very integrity of the neurons in the optic system depends on external stimulation for alimentation. In assimilation, the organism takes in the new in terms of the familiar and acts in the present as it has in the past. In the process of accommodation, the organism is modified by the demands—that is, the novelties—of the environment. Accommodation leads to a reorganization of the programs of the organism as it struggles to cope more effectively with the mismatch between its available action patterns and the new requirements of its current environment.

Development of the social bond. As sensory development progresses, there is for all social organisms a parallel task of fashioning a tie between the newborn and its species. In recent years, much attention has been focused on the concepts of ethology. Ethologists have demonstrated, primarily in birds but also in ungulates, that there is a critical period shortly after birth in which the newborn becomes imprinted on a moving, sound-producing object that from then on serves to elicit following behavior, just as the mother does in the natural situation. Birds imprinted on artificial objects become isolates from the flock and may be unable to mate. For all of the undoubted importance of imprinting in certain species, it should be emphasized that imprinting has not been demonstrated in man or in other primates.

The effects of total social isolation in subhuman species are of great interest in studying the socialization process. Puppies isolated in individual cages for six months exhibit a peculiar syndrome characterized by overactivity, distractibility, inadequate response to pain, whirling fits, inferiority to pet-reared and colony-reared dogs in problem-solving and in food competition, and inability to be effectively socialized thereafter. Monkeys reared as isolates, even when offered surrogate mothers (objects for clinging), are subsequently unable to adjust to a colony existence and have extraordinary difficulty in learning to mate. When impregnated, isolate-reared females fail to mother their young. The behavioral peculiarities of these isolates were initially attributed to the lack of mothering in infancy, but Harlow's more recent studies have demonstrated that an opportunity for peer interaction between two nonmothered infant monkeys apparently suffices for the development of social behavior.

Harlow traced five affectional systems in the development of the monkey: infant-mother; peer; heterosexual; maternal; and paternal. The infant-mother affectional system is modulated via body contact, clinging, nursing, rocking, warmth, and visual stimulation. It passes through four stages: reflex, attachment, security, and separation. The peer system exhibits successive stages of presocial exploration, interactive play, aggressive play, and developing social status. Heterosexual differentiation includes the passivity pattern and pelvic thrusts of the female; the threat pattern, pelvic thrusts, and clasps of the male; grooming behavior; and full adult sexual behavior. The maternal affectional system develops through stages of attachment and protection, ambivalence, and separation and rejection. The paternal system includes such behaviors as retrieval, protection, and punishment.

Schneirla and Rosenblatt, in studying the suckling behaviors of kitten and cat, have emphasized the interactive nature of the developmental process. The maturation of the kitten, its acquisition of experience, and the interactions of the behaviors of kitten and cat contribute to the sequence. The suckling period, some sixty days in the cat, can be divided into three phases. In the first to the twentieth day, the female approaches the kittens, arches her body in a "U" to present the mammary surface, and licks and so orients the kittens toward her. In response to tactile stimulation, the kittens acquire increasing skill in nipple localization and suckling. During the second phase, from the twentieth to the thirtieth day, both the kittens and the cat initiate approaches. The kittens display increasing perceptual organization and orient to the home corner of the cage and to the cat. The cat responds with a "U" to the approach of the kittens. The kittens begin to play with one another. During the third and final phase, from the thirtieth to the sixtieth day, most suckling occurs at the initiative of the kittens, who pursue the mother vigorously. The cat now responds irregularly and avoids the kittens more and more until she no longer accepts them. Summarizing their findings, Schneirla and Rosenblatt stated:

> These considerations favor a very different view of the concept of critical periods from the one now held by many writers. In the social development of the cat . . . striking changes in the essential progression are grounded not only in the growth-dependent processes of maturation but also, at the same time, in opportunities for experience and learning arising in the standard female-litter situation. This conception of social ontogeny encourages stressing not just one or a few chronologically marked changes in the behavior pattern, but rather indicates that normally each age period is crucial for the development of particular aspects in a complex progressive pattern of adjustment . . . critical periods in social development are not matters of maturation per se. Rather, time-conditioned factors depending upon experience in the normal situation, in close conjunction with growth-dependent factors, are necessary for both the turning points and the intervening progress in social adjustment. . . . Mammalian social development is thus seen as advancing from birth in ways that, for the species-characteristic outcome, continuously require not only the standard conditions of organic maturation but also the presence of the standard developmental setting with its progessively changing behavioral properties.

Social deprivation syndromes.   What happens to the human infant deprived of normal social and cognitive experience? Pediatricians have long known and repeatedly recorded the severe developmental retardation that accompanies maternal rejection and neglect. Infants in institutions characterized by low staff-to-infant ratios and frequent turnover of personnel, even when physical care and freedom from infection are adequate, display marked developmental retardation. The same infants, if placed in adequate foster or adoptive care, undergo marked acceleration in development. Bowlby, in 1952, on the basis of an extensive review of the literature, concluded that early separation had persistent and irreversible effects on personality and intelligence. The most persuasive evidence for this conclusion was that provided by Goldfarb, who compared the behavior in adolescence of two groups of children abandoned in infancy. The first group remained in an orphanage for the first three years of life and then were placed in foster care; the second group were placed in foster care in infancy. The foster homes for the two groups were said to be substantially alike; the possibility of differential placement because of the initial characteristics of the infants was denied by the social agency. As adolescents, the children institutionalized for the first three years showed lower I.Q.s, inferior school performance, and sociopathic traits. Bowlby's later studies of children who had been separated from their families early in life because of tuberculosis failed to confirm the anticipated severe psychological consequences. Such factors as the quality of institutional care, the care received before and after institutionalization, the reasons for removal from the family, and the maintenance of a relationship with parents by visiting during the period of separation are important variables in determining outcome.

The most striking evidence that early damage can be reversed by adequate subsequent care was provided by the studies of Skeels. He identified twenty-five children in an orphanage, thirteen of whom were removed for placement in an experimental program. They were placed in the care of older female retardates as foster mothers and were enrolled in a preschool enrichment program. Two years later, the experimental group, with a mean initial I.Q. of 64.3, had attained an I.Q. of 91.8, whereas the control group left in the orphanage, initially at 86.7, had declined to 60.5. Eleven of the thirteen experimental children were adopted. Three years later, their mean I.Q. was 95.9, compared with 66.1 for the controls. Current information on the adult adjustment of the study subjects revealed that all thirteen of the experimental children are self-supporting, and eleven are married and parents of nine normal children. This group had attained a median education of twelfth grade. In contrast, the twelve controls had a median third grade education. One had died in adolescence, one is in a mental hospital, four are in institutions for the retarded, three are unemployed, two are unskilled laborers, and only one is a skilled worker. The median cost to the state for the experimental program was about $1,000 a child; the control group, most of whom remained in care throughout their lives, had cost from $7,000 to $24,000 each.

Bowlby's monograph on maternal deprivation, reviewed and critically assessed by a later World Health Organization publication, served to call attention to the disastrous and far-reaching effects of early neglect. Its stress on the irreversibility of the damage was unfortunate; the early studies confounded the effects of separation and institutionalization with the poor care provided the children once they were removed from the initially depriving situation. The consequences of deprivation vary with the severity and duration of the depriving experience, the age of the child at which the deprivation occurs, and the adequacy of restitutive measures.

Temperamental differences. But what of the normal newborn in his own family? Is he a *tabula rasa*, a smooth slate on which characteristics are engraved with greater or lesser ease? Though a definitive answer to this question is not possible with present evidence, there are strong suggestions of congenital differences. Lipton et al. and Bridger have demonstrated wide individual differences among infants in autonomic reactivity, differences that persist over the newborn period but whose long-range consequences are not yet known. The studies of Thomas et al. have demonstrated temperamental characteristics already evident by the third month of life. In a careful longitudinal study of 130 middle-class infants, the researchers were able to identify nine behavioral dimensions on which reliable ratings can be obtained: activity-passivity, regularity-irregularity, intensity, approach-withdrawal, adaptive-nonadaptive, high-low threshold of response to stimulation, positive-negative mood, high-low selectivity, and high-low distractibility. The ratings on individual children showed substantial correlations between 3 months and 2 years but much lower correlations at 5 years. During the course of the study, twenty-seven of the children presented clinical psychiatric problems. Chess et al. were able to discern a relationship between the initial characteristics of the infant, the mode of parental management, and the subsequent appearance of symptoms.

Clinicians are coming to the view that the infant is an important actor in the family drama, one who in part determines its course. The behavior of the infant serves to control the behavior of his mother, just as her behavior modulates his. The calm, smiling, predictable, good infant is a powerful reward for tender maternal care. The jittery, irregular, irritable infant tries a mother's patience; if her capacities for giving are marginal, his traits may cause her to turn away from him and thus complicate his already inadequate beginnings.

Cognitive development. At birth all infants have a repertoire of reflex behaviors—breathing, crying, defecating, head-turning toward the stimulated cheek, mouthing of a nipple touching the lips, sucking, and swallowing. Recent studies have indicated that both vision and hearing are more highly developed in the newborn than they had been thought to be. By 1 to 2 weeks of age, the infant "smiles"; this response is endogenously determined, as evident by smiling in blind infants. By 2 to 4 weeks of age, visual fixation and visual following are evident, behaviors that may be compared to the following movements in subhuman forms. By 4 to 8 weeks, social smiling is elicited by the face or voice of the caretaker. By 16 to 18 weeks, vocalization or babbling has appeared in the child in a language-rich environment. The persistence and further evolution of this vocalization depend on rewarding consequences from the human environment. By 18 to 20 weeks, selective social smiling is apparent to familiar faces. This smile has been shaped by the response of adults and is in turn a powerful mechanism for controlling the adults. By 6 to 8 months, the child sits; by 9 to 12 months, he stands; and between 12 and 15 months, he usually walks and speaks his first words. Details of the sequence of motor and adaptive behaviors exhibited by the normally developing infant have been described by Gesell, whose scales permit comparison of the accomplishments of a particular infant with normative standards.

In contrast to the normative approach taken by Gesell, who views development as the unfolding of a genetically determined sequence, is Piaget's epigenetic theory of intelligence, summarized recently by Flavell. To Piaget, intelligence is but a special instance of biological adaptation within the context of life, which he views as a continuous creative interaction between the organism and its environment. The outer manifestation of this interaction is coping behavior; the inward reflection is the functional organization of the mental apparatus. Adaptive coping continuously reorganizes the structures of the mind. This theory is dissonant with most philosophical systems since Plato, which take the logical structures of space, causality, and time as given rather than as evolving epigenetically.

Piaget divided the development of intelligence into three major periods: sensorimotor, birth to 2 years; concrete operations, 2 to 12 years; and formal operations, 12 years through adult life. The sensorimotor period is one in which the congenital sensorimotor schemata or reflexes are generalized, related to one another, and differentiated to become the elementary operations of intelligence. The period of concrete operations is divided into a preconceptual phase, from 2 to 4 years of age, during which symbols are constructed; the intuitive phase of acquiring concepts of space, causality, and time, from 4 to 7; and the phase of concrete operations, in which thought becomes decentered from perception and action— that is, the increasing autonomy of central processes permits the activities of classifying, ordering, and numbering. The period of formal operations is one of systematization and recombination of the concrete operations, in the course of which the logical structures of abstract thought are mastered.

A review of the first few stages of the sensorimotor period may serve to convey Piaget's method of analysis. In its first stage, from birth to 2 months, the exercise of the ready-made reflexes leads to a transition from passive release by stimulation to active groping. Reflex sucking is accompanied by search and discrimination; vision moves from the pupillary reflex response to light to following and active search; prehension moves from the grasp reflex to separate finger movements. The exercise of a function brings inherent satisfaction or what Buhler called function pleasure. This notion of function pleasure is to be distinguished from the widely held concept that the satisfaction of a physiological need is the governing principle of behavior. The varying circumstances of stimulation during this period promote accommodation of the organism to the necessities of the external world; that is, the infant shapes his response to the particularities of the stimulating object—be it finger, nipple, or spoon—and, in so doing, changes himself.

The next stage, primary circular reactions, from 2 to 5 months, is one of reciprocal coordination between the hand and the sucking movements of the mouth, between the hearing and the seeing of a visible and audible object, between the seeing and the grasping of a visible and palpable object, etc. New objects elicit greater interest than overly familiar ones. Recent studies have demonstrated that infants will view complex patterns for longer periods than they will simple patterns. As the infant's hands come into his visual field by chance, he stares at them and then begins to move them as he watches them. Something looked at becomes something to grasp, and something grasped becomes something to suck. However, at this stage reality remains subjective—that is, there is no further search for an object that disappears from the visual field. The child has no general space but only a buccal, a kinesthetic, a visual, an auditory space.

The third stage, secondary circular reactions, from 5 to 9 months, is one in which the coordinations of the second stage become dissociated and regrouped in new ways and acquire the independence of learning sets. The rudiments of intentionality appear as the child begins to anticipate the consequences of his own acts. The infant no longer merely utilizes adventitious circumstances but begins to bring definite actions to bear on these circumstances. Ends, the outcomes sought, are differentiated from the means, his own actions. The infant dandled on his father's knee will begin to bounce up and down when the knee stops, as if this were intended to cause the knee to bounce him. Recognition is manifested by outlined or abbreviated acts. Thus, the infant who had enjoyed the movements of a toy brought about by the shaking of his legs will briefly shake his legs when he sees the toy again. It is at this stage that the elementary constructions of reality are undertaken. Objects begin to acquire permanence. Prior to this point, the rest of the world exists for the infant only insofar as it impinges on his sensations or is subject to his actions. Once removed from his immediate presence, objects have no further meaning for him. But now, if an object is dropped in front of him, he will look down to the ground to search for it; that is, he behaves for the first time as though the object had a reality outside of him, although true object permanence is not attained until well into the second year of life. Another important acquisition in this stage is the beginning of imitation.

The remaining stages of the sensorimotor period—coordination of the secondary schemata, the tertiary circular reactions, and the invention of new means through mental combination—cannot here be described, nor can the periods of concrete operations and formal operations. They will, however, repay careful study in Flavell's synthesis of Piaget's many volumes or, better yet, in the originals. Piaget has emphasized throughout the role of intervening experience on the maturation of cognitive functions. It is the richness, complexity, and diversity of stimulation in a favorable environment that results in the accommodation of mental structures to the nuances of reality and in the elaboration of the highest mental functions. Although Piaget's studies have until recently been limited to normal children of favorable circumstance, the framework he developed is a useful one in cross-cultural and cross-class comparisons. Currently, there are active efforts to develop intelligence tests based on the Piagetan scheme of the epigenetic development of intelligence.

Emotional development. Parallel to the stages of cognitive development are the stages of emotional development. Despite the conventional practice of separating them, they are clearly interdependent. Indeed, it is the care-taking person who provides the major stimulus to both aspects of mental growth. The human infant is totally dependent on adult caretakers for sheer survival. It is in relation to regular and hence predictable events of care-taking that an affectional tie between infant and care-taker develops; his behavioral repertoire expands as his acts have consequences in the form of social responses from the care-takers.

The Freudian formulation that the tie to the mother develops solely or principally by extension from the nursing act takes far too restricted a view of the interoceptive and exteroceptive channels stimulated by mothering and important to the sensory hierarchy of the infant. Contact does not play the role in the human infant demonstrated by Harlow for the monkey, but touch, smell, sight, sound, warmth, kinesthetic stimulation, and the infant's own behavior do enter into the complex of care. As perceptual and cognitive maturation occurs, the infant is able to relate these initially disconnected and separate experiences to the person who provides them and to distinguish her from other persons in the environment.

The severity of the effects resulting from deprivation of mothering care attests to the central role of mothering—*and fathering*—in the normal developmental process. However, just as with Bowlby's initial view that irreversible harm results from early lack, Erikson's concept that a sense of trust—confident expectation that needs will be met—is elaborated primarily from need satisfaction in the *first year* of life is one-sided and incomplete. The basis for trust in others *begins* to emerge from good care in infancy, but trust is in no sense a final acquisition of this first year and must be continuously reinforced during all of childhood and adolescence if it is to become a prevailing trait. A more accurate formulation would be that the nucleus of trust is established in infancy but that the issue is far from settled.

Toddler Stage

The second year of life is marked by acceleration of motor and intellectual development. The ability to walk confers on the toddler a degree of control over his own actions that allows him to determine when to approach and when to withdraw. The acquisition of speech profoundly extends his horizons. Typically the child learns to say "no" before he learns to say "yes." Correspondingly, the infant knows what he doesn't want long before he is able to formulate what he does want. The negativism of the toddler is a vital stage in individuation. "It is useless to be able to do what one cannot stop doing," noted Lao-Tse.

The second and third years of life are a period of increasing social demands on the child. The clinical observation that toilet-training can become a focus of struggle between mother and child has led to the simplistic formulation that toilet-training in itself is a critical event for character formation. The prolific literature on this subject implies that training is inevitably a traumatic event, but this is a distorted formulation based on one-sided experience with disturbed families. It *can* be elevated to a central issue by a rigid, severe, and restricting mother, but it varies with the culture and with the temperamental characteristics of mother and child. The fortunate mother whose child has regular bowel function with predictable evacuations can train him with a minimum of effort, in contrast to the potential for trouble provided by an irregular youngster. When toilet-training problems are associated with clinical psychiatric disorders, it is not necessarily because of the toilet-training itself but rather because toilet-training serves a paradigm of the general training practices of the family—that is, the mother who is overly severe in this area is likely to be punitive and restrictive in others as well. Thus, what appears to be a consequence of toilet-training is a consequence of general child-rearing practices, of which this is only an instance. The child's ability to accommodate himself to social demands by the acquisition of self-control can lead to pride in self and zestful striving for a new accomplishment; if he surrenders to parental coercion with shame at his physiological functions and doubt as to his own worth, he emerges inhibited, fearful, and stereotyped; if he rebels, he may remain stubborn and oppositional.

Parallel to the changing tasks for the child are changing tasks for his parents. Whereas in the stage of infancy the major responsibility for parents is to meet the infant's needs in a sensitive and giving fashion, without so anticipating and so fulfilling his needs that he never experiences tension, the parental task at the toddler stage is a requirement for firmness about the boundaries of acceptable behavior and encouragement of the progressive emancipation of the child. The child must be allowed to do for himself insofar as he is able, but he must be protected and assisted when the challenges are beyond him.

In the fourth year of life, there is further augmentation of the youngster's capacities, which, however, still run well behind his aspirations; he often undertakes things he cannot complete successfully. He becomes capable of anticipation as a basis for accepting the postponement of immediate gratification. There is a flowering of imagination, as revealed in controlled fantasy and play. Play is a central psychological activity for this period. It is, to begin with, fun: the sheer pleasure of exercising new executive capacities and acquiring mastery. It serves the function of releasing tension and energy. Following stress, it can provide emotional catharsis. But perhaps most important of all, the trial roles assumed in dramatic play allow the child to try out the adult identities he will one day have to understand and to assume. It is during this era that sexual identity is firmly established.

Psychosexual development. The forerunners of sexual differentiation are evident from birth when parents dress infants differently and treat them differently because of the differential expectations evoked by sex typing. The child through imitation, reward, and coercion assumes the behaviors that his culture defines for his sexual role. The way he walks, talks, and gestures; the level of activity he is permitted; the games he plays—all are differential by sex, and all serve to identify him to others and to tell him about himself as his role becomes crystallized. He exhibits active curiosity about anatomical sex. If this curiosity is recognized as healthy and is met with honest and age-appropriate replies, he acquires a sense of the wonder of life and comfort about his own role in it. If the subject is taboo and his questions rebuffed, he responds with shame and discomfort.

At this stage he is likely to struggle for the exclusive affection and attention of his parents. This includes both rivalry with his siblings and with one or another parent for the star role in the family. Although he is beginning to be able to share, he gives up only with difficulty. Psychoanalysis has emphasized the competition for the exclusive possession of the parent of the opposite sex and rivalry with the same-sexed parent, the oedipal conflict. Here again, the elaboration of theory based on the study of disturbed patients—indeed, of adult patients whose recollections of early childhood are distorted by fantasy—has led to an unwarranted focus on the oedipal problem. It is more useful to conceptualize the developmental task as one of acquiring a comfortable sharing of love roles in the family rather than a distorted love affair with a parent whose response sexualizes the child's search for security and comfort. If the demands for exclusive possession are not effectively resolved, the result is likely to be jealous competitiveness in relations with peers and lovers. The fantasies aroused by the struggle lead to fear of retaliation and displacement of fear onto external objects. These issues are important in elaborating the basis for conscience. In an equitable, loving family, the child elaborates a moral system of ethical rights freely contracted. This contrasts with conscience based on terror, with fear of retaliation for unchecked cupidity, leading to ritualized and rigid moralism.

School Period

As the child enters kindergarten and elementary school, the formal mands for academic learning, particularly in Western society, becor jor determinants of further personality development. So cruci´ task of developing competence that success or failure in i⊢

child's image of himself as a capable and adequate person or as an inferior and feckless one.

Intelligence measurement. Although the child's intelligence as measured by I.Q. tests is the single variable that correlates most highly with academic success, the coefficient of correlation between I.Q. and grades does not exceed 0.6 to 0.7, thus accounting for no more than a third to a half of the variance. Equally salient are motivation, work habits, creativity, and other traits for which there are as yet no quantitative measures. There is impressive evidence that the disadvantageous circumstances associated with urban slum life depress motivation, measured I.Q., and academic accomplishment. Eisenberg reported in 1966 that from a third to a half of children from urban slums are more than two years retarded in reading by the sixth grade, and the gap is even greater by the ninth grade. These are the youngsters who are likely to drop out of school and to join the mass of chronically unemployable adults because of lack of salable skills.

Unfortunately, by a process of circular reasoning, the poor school performance is commonly explained by the poor I.Q., which is attributed to the genetic consequences of assortative mating—that is, the inferior academic accomplishments of slum dwellers are attributed to biological inadequacy. This viewpoint has been espoused at least since the time of Plato, who invented the myth of the men of gold, silver, brass, and iron as a useful falsehood to persuade citizens to accept their destiny in the state. In its contemporary version, its advocates justify the conclusion that the poor are inferior by pointing to their school performance, without recognizing the role of the inadequacy of the education provided to them in determining that performance.

The children of the urban slum, of migrant workers, of ghettoized minority groups are doubly disadvantaged. They arrive at school poorly motivated, unfamiliar with the academic materials that are commonplace in the middle-class home, with short attention span, with language deficient in vocabulary and in syntactical structure, rich in survival behaviors suitable for the alleys of the city but highly inappropriate in school. Once they arrive, they are faced with schools that are overcrowded, obsolescent in physical structure, inadequately staffed, and frequently staffed by ill-trained and poorly motivated teachers. Is it then a wonder that serial measures, both of I.Q. and of academic attainment, show a progressively widening gap between these children and those more favored?

Indeed, one of the most pernicious of myths is the notion of constancy of the I.Q. Though it is true that I.Q. measures on groups of children show remarkable apparent constancy over a period of several years, the scores for individual children within the group, even of middle-class children, show wide variation. For example, in the Fels study of I.Q. from age 3 to age 12, two-thirds of the children varied more than 15 points in I.Q.—and one showed as much as a 58-point change—despite a mean group I.Q. that remained at about 120. Noteworthy in these studies was the observation that children who at 5 displayed the traits associated with achievement motivation—independence, competitiveness, self-initiation— were among those likely to show I.Q. gains, whereas those low on these measures were characterized by declining I.Q. figures.

Indeed, all this was said by Binet, whose psychometric methods have been suborned for a purpose he deplored:

> Some recent philosophers appear to have given their moral support to the deplorable verdict that the intelligence of the individual is a fixed quantity. . . . We must protest and act against this brutal pessimism. . . . A child's mind is like a field for which an expert farmer has advised a change in the method of cultivating, with the result that in place of desert land, we now have a harvest. It is in this particular sense, the one which is significant, that we say that the intelligence of children may be increased. One increases that which constitutes the intelligence of a school child, namely, the capacity to learn, to improve with instruction.

That Binet was indeed correct is evident from the modification of cognitive performance by preschool enrichment programs for disadvantaged 5-year-old slum-dwellers. In studies on Project Head Start in Baltimore in the summer of 1965, the Peabody Picture Vocabulary Test (PPVT) and the Harris-Goodenough Draw-a-Person (DAP), which correlate respectably with standard I.Q. measures on the usual population samples, were administered to the Head Start children and to a control group. On the PPVT, the controls and the Head Start children showed no significant difference on the pretest, but the Head Start children showed improvement during and after the program (see Table I).

In the DAP, Head Start children also showed improvement, but the

TABLE I

Raw Scores for Head Start Subjects and Controls in Peabody Picture Vocabulary Test (PPVT) and Harris-Goodenough Draw-a-Person (DAP)

| | Head Start | | | | | | | |
| | First week of program | | Sixth week of program | | Two weeks after program | | Controls[a] | |
	PPVT	DAP	PPVT	DAP	PPVT	DAP	PPVT	DAP
Mean	32.63	7.71	36.83	9.10	39.74	9.75	33.65	8.91
Standard deviation	12.33	4.79	10.82	4.20	11.34	4.41	11.70	4.98
Number of cases	(424)	(500)	(423)	(476)	(413)	(435)	(402)	(420)

[a] Controls were tested two weeks after the end of the Head Start program.

controls scored about the same as the Head Start children half-way through the program (see Table I). This suggests either that the function tapped by the DAP matures with less dependence on outside stimulation or that the stimulus configurations necessary for its development are relatively more available in the slum environment.

The question remains: What has changed in relation to the Head Start experience? That the difference is not simply ascribable to test practice is suggested by test-retest data reported by others. That the effects are substantial and reproducible is indicated by the studies of Gray and Klaus and of Dunn and Mueller with children given longer enrichment experiences. It is not at all clear whether Head Start has improved understanding of instructions, involvement in the test situation, attentiveness, planfulness, familiarity with test materials and methods, hearing vocabulary, verbal intelligence, visuomotor performance, or intellectual maturity.

The dependence of intelligence, that which cognitive tests attempt to measure, on such primary traits as the ability to sustain attention and to inhibit impulsive responding is illustrated by findings in the treatment of children with hyperkinetic behavior disorders with stimulant drugs (dextroamphetamine and methylphenidate). The patients were given Porteus Maze Tests before and after treatment by active drug or placebo in a double-blind design. As Table II indicates, the children treated by the

TABLE II

Porteus Maze Test Quotient Scores Before and After Treatment[a]

	Drug		Placebo	
	Before	After	Before	After
Number of cases	(19)	(19)	(19)	(17)
Mean	102.79	118.63	105.63	107.59
Standard deviation	16.37	10.41	17.14	18.66

[a] The drug given was a stimulant, either dextroamphetamine or methylphenidate. $t(df = 34) = 3.32; P < 0.01$.

stimulant drug showed a highly significant improvement in Porteus I.Q., whereas the placebo group showed no change. Was intelligence increased? Or did the drug, by diminishing impulsiveness, reveal the intelligence that was really there? Clearly, the answer depends on what is included in the definition of intelligence.

There is no innate intelligence. Intelligence is as intelligence does, for it is *behavior* that is measured. Intelligent behavior emerges from the interaction between the characteristics of the child and the demands and opportunities of his environment. These statements do not represent a denial of the reality of individual differences. The emphasis on nature *or* nurture in polemics on intelligence is a false issue. *All* behavior is inherited; *all* behavior is acquired. It is as meaningful to ask how much is inherited and how much acquired as it is to ask how much of the area of a rectangle is due to the length and how much to the width. There can be no behavior without both nature and nurture. The relevant questions are: With nature held constant, what is the variance produced by differences in nurture? With nurture held constant, how much variance can be produced by differences in nature?

Aggressive behavior. The frequency of aggressive behavior in children is often used as an argument for an innate aggressive instinct. Here is yet another instance of the widespread tendency to substitute for the actual study of infantile behavior the mere a priori assignment of motives on the basis of spurious analogies with adult motivations. In the normal child, aggression can be effectively understood in terms of the motives—defense, mastery, curiosity—for which aggressiveness is a suitable mediator. Its greater frequency in the abnormal child can be correlated with defects in the organism, as in the case of brain injury, or with distortions in his environment, as in the case of faulty identification models. Moreover, the frequency of display of aggressive behavior is a function of the culture in which the child is reared. Aggressive fantasy materials—movies, crime comics, and so on—rather than affording catharsis for instinctual aggressiveness, generate the very tensions they profess to release. It is not the ubiquity of aggression that needs to be accounted for; it is its remarkably wide variation from culture to culture, from time to time in a given culture, and from individual to individual in a given culture at a given time.

A central issue is the meaning to be ascribed to the term "aggression." If a child is observed taking apart a watch, this behavior can be described as aggressive. In a given instance, it may be—if, for example, the watch belongs to the child's father, and the father has just punished him. On the other hand, if the watch is an old one in his stock of toys, his motive may be curiosity about its mechanism—a belief more readily accepted if his delight as he is able to reassemble it in working order is observed. If he strikes another child, this can be an act of aggression. It well may be if the victim is the baby sister his parents have just embraced. Or it may be defensive if the victim has made a threatening gesture or has tried to seize a favorite toy. Homely anecdotes serve to make the point, but documented experimental examples are readily available—children emulating adult models, children systematically subjected to frustration, children watching films of aggressive behavior—all of whom show predictable increases in aggressiveness.

The doctrine of aggressive instincts exhibits a curious indirectness of reasoning. All active behavior is labeled aggressive. The label is then taken as sufficient to represent the source. In so doing, this argument reflects the ambiguity of everyday language, in which aggressive is defined at one and the same time as "assaultive and violent" and as "energetic and vigorous." Surely, there is a world of difference between an assault intended to destroy and a vigorous effort to cope adaptively. To argue that the latter is but a sublimated equivalent of the former is to substitute mere verbal trickery for detailed behavioral analysis. The capacity for aggression is indeed inherent in the biological organization of man, as it is in all mammals; its display is, however, conditioned by other determinants.

ADOLESCENCE

Adolescence is a critical period of development, with manifestations at the biological, psychological, and social levels of integration; it is a period of variable onset and duration, marking the end of childhood and setting the foundation for maturity. Biologically, its onset is signaled by the final phase of acceleration of growth and the beginnings of secondary sexual development, and its termination is marked by epiphyseal fusion and the completion of sexual differentiation. Psychologically, it is marked by an acceleration of cognitive growth and personality formation and is succeeded by the stage of parenthood and the acquisition of an adult work role. Socially, it is a period of intensified preparation for the assumption of an adult role, and its termination is signaled when the individual is accorded full adult prerogatives, the timing and nature of which vary widely from society to society.

Development at the biological, psychological, and social levels of integration is marked by significant interaction between levels, with events at any one level being able to impede or accelerate development at each of the others. Although the time at which the hypothalamic-pituitary axis initiates growth acceleration and sexual maturation is a function of individual heredity, it may be delayed or advanced by environmental factors. The ultimate height attained by adolescents in economically developing countries has shown striking gains as nutrition has improved—as, for example, in Japan since the war. Similarly, the time of menarche has shown a trend toward acceleration in countries with improving standards of nutrition and health; these physiological trends are the result of industrial and social organization.

In similar fashion, biological maturation provides the muscular strength and dexterity that permits the adolescent to participate successfully in the activities of his peer group, success at which promotes a psychological feeling of adequacy. At the same time, positive psychological motivation is a prerequisite for task perseverance and the search for variety of experience, which provides the conditions necessary for full muscular development through exercise. Folk beliefs about diet may lead to inadequate nutritional intake; social prejudices against minority group members may deny them the experiences necessary for full individuation. The importance of these reciprocal influences is underscored by the fact that each society is ultimately dependent on its adolescents as its future adults. Failure to provide the conditions necessary for their optimal development will handicap the growth potential of the society.

Biological factors. Biological factors set wide limits for the onset, termination, and achievements of adolescence. Onset in normal children may occur as early as age 7 or 8 or as late as 17 or 18; termination may be as early as 15 or 16 or as late as 24 or 25. The timing is a function both of internal factors, such as sex and inheritance, and of external factors, such as nutrition and medical care.

Social factors. Adolescence as a social phenomenon, though restricted by biological limits, is a function of cultural norms. The more sophisticated a society in its technology, the more prolonged the period of adolescence, since the complexity of the preparation required for adult roles depends on the demands the society sets. In the United States the long period of study required for specialized occupational roles delays the age of self-support, the opportunity for marriage, and the age of creative contribution to society—all attributes of the adult role.

In many cultures the onset of adolescence is clearly signaled by puberty rites, usually in the form of tests of strength and courage. In technologically advanced societies, there is no such clear signification of the end of childhood; moreover, the requirements for adulthood are less sharply defined; the individual must undergo a more prolonged and, at times, confused struggle to attain adult status.

Psychological factors. At a psychological level, the most striking attainment during adolescence is the ability for abstract conceptualization. It is here that the foundations of scientific contribution and of creativity are to be found. The adolescent's capacity for abstract thought accounts for his increasing concern with national and international problems and with the basic meanings and values of human existence. This idealism of adolescents is shaped by the cultural envelope that surrounds the individual, but its very existence leads to questioning, to examination of basic premises, and to dissatisfaction with the imperfections in the world as it is. Fostering and strengthening this suprapersonal psychological trait in adolescence leads to the creation of adults who enhance the society that bred them. The denial of opportunity for its positive expression warps development and leads to a generation of self-preoccupied adults who may fail to meet the challenge of history.

A related theme of adolescence is the search for a sense of personal identity, in the cogent terminology of Erikson. No longer a child and not yet an adult, the adolescent engages busily in determining who he is and what he is to become. He examines his parents from a more critical perspective and leans more to peer groups for his sense of belonging. If his relations with his parents have been soundly constructed and if they meet his doubts and criticisms with sympathetic understanding, this temporary unsettling of his prior role leads to a resynthesis of his relations with them on a firm and lasting basis, one marked by reciprocal respect and by personal independence without abandonment of filial loyalty. Where the prior parent-child relationship has been one of excessive dependence or excessive hostility, adolescent turmoil may be prolonged and lead either to failure of emancipation or to rejection of family ties and a lasting sense of isolation.

A third major psychological issue is the further evolution of psychosexual role. The development of adult sexual characteristics and the experience of a bewildering array of new physical sensations, both of which lead to an upsurge of interest in physical sex and a psychological sensitization to a new aspect of interpersonal relationships, challenge the psychosexual structures of childhood. Comparative studies indicate that, as the scale of evolution is ascended, sexual behavior is less dependent on hormones and more dependent on learning. In man the role of hormones is limited to priming the organism for biological maturation and to influencing but not determining solely the level of libido; the direction, nature, and adequacy of sexual performance are controlled by psychosocial factors. The many investigations of the biology of sex deviants have failed to identify chromosomal, hormonal, or gonadal aberrations. The remarkable variation in sexual behavior between societies and between social classes within a single society emphasizes the cultural determinants of sexual behavior, given adequate biological maturation.

The ambivalence of Western society toward sexuality—manifested by the conflicts between official attitudes and private behaviors and the pervasive emphasis on sex side by side with sanctions against its expression—contributes to the difficulty, so common in adolescence, of attaining the basis for a sense of competence, freedom, and pleasure as a sexually functioning adult. Adolescents are entitled to full and unambiguous information about the physiology of sex *and* its ethical significance as an intimate relationship between human beings. Commonly expressed fears that providing such information to adolescents will lead to premature experimentation run contrary to clinical experience, which indicates that ignorance of sex and impoverishment of human relationships account for sexual misadventures. A sense of inadequacy in sexuality not only impairs sexual function but leads to disabilities in other adult roles.

The search for identity is markedly influenced by peer groups. If these are constructive social groups that provide creative outlets for adolescent energy, the result is a sense of meaningful membership in the community and identification with its goals. But if the peer group is a delinquent gang, with values antagonistic to the larger society, the result is likely to be antisocial personality organization. The experience of growing up as a member of a disadvantaged minority group, with attendant humiliation and denial of opportunity, makes it difficult for the adolescent to identify with the values of the society at large and favors instead hostility toward its norms and a disposition to anarchistic individualism. However, even under these circumstances, leadership and social forms that permit the disadvantaged adolescent to employ his energy in efforts to change unjust social patterns can foster his emergence into creative adulthood.

The family is an important agent in transmitting the behavior patterns and values expected of the adolescent by society. Distortions in family structure, whether idiosyncratic or socially induced, inevitably have profound effects on individual development. The social consequences of economic disadvantage—poor health, reduced longevity, poor education, extralegal marital arrangements, the necessity for exploiting children economically—erode family structure. The unemployed drifting father and the unmarried deserted mother not only fail to provide their children with adequate nurture but also serve as poor identification models. The aggregation of disadvantaged families in decaying neighborhoods all too often reinforces family psychopathology by exposing the adolescent to delinquent gangs and ineffective schooling.

The sensitivity of the adolescent to the good opinion of his peers and the dependence of his sense of identity on the attainment of competence in an adult role render him psychologically vulnerable to variations in physiological development, such as precocious or delayed growth, acne, obesity, enlarged mammary glands in the males, and inadequate or overabundant breast development in the female. These deviations from expected patterns of maturation, though they may be without great medical significance, can lead to major psychological harm if not offset by sensitive guidance by the physician. The adolescent with limited intellectual or physical capacity can develop a persisting and even unchangeable feeling of inferiority if he is forced to compete in situations in which he repeatedly experiences failure. The individualization of education and vocational training for adolescents is essential, both to permit the talented individual to exploit his abilities and to direct the youngster with specific limitations to activities that develop the capacities he does have.

The characteristic fluidity of psychological structure in adolescence results in the common display of transient symptoms, many of which resemble the psychopathological syndromes of adulthood. The clinician must exercise great caution lest he misinterpret the turbulent but temporary maladaptive patterns manifested by the adolescents. Incorrect diagnostic formulations may lead to social consequences that freeze into permanence an otherwise readily correctable deviation in the normal growth pattern. It is, of course, true that schizophrenia and manic-depressive psychosis appear at significant rates for the first time in adolescence. However, these remain relatively uncommon disorders and must be discriminated from panic states in a youngster confronted by overwhelming internal and external stimulation.

The psychological basis for a sense of individual worth as an adult rests on the acquisition of competence in a work role during adolescence. A sense of competence is acquired not by being reassured but by experiencing success in a socially important task. The educational challenge is to stimulate abilities to the utmost without setting standards so high that they lead to inevitable defeat. The educational accomplishment must be matched by an opportunity for the individual to exercise his competence as a worker in the economic world. The sustained motivation necessary for mastering a difficult work role is only possible when there is a real likelihood of fulfilling that role in adult life and of having it respected by others. The task of providing full employment in a world in which automation is revolutionizing traditional work roles is a challenge to the citizenry and the government.

The capacity for engagement in meaningful social activity is present in young people in every country of the world. For all the dismay caused by the disengagement and alienation experienced by many American adolescents, the dedication, zest for life, and commitment displayed by workers in the Peace Corps, VISTA, and the civil rights movement give us faith that this is a generation better than our own. The provision of an optimal framework for adolescent development is inseparable from the struggle to create a better world by helping to mold the citizens who will build it.

AFTER ADOLESCENCE

Development continues as long as life continues. As social roles change, as intellectual and physical capacities first advance and later recede, new challenges demand new adaptations. Studies of sensory deprivation in the normal volunteer have emphasized the role of sensory input in maintaining reality-testing and perceptual organization. Social input is necessary for the maintenance of personality organization. What appear to be remarkable constancies of personality over a lifetime are not to be taken as evidence of a crystallized and unchangeable structure; rather, they result from the constant reinforcement of personality traits by the social environment in which the individual moves. Changes in the social field—brought about by chance, social change, or catastrophe—can lead to profound alterations in personal function.

The adult psychiatrist, no less than the child psychiatrist, must view his patient in dynamic terms as an organism with a history, with a set of attitudes and expectations, and with profound dependence on the forces in his social field. The patient should be assessed as much in terms of his abilities as his disabilities, as much in terms of what he can become as what he has been and what he is. Clinical diagnosis and treatment are most effective when based on a view that stresses personality as an emergent, constantly in the process of formation and never fully complete.

REFERENCES

Ainsworth, M. D. The effects of maternal deprivation: review of findings and controversy in the context of research strategy. In *Deprivation of Maternal Care*. Public Health Papers, No. 14, p. 97. World Health Organization, Geneva, 1962.
Aries, P. *Centuries of Childhood*. Alfred A. Knopf, New York, 1962.

Binet, A. *Les Idées Modernes sur les Enfants*. Ernest Flammarion, Paris, 1909.

Bowlby, J. *Maternal Care and Mental Health*, ed. 2. Monograph Series No. 2. World Health Organization, Geneva, 1952.

Bridger, W. H. Sensory habituation and discrimination in the human neonate. Amer. J. Psychiat., 117: 991, 1961.

Conel, J. L. *The Postnatal Development of the Human Cerebral Cortex*, 5 vols. Harvard University Press, Cambridge, 1939–1955.

Conners, C. K., and Eisenberg, L. The effects of methylphenidate on symptomatology and learning in disturbed children. Amer. J. Psychiat., 120: 458, 1963.

DeVore, I. *Primate Behavior*. Holt, Rinehart and Winston, New York, 1965.

Eisenberg, L. If not now, when? Amer. J. Orthopsychiat., 32: 781, 1962.

Eisenberg, L. Reading retardation I. Psychiatric and sociologic aspects. Pediatrics, 37: 352, 1966.

Eisenberg, L., Conners, C. K., and Sharpe, L. A controlled study of the differential application of outpatient psychiatric treatment for children. Jap. J. Child Psychiat., 6: 125, 1965.

Erikson, E. H. *Identity and the Life Cycle*. Psychological Issues, Monograph No. 1. International Universities Press, New York, 1959.

Flavell, J. H. *The Developmental Psychology of Jean Piaget*. D. Van Nostrand, New York, 1963.

Freud, S. *Reflections on War and Death*. Moffat, Yard, & Co., New York, 1918.

Gesell, A. *The First Five Years of Life*. Harper & Bros., New York, 1940.

Goldfarb, W. Emotional and intellectual consequences of deprivation in infancy: a re-evaluation. In *Psychopathology of Childhood*, P. H. Hoch and J. Zubin, editors. Grune & Stratton, New York, 1965.

Goodall, J. Tool using and aimed throwing in a community of free-living chimpanzees. Nature, 201: 1264, 1964.

Gray, S. W., and Klaus, R. A. An experimental preschool program for culturally deprived children. Child Develop., 36: 887, 1965.

Harlow, H. F. The nature of love. Amer. Psychologist, 13: 673, 1958.

Harlow, H. F., and Harlow, M. K. *The Affectional Systems in Behavior of Non-Human Primates*, A. M. Schrier, H. F. Harlow, and F. Stollnitz, editors, vol. 2. Academic Press, New York, 1965.

Held, R., and Hein A., Movement-produced stimulation in the development of visually guided behavior. J. Comp. Physiol. Psychol., 56: 872, 1963.

Hewes, G. W. Hominid bipedalism: independent evidence for the food-carrying theory. Science, 146: 416, 1964.

Hunt, J. McV. *Intelligence and Experience*. Ronald Press, New York, 1961.

Jung, C. G. *Psychology of the Unconscious*. Dodd, Mead, & Co., New York, 1927.

Kessen, W. *The Child*. Wiley, New York, 1965.

Lehrman, D. S. The reproductive behavior of ring doves. Sci. Amer., 211: 48, 1964.

Lipton, E. L., Steinschneider, A., and Richmond, J. B. The autonomic nervous system in early life. N. Eng. J. Med., 273: 147, 201, 1965.

Needham, J. *A History of Embryology*. Abelard-Schuman, New York, 1959.

Pasamanick, B., and Knobloch, H. Retrospective studies on the epidemiology of reproductive casualty: old and new. Merrill-Palmer Quart. Behav. Develop., 12: 7, 1966.

Riesen, A. H. Effects of stimulus deprivation on the development and atrophy of the visual sensory system. Amer. J. Orthopsychiat., 30: 23, 1960.

Rose, J. E., Malis, L. I., Kruger, L., and Baker, C. P. Effects of heavy, ionizing, monoenergetic particles on the cerebral cortex. II. Histological appearance of laminar lesions and growth of nerve fibers after laminar destruction. J. Comp.

Neurol., 115: 243, 1960.

Sayegh, Y., and Dennis, W. The effect of supplementary experiences upon the behavioral development of infants in institutions. Child Develop., 36: 81, 1965.

Schneirla, T. C., and Rosenblatt, J. S. Behavioral organization and genesis of the social bond in insects and mammals. Amer. J. Orthopsychiat., 31: 223, 1961.

Skeels, H. M. Adult status of children with contrasting early life experiences. Monogr. Soc. Res. Child Develop., 31: Ser. 105, No. 3, 1966.

Skeels, H. M., and Dye, H. B. A study of the effects of differential stimulation on mentally retarded children. Proc. Amer. Assoc. Ment. Def., 44: 114, 1939.

Sontag, L. W., Baker, C. T., and Nelson, V. L. Mental growth and personality formation. Monogr. Soc. Res. Child Develop., 23: Ser. 68, No. 2, 1958.

Thomas, A., Birch, H. G., Chess, S., Hertzig, M. E., and Korn, S. Behavioral Individuality in Early Childhood. New York University Press, New York, 1965.

Wiesel, T. N., and Hubel, D. H. Effects of visual deprivation on morphology and physiology of cells in the cat's lateral geniculate body. J. Neurophysiol., 26: 978, 1963.

Wiesel, T. N., and Hubel, D. H. Single cell responses in striate cortex of kittens deprived of vision in one eye. J. Neurophysiol., 26: 1003, 1963.

AREA B

---

*Assessment in
Child Psychiatry*

CHAPTER THREE

Classification of Child Psychiatric Disorders

HAROLD I. KAPLAN, M.D.

THE FIRST EDITION of *Diagnostic and Statistical Manual: Mental Disorders* (DSM-I) was published by the American Psychiatric Association in 1952. In 1968 the second edition, DSM-II, appeared. DSM-II presents what is now the official psychiatric nomenclature used in the United States. The diagnostic terms in DSM-II are defined in Table I. The reader should note that this table includes only a few specific categories limited to children—IX. Behavior Disorders of Childhood and Adolescence. Table II compares DSM-I and DSM-II.

In 1966 the Group for the Advancement of Psychiatry published its own classification of child psychiatric disorders in *Psychopathological Disorders in Childhood: Theoretical Considerations and a Proposed Classification*. This classification, although unofficial, is of importance and is listed in Table III. There is still much dissatisfaction about the child psychiatric classifications in DSM-II. The reader is referred to Fish's discussion in Chapter 4 for an evaluation of the assets and weaknesses of the new official classification and a comparison of DSM-II and the GAP classification.

The nosology used in this book is a combination of DSM-II, DSM-I, and the GAP report. However, since the official nomenclature must be used in records and official reports, the reader may translate all diagnostic terms used in this book into DSM-II terminology by using Tables I and II.

TABLE I
The New Diagnostic Nomenclature of Mental Disorders:
Definition of Terms

I. MENTAL RETARDATION [1] (310–315)

Mental retardation refers to subnormal general intellectual functioning which originates during the developmental period and is associated with impairment of either learning and social adjustment or maturation, or both. (These disorders were classified under "Chronic brain syndrome with mental deficiency" and "Mental deficiency" in DSM-I.) The diagnostic classification of mental retardation relates to IQ as follows[2]:

310 Borderline mental retardation–IQ 68–83
311 Mild mental retardation–IQ 52–67
312 Moderate mental retardation–IQ 36–51
313 Severe mental retardation–IQ 20–35
314 Profound mental retardation–IQ under 20

Classifications 310–314 are based on the statistical distribution of levels of intellectual functioning for the population as a whole. The range of intelligence subsumed under each classification corresponds to one standard deviation, making the heuristic assumption that intelligence is normally distributed. It is recognized that the intelligence quotient should not be the only criterion used in making a diagnosis of mental retardation or in evaluating its severity. It should serve only to help in making a clinical judgment of the patient's adaptive behavioral capacity. This judgment should also be based on an evaluation of the patient's developmental history and present functioning, including academic and vocational achievement, motor skills, and social and emotional maturity.

315 Unspecified mental retardation

This classification is reserved for patients whose intellectual functioning has not or cannot be evaluated precisely but which is recognized as clearly subnormal.

Reprinted with permission from the second edition of *Diagnostic and Statistical Manual of Mental Disorders* (DSM-II), published by the American Psychiatric Association, 1968.

[1] For a fuller definition of terms see the "Manual on Terminology and Classification in Mental Retardation" (supplement to *American Journal of Mental Deficiency*, second edition, 1961), from which most of this section has been adapted.

[2] The IQ's specified are for the Revised Stanford-Binet Tests of Intelligence, Forms L and M. Equivalent values for other tests are listed in the manual cited in the footnote above.

CLINICAL SUBCATEGORIES OF MENTAL RETARDATION

These will be coded as fourth digit subdivisions following each of the categories 310–315. When the associated condition is known more specifically, particularly when it affects the entire organism or an organ system other than the central nervous system, it should be coded additionally in the specific field affected.

.0 Following infection and intoxication

This group is to classify cases in which mental retardation is the result of residual cerebral damage from intracranial infections, serums, drugs, or toxic agents. Examples are:

Cytomegalic inclusion body disease, congenital. A maternal viral disease, usually mild or subclinical, which may infect the fetus and is recognized by the presence of inclusion bodies in the cellular elements in the urine, cerebrospinal fluid, and tissues.

Rubella, congenital. Affecting the fetus in the first trimester and usually accompanied by a variety of congenital anomalies of the ear, eye, and heart.

Syphilis, congenital. Two types are described, an early meningovascular disease and a diffuse encephalitis leading to juvenile paresis.

Toxoplasmosis, congenital. Due to infection by a protozoanlike organism, Toxoplasma, contracted in utero. May be detected by serological tests in both mother and infant.

Encephalopathy associated with other prenatal infections. Occasionally fetal damage from maternal epidemic cerebrospinal meningitis, equine encephalomyelitis, influenza, etc., has been reported. The relationships have not as yet been definitely established.

Encephalopathy due to postnatal cerebral infection. Both focal and generalized types of cerebral infection are included and are to be given further anatomic and etiologic specification.

Encephalopathy, congenital, associated with maternal toxemia of pregnancy. Severe and prolonged toxemia of pregnancy, particularly eclampsia, may be associated with mental retardation.

Encephalopathy, congenital, associated with other maternal intoxications. Examples are carbon monoxide, lead, arsenic, quinine, ergot, etc.

Bilirubin encephalopathy (Kernicterus). Frequently due to Rh, A, B, O blood group incompatibility between fetus and mother but may also follow prematurity, severe neonatal sepsis, or any condition producing high levels of serum bilirubin. Choreoathetosis is frequently associated with this form of mental retardation.

Post-immunization encephalopathy. This may follow inoculation with serum, particularly antitetanus serum, or vaccines such as smallpox, rabies, and typhoid.

Encephalopathy, other, due to intoxication. May result from such toxic agents as lead, carbon monoxide, tetanus, and botulism exotoxin.

.1 Following trauma or physical agent

Further specification within this category follows:

Encephalopathy due to prenatal injury. This includes prenatal irradiation and asphyxia, the latter following maternal anoxia, anemia, and hypotension.

Encephalopathy due to mechanical injury at birth. These are attributed to difficulties of labor due to malposition, malpresentation, disproportion, or other complications leading to dystocia which may increase the probability of damage to the infant's brain at birth, resulting in tears of the meninges, blood vessels, and brain substance. Other reasons include venous-sinus thrombosis, arterial embolism, and thrombosis. These may result in sequelae which are indistinguishable from those of other injuries, damage, or organic impairment of the brain.

Encephalopathy due to asphyxia at birth. Attributable to the anoxemia following interference with placental circulation due to premature separation, placenta praevia, cord difficulties, and other interferences with oxygenation of the placental circulation.

Encephalopathy due to postnatal injury. The diagnosis calls for evidence of severe trauma such as a fractured skull, prolonged unconsciousness, etc., followed by a marked change in development. Postnatal asphyxia, infarction, thrombosis, laceration, and contusion of the brain would be included and the nature of the injury specified.

.2 With disorders of metabolism, growth, or nutrition

All conditions associated with mental retardation directly due to metabolic, nutritional, or growth dysfunction should be classified here, including disorders of lipid, carbohydrate, and protein metabolism and deficiencies of nutrition.

Cerebral lipoidosis, infantile (Tay-Sach's disease). This is caused by a single recessive autosomal gene and has infantile and juvenile forms. In the former there is gradual deterioration, blindness after the pathognomonic "cherry-red spot," with death occurring usually before age 3.

Cerebral lipoidosis, late infantile (Bielschowsky's disease). This differs from the preceding by presenting retinal optic atrophy instead of the "cherry-red spot."

Cerebral lipoidosis, juvenile (Spielmeyer-Vogt disease). This usually appears between the ages of 5 and 10 with involvement of the motor systems, frequent seizures, and pigmentary degeneration of the retina. Death follows in five to ten years.

Cerebral lipoidosis, late juvenile (Kuf's disease). This is categorized under mental retardation only when it occurs at an early age.

Lipid histiocystosis of kerasin type (Gaucher's disease). As a rule this condition causes retardation only when it affects infants. It is characterized by Gaucher's cells in lymph nodes, spleen, or marrow.

Lipid histiocystosis of phosphatide type (Niemann-Pick's disease). Distinguished from Tay-Sach's disease by enlargement of liver and spleen. Biopsy of spleen, lymph, or marrow show characteristic "foam cells."

Phenylketonuria. A metabolic disorder, genetically transmitted as a simple autosomal recessive gene, preventing the conversion of phenylalanine into tyrosine with an accumulation of phenylalanine, which in turn is converted to phenylpyruvic acid detectable in the urine.

Hepatolenticular degeneration (Wilson's disease). Genetically transmitted as a simple autosomal recessive. It is due to inability of ceruloplasmin to bind copper, which in turn damages the brain. Rare in children.

Porphyria. Genetically transmitted as a dominant and characterized by excretion of porphyrins in the urine. It is rare in children, in whom it may cause irreversible deterioration.

Galactosemia. A condition in which galactose is not metabolized, causing its accumulation in the blood. If milk is not removed from the diet, generalized organ deficiencies, mental deterioration, and death may result.

Glucogenosis (Von Gierke's disease). Due to a deficiency in glycogen-metabolizing enzymes with deposition of glycogen in various organs, including the brain.

Hypoglycemosis. Caused by various conditions producing hypoglycemia which, in the infant, may result in epilepsy and mental defect. Diagnosis may be confirmed by glucose tolerance tests.

.3 Associated with gross brain disease (postnatal)

This group includes all diseases and conditions associated with neoplasms, but not growths that are secondary to trauma or infection. The category also includes a number of postnatal diseases and conditions in which the structural reaction is evident but the etiology is unknown or uncertain, though frequently presumed to be of hereditary or familial nature. Structural reactions may be degenerative, infiltrative, inflammatory, proliferative, sclerotic, or reparative.

Neurofibromatosis (Neurofibroblastomatosis, von Recklinghausen's disease). A disease transmitted by a dominant autosomal gene but with reduced penetrance and variable expressivity. It is characterized by cutaneous pigmentation ("café au lait" patches) and neurofibromas of nerve, skin, and central nervous system with intellectual capacity varying from normal to severely retarded.

Trigeminal cerebral angiomatosis (Sturge-Weber-Dimitri's disease). A condition characterized by a "port wine stain" or cutaneous angioma, usually in the distribution of the trigeminal nerve, accompanied by vascular malformation over the meninges of the parietal and occipital lobes with underlying cerebral maldevelopment.

Tuberous sclerosis (Epiloia, Bourneville's disease). Transmitted by a dominant autosomal gene, characterized by multiple gliotic nodules in the central nervous system, and associated with adenoma sebaceum of the face and tumors in other organs. Retarded development and seizures may appear early and increase in severity along with tumor growth.

Intracranial neoplasm, other. Other relatively rare neoplastic diseases leading to mental retardation should be included in this category and specified when possible.

Encephalopathy associated with diffuse sclerosis of the brain. This category includes a number of similar conditions differing to some extent in their pathological and clinical features but characterized by diffuse demyelination of the white matter with resulting diffuse glial sclerosis and accompanied by intellectual deterioration. These diseases are often familial in character and, when possible, should be specified under the following:

ACUTE INFANTILE DIFFUSE SCLEROSIS (KRABBE'S DISEASE).

DIFFUSE CHRONIC INFANTILE SCLEROSIS (MERZBACHER-PELIZAEUS DISEASE, APLASIA AXIALIS EXTRACORTICALIS CONGENITA).

INFANTILE METACHROMATIC LEUKODYSTROPHY (GREENFIELD'S DISEASE).

JUVENILE METACHROMATIC LEUKODYSTROPHY (SCHOLZ'S DISEASE).

PROGRESSIVE SUBCORTICAL ENCEPHALOPATHY (ENCEPHALITIS PERIAXIALIS DIFFUSA, SCHILDER'S DISEASE).

SPINAL SCLEROSIS (FRIEDREICH'S ATAXIA). Characterized by cerebellar degeneration, early onset followed by dementia.

Encephalopathy, other, due to unknown or uncertain cause with the structural reactions manifest. This category includes cases of mental retardation associated with progressive neuronal degeneration or other structural defects which cannot be classified in a more specific, diagnostic category.

.4 Associated with diseases and conditions due to unknown prenatal influence

This category is for classifying conditions known to have existed at the time of or prior to birth but for which no definite etiology can be established. These include the primary cranial anomalies and congenital defects of undetermined origin as follows:

Anencephaly (including hemianencephaly).

Malformations of the gyri. This includes agyria, macrogyria (pachygyria), and microgyria.

Porencephaly, congenital. Characterized by large funnel-shaped cavities occurring anywhere in the cerebral hemispheres. Specify, if possible, whether the porencephaly is a result of asphyxia at birth or postnatal trauma.

Multiple-congenital anomalies of the brain.

Other cerebral defects, congenital.

CRANIOSTENOSIS. The most common conditions included in this category are acrocephaly (oxycephaly) and scaphocephaly. These may or may not be associated with mental retardation.

HYDROCEPHALUS, CONGENITAL. Under this heading is included only that type of hydrocephalus present at birth or occurring soon after delivery. All other types of hydrocephalus, secondary to other conditions, should be classified under the specific etiology when known.

HYPERTELORISM (GREIG'S DISEASE). Characterized by abnormal development of the sphenoid bone increasing the distance between the eyes.

MACROCEPHALY (MEGALENCEPHALY). Characterized by an increased size and weight of the brain due partially to proliferation of glia.

MICROCEPHALY, PRIMARY. True microcephaly is probably transmitted as a single autosomal recessive. When it is caused by other conditions, it should be classified according to the primary condition, with secondary microcephaly as a supplementary term.

LAURENCE-MOON-BIEDL SYNDROME. Characterized by mental retardation associated with retinitis pigmentosa, adiposo-genital dystrophy, and polydactyly.

.5 With chromosomal abnormality

This group includes cases of mental retardation associated with chromosomal abnormalities. These may be divided into two sub-groups, those associated with an abnormal number of chromosomes and those with abnormal chromosomal morphology.

Autosomal trisomy of group G (Trisomy 21, Langdon-Down disease, Mongolism). This is the only common form of mental retardation due to chromosomal abnormality. (The others are relatively rare.) It ranges in degree from moderate to severe with infrequent cases of mild retardation. Other congenital defects are frequently present, and the intellectual development decelerates with time.

Autosomal trisomy of group E.

Autosomal trisomy of group D.

Sex chromosome anomalies. The only condition under the category which has any significant frequency is Klinefelter's syndrome.

Abnormal number of chromosomes, other. In this category would be included monosomy G and possibly others as well as other forms of mosaicism.

Short arm deletion of chromosome 5—group B (Cri du chat). A quite rare condition characterized by congenital abnormalities and a catlike cry during infancy which disappears with time.

Short arm deletion of chromosome 18—group E.
Abnormal morphology of chromosomes, other. This category includes a variety of translocations, ring chromosomes, fragments, and
isochromosomes associated with mental retardation.

.6 Associated with prematurity

This category includes retarded patients who had a birth weight of less
than 2,500 grams (5.5 pounds) and/or a gestational age of less than
thirty-eight weeks at birth, and who do not fall into any of the preceding
categories. This diagnosis should be used only if the patient's mental retardation cannot be classified more precisely under categories .0 to .5
above.

.7 Following major psychiatric disorder

This category is for mental retardation following psychosis or other
major psychiatric disorder in early childhood when there is no evidence
of cerebral pathology. To make this diagnosis, there must be good evidence that the psychiatric disturbance was extremely severe. For example,
retarded young adults with residual schizophrenia should not be classified
here.

.8 With psychosocial (environmental) deprivation

This category is for the many cases of mental retardation with no
clinical or historical evidence of organic disease or pathology but for
which there is some history of psychosocial deprivation. Cases in this
group are classified in terms of psychosocial factors which appear to bear
some etiological relationship to the condition as follows:
   Cultural-familial mental retardation. Classification here requires that
   evidence of retardation be found in at least one of the parents and
   in one or more siblings, presumably because some degree of cultural
   deprivation results from familial retardation. The degree of retardation
   is usually mild.
   Associated with environmental deprivation. An individual deprived
   of normal environmental stimulation in infancy and early childhood
   may prove unable to acquire the knowledge and skills required to function normally. This kind of deprivation tends to be more severe than
   that associated with familial mental retardation (q.v.). This type of
   deprivation may result from severe sensory impairment, even in an
   environment otherwise rich in stimulation. More rarely it may result
   from severe environmental limitations or atypical cultural milieus. The
   degree of retardation is always marginal or mild.

.9 With other [and unspecified] condition

II. ORGANIC BRAIN SYNDROMES

(Disorders caused by or associated with impairment of brain tissue function)

These disorders are manifested by the following symptoms:

(a) Impairment of orientation
(b) Impairment of memory
(c) Impairment of all intellectual functions such as comprehension, calculation, knowledge, learning, etc.
(d) Impairment of judgment
(e) Lability and shallowness of affect

The organic brain syndrome is a basic mental condition characteristically resulting from diffuse impairment of brain tissue function from whatever cause. Most of the basic symptoms are generally present to some degree regardless of whether the syndrome is mild, moderate, or severe.

The syndrome may be the only disturbance present. It may also be associated with psychotic symptoms and behavioral disturbances. The severity of the associated symptoms is affected by and related to not only the precipitating organic disorder but also the patient's inherent personality patterns, present emotional conflicts, his environmental situation, and interpersonal relations.

These brain syndromes are grouped into psychotic and nonpsychotic disorders according to the severity of functional impairment. The psychotic level of impairment is described on page 23 [54 in this book] and the nonpsychotic on pages 31–32 [61].

It is important to distinguish "acute" from "chronic" brain disorders because of marked differences in the course of illness, prognosis and treatment. The terms indicate primarily whether the brain pathology and its accompanying organic brain syndrome is reversible. Since the same etiology may produce either temporary or permanent brain damage, a brain disorder which appears reversible (acute) at the beginning may prove later to have left permanent damage and a persistent organic brain syndrome which will then be diagnosed "chronic." Some brain syndromes occur in either form. Some occur only in acute forms (e.g., *Delirium tremens*). Some occur only in chronic form (e.g., *Alcoholic deterioration*). The acute and chronic forms may be indicated for those disorders coded in four digits by the addition of a fifth qualifying digit: .x1 *acute* and .x2 *chronic*.

THE PSYCHOSES

Psychoses are described in two places in this Manual, here with the organic brain syndromes and later with the functional psychoses. The general discussion of psychosis appears here because organic brain syndromes are listed first in DSM-II.

Patients are described as psychotic when their mental functioning is sufficiently impaired to interfere grossly with their capacity to meet the ordinary demands of life. The impairment may result from a serious distortion in their capacity to recognize reality. Hallucinations and delusions, for example, may distort their perceptions. Alterations of mood may be so profound that the patient's capacity to respond appropriately is grossly impaired. Deficits in perception, language, and memory may be so severe that the patient's capacity for mental grasp of his situation is effectively lost.

Some confusion results from the different meanings which have become attached to the word "psychosis." Some nonorganic disorders (295–298), in the well-developed form in which they were first recognized, typically rendered patients psychotic. For historical reasons these disorders are still classified as psychoses, even though it now generally is recognized that many patients for whom these diagnoses are clinically justified are not in fact psychotic. This is true particularly in the incipient or convalescent stages of the illness. To reduce confusion, when one of these disorders listed as a "psychosis" is diagnosed in a patient who is not psychotic, the qualifying phrase *not psychotic* or *not presently psychotic* should be noted and coded .x6 with a fifth digit.

Example: 295.06 *Schizophrenia, simple type, not psychotic.*

It should be noted that this Manual permits an organic condition to be classified as a psychosis only if the patient is psychotic during the episode being diagnosed.

If the specific physical condition underlying one of these disorders is known, indicate it with a separate, additional diagnosis.

II. A. PSYCHOSES ASSOCIATED WITH ORGANIC BRAIN SYNDROMES (290–294)

290 Senile and Presenile dementia

290.0 *Senile dementia*

This syndrome occurs with senile brain disease, whose causes are largely unknown. The category does not include the presenile psychoses nor other degenerative diseases of the central nervous system. While senile brain disease derives its name from the age group in which it is most commonly seen, its diagnosis should be based on the brain disorder present and not on the patient's age at times of onset. Even mild cases will manifest some evidence of organic brain syndrome: self-centeredness, difficulty in assimilating new experiences, and childish emotionality. Deterioration may be minimal or progress to vegetative existence. (This condition was called "Chronic Brain Syndrome associated with senile brain disease" in DSM-I.)

290.1 *Presenile dementia*

This category includes a group of cortical brain diseases presenting clinical pictures similar to those of senile dementia but appearing characteristically in younger age groups. Alzheimer's and Pick's diseases are the two best known forms, each of which has a specific brain pathology. (In DSM-I Alzheimer's disease was classified as "Chronic Brain Syndrome with other disturbance of metabolism." Pick's disease was "Chronic Brain Syndrome associated with disease of unknown cause.") When the impairment is not of psychotic proportion the patient should be classified under *Nonpsychotic OBS with senile or presenile brain disease.*

291 Alcoholic psychoses

Alcoholic psychoses are psychoses caused by poisoning with alcohol (see page 23 [53]). When a preexisting psychotic, psychoneurotic, or other disorder is aggravated by modest alcohol intake, the underlying condition, not the alcoholic psychosis, is diagnosed.

Simple drunkenness, when not specified as psychotic, is classified under *Nonpsychotic OBS with alcohol.*

In accordance with ICD-8, this Manual subdivides the alcoholic psychoses into *Delirium tremens, Korsakov's psychosis, Other alcoholic hallucinosis,* and *Alcoholic paranoia.* DSM-II also adds three further subdivisions: *Acute alcohol intoxication, Alcoholic deterioration,* and *Pathological intoxication.* (In DSM-I "Acute Brain Syndrome, alcohol intoxication" included what is now *Delirium tremens, Other alcoholic hallucinosis, Acute alcohol intoxication,* and *Pathological intoxication.*)

291.0 Delirium tremens

This is a variety of acute brain syndrome characterized by delirium, coarse tremors, and frightening visual hallucinations usually becoming more intense in the dark. Because it was first identified in alcoholics and until recently was thought always to be due to alcohol ingestion, the term is restricted to the syndrome associated with alcohol. It is distinguished from *Other alcoholic hallucinosis* by the tremors and the disordered sensorium. When this clinical picture is due to a nutritional deficiency rather than to alcohol poisoning, it is classified under *Psychosis associated with metabolic or nutritional disorder.*

291.1 Korsakov's psychosis (alcoholic) Also "Korsakoff"

This is a variety of chronic brain syndrome associated with long-standing alcohol use and characterized by memory impairment, disorientation, peripheral neuropathy, and particularly by confabulation. Like delirium tremens, Korsakov's psychosis is identified with alcohol because of an initial error in identifying its cause, and therefore the term is confined to the syndrome associated with alcohol. The similar syndrome due to nutritional deficiency unassociated with alcohol is classified *Psychosis associated with metabolic or nutritional disorder.*

291.2 Other alcoholic hallucinosis

Hallucinoses caused by alcohol which cannot be diagnosed as delirium tremens, Korsakov's psychosis, or alcoholic deterioration fall in this category. A common variety manifests accusatory or threatening auditory hallucinations in a state of relatively clear consciousness. This condition must be distinguished from schizophrenia in combination with alcohol intoxication, which would require two diagnoses.

291.3 Alcohol paranoid state ((Alcoholic paranoia))[3]

This term describes a paranoid state which develops in chronic alcoholics, generally male, and is characterized by excessive jealousy and delusions of infidelity by the spouse. Patients diagnosed under primary paranoid states or schizophrenia should not be included here even if they drink to excess.

291.4* Acute alcohol intoxication* [4]

All varieties of acute brain syndromes of psychotic proportion caused by alcohol are included here if they do not manifest features of delirium tremens, alcoholic hallucinosis, or pathological intoxication. This diagnosis is used alone when there is no other psychiatric disorder or as an additional diagnosis with other psychiatric conditions including alcoholism. The condition should not be confused with *simple drunkenness*, which does not involve psychosis. (All patients with this disorder would have been diagnosed "Acute Brain Syndrome, alcohol intoxication" in DSM-I.)

291.5* Alcoholic deterioration*

All varieties of chronic brain syndromes of psychotic proportion caused by alcohol and not having the characteristic features of Korsakov's psychosis are included here. (This condition and Korsakov's psychosis were both included under "Chronic Brain Syndrome, alcohol intoxication with psychotic reaction" in DSM-I.)

291.6* Pathological intoxication*

This is an acute brain syndrome manifested by psychosis after minimal alcohol intake (In DSM-I this diagnosis fell under "Acute Brain Syndrome, alcohol intoxication.")

291.9 Other [and unspecified] [5] alcoholic psychosis

This term refers to all varieties of alcoholic psychosis not classified above.

292 Psychosis associated with intracranial infection

292.0 General paralysis

This condition is characterized by physical signs and symptoms of parenchymatous syphilis of the nervous system, and usually by positive serology, including the paretic gold curve in the spinal fluid. The condition may simulate any of the other psychoses and brain syn-

---

[3] Double parentheses indicate ICD-8 terms equivalent to U. S. terms.
[4] Asterisk indicates categories added to ICD-8 for use in the United States only.
[5] Brackets indicate ICD-8 categories to be avoided in the United States or used by record librarians only.

dromes. If the impairment is not of psychotic proportion, it is classified *Nonpsychotic OBS with intracranial infection*. If the specific underlying physical condition is known, indicate it with a separate, additional diagnosis. (This category was included under "Chronic Brain Syndrome associated with central nervous system syphilis (meningoencephalitic)" in DSM-I.)

292.1 Psychosis with other syphilis of central nervous system

This includes all other varieties of psychosis attributed to intracranial infection by **Spirochaeta pallida**. The syndrome sometimes has features of organic brain syndrome. The acute infection is usually produced by meningovascular inflammation and responds to systemic antisyphilitic treatment. The chronic condition is generally due to gummata. If not of psychotic proportion, the disorder is classified *Nonpsychotic OBS with intracranial infection*. (In DSM-I "Chronic Brain Syndrome associated with other central nervous system syphilis" and "Acute Brain Syndrome associated with intracranial infection" covered this category.)

292.2 Psychosis with epidemic encephalitis
        (von Economo's encephalitis)

This term is confined to the disorder attributed to the viral epidemic encephalitis that followed World War I. Virtually no cases have been reported since 1926. The condition, however, is differentiated from other encephalitis. It may present itself as acute delirium and sometimes its outstanding feature is apparent indifference to persons and events ordinarily of emotional significance, such as the death of a family member. It may appear as a chronic brain syndrome and is sometimes dominated by involuntary, compulsive behavior. If not of psychotic proportions, the disorder is classified under *Nonpsychotic OBS with intracranial infection*. (This category was classified under "Chronic Brain Syndrome associated with intracranial infection other than syphilis" in DSM-I.)

292.3 Psychosis with other and unspecified encephalitis

This category includes disorders attributed to encephalitic infections other than epidemic encephalitis and also to encephalitis not otherwise specified.[6] When possible, the type of infection should be indicated. If not of psychotic proportion, the disorder is classified under *Nonpsychotic OBS with intracranial infection*.

292.9 Psychosis with other [and unspecified] intracranial infection

This category includes all acute and chronic conditions due to nonsyphilitic and nonencephalitic infections, such as meningitis and brain abscess. Many of these disorders will have been diagnosed as the acute form early in the course of the illness. If not of psychotic proportion,

[6] A list of important encephalitides may be found in *A Guide to the Control of Mental Disorders*, American Public Health Association, Inc., New York, 1962, pp. 40 ff.

the disorder should be classified under *Nonpsychotic OBS with intra-cranial infection.* (In DSM-I the acute variety was classified as "Acute Brain Syndrome associated with intracranial infection" and the chronic variety as "Chronic Brain Syndrome associated with intracranial infection other than syphilis.")

293 Psychosis associated with other cerebral condition

This major category, as its name indicates, is for all psychoses associated with cerebral conditions *other* than those previously defined. For example, the degenerative diseases following do *not* include the previous senile dementia. If the specific underlying physical condition is known, indicate it with a separate, additional diagnosis.

293.0 Psychosis with cerebral arteriosclerosis

This is a chronic disorder attributed to cerebral arteriosclerosis. It may be impossible to differentiate it from senile dementia and pre-senile dementia, which may coexist with it. Careful consideration of the patient's age, history, and symptoms may help determine the pre-dominant pathology. Commonly, the organic brain syndrome is the only mental disturbance present, but other reactions, such as depression or anxiety, may be superimposed. If not of psychotic proportion, the condition is classified under *Nonpsychotic OBS with circulatory disturbance.* (In DSM-I this was called "Chronic Brain Syndrome associated with cerebral arteriosclerosis.")

293.1 Psychosis with other cerebrovascular disturbance

This category includes such circulatory disturbances as cerebral thrombosis, cerebral embolism, arterial hypertension, cardio-renal disease, and cardiac disease, particularly in decompensation. It excludes conditions attributed to arteriosclerosis. The diagnosis is determined by the underlying organ pathology, which should be specified with an additional diagnosis. (In DSM-I this category was divided between "Acute Brain Syndrome associated with circulatory disturbance" and "Chronic Brain Syndrome associated with circulatory disturbance other than cerebral arteriosclerosis.")

293.2 Psychosis with epilepsy

This category is to be used only for the condition associated with "idiopathic" epilepsy. Most of the etiological agents underlying chronic brain syndromes can and do cause convulsions, particularly syphilis, intoxication, trauma, cerebral arteriosclerosis, and intracranial neoplasms. When the convulsions are symptomatic of such diseases, the brain syndrome is classified under those disturbances rather than here. The disturbance most commonly encountered here is the clouding of consciousness before or after a convulsive attack. Instead of a convulsion, the patient may show only a dazed reaction with deep confusion, bewilderment, and anxiety. The epileptic attack may also take the form of an episode of excitement with hallucinations, fears, and violent outbreaks. (In DSM-I this was included in "Acute Brain Syndrome associated with convulsive disorder" and "Chronic Brain Syndrome associated with convulsive disorder.")

293.3 Psychosis with intracranial neoplasm

Both primary and metastatic neoplasms are classified here. Reactions to neoplasms other than in the cranium should not receive this diagnosis. (In DSM-I this category included "Acute Brain Syndrome associated with intracranial neoplasm" and "Chronic Brain Syndrome associated with intracranial neoplasm.")

293.4 Psychosis with degenerative disease of the central nervous system

This category includes degenerative brain diseases not listed previously. (In DSM-I this was part of "Acute Brain Syndrome with disease of unknown or uncertain cause" and "Chronic Brain Syndrome associated with diseases of unknown or uncertain cause.")

293.5 Psychosis with brain trauma

This category includes those disorders which develop immediately after severe head injury or brain surgery and the post-traumatic chronic brain disorders. It does not include permanent brain damage which produces only focal neurological changes without significant changes in sensorium and affect. Generally, trauma producing a chronic brain syndrome is diffuse and causes permanent brain damage. If not of psychotic proportions, a post-traumatic personality disorder associated with an organic brain syndrome is classified as a *Nonpsychotic OBS with brain trauma*. If the brain injury occurs in early life and produces a developmental defect of intelligence, the condition is also diagnosed *Mental retardation*. A head injury may precipitate or accelerate the course of a chronic brain disease, especially cerebral arteriosclerosis. The differential diagnosis may be extremely difficult. If, before the injury, the patient had symptoms of circulatory disturbance, particularly arteriosclerosis, and now shows signs of psychosis, he should be classified *Psychosis with cerebral arteriosclerosis*. (In DSM-I this category was divided between "Acute Brain Syndrome associated with trauma" and "Chronic Brain Syndrome associated with brain·trauma.")

293.9 Psychosis with other [and unspecified] cerebral condition

This category is for cerebral conditions other than those listed above, and conditions for which it is impossible to make a more precise diagnosis. [Medical record librarians will include here *Psychoses with cerebral condition, not otherwise specified*.]

294 Psychosis associated with other physical condition

The following psychoses are caused by general systemic disorders and are distinguished from the *cerebral* conditions previously described. If the specific underlying physical condition is known, indicate it with a separate, additional diagnosis.

294.0 Psychosis with endocrine disorder

This category includes disorders caused by the complications of diabetes other than cerebral arteriosclerosis and disorders of the thyroid, pituitary, adrenals, and other endocrine glands. (In DSM-I "Chronic Brain Syndrome associated with other disturbances of metabolism, growth, or nutrition" included the chronic variety of these disorders. DSM-I defined these conditions as "disorders of metabolism," but they here are considered endocrine disorders.)

294.1 Psychosis with metabolic or nutritional disorder

This category includes disorders caused by pellagra, avitaminosis, and metabolic disorders. (In DSM-I this was part of "Acute Brain Syndrome associated with metabolic disturbance" and "Chronic Brain Syndrome associated with other disturbance of metabolism, growth, or nutrition.")

294.2 Psychosis with systemic infection

This category includes disorders caused by severe general systemic infections, such as pneumonia, typhoid fever, malaria, and acute rheumatic fever. Care must be taken to distinguish these reactions from other disorders, particularly manic-depressive illness and schizophrenia, which may be precipitated by even a mild attack of infectious disease. (In DSM-I this was confined to "Acute Brain Syndrome associated with systemic infection.")

294.3 Psychosis with drug or poison intoxication (other than alcohol)

This category includes disorders caused by some drugs (including psychedelic drugs), hormones, heavy metals, gases, and other intoxicants except alcohol. (In DSM-I these conditions were divided between "Acute Brain Syndrome, drug or poison intoxication" and "Chronic Brain Syndrome, associated with intoxication." The former excluded alcoholic acute brain syndromes, while the latter included alcoholic chronic brain syndromes.)

294.4 Psychosis with childbirth

Almost any type of psychosis may occur during pregnancy and the post-partum period and should be specifically diagnosed. This category is not a substitute for a differential diagnosis and excludes other psychoses arising during the puerperium. Therefore, this diagnosis should not be used unless all other possible diagnoses have been excluded.

294.8 Psychosis with other and undiagnosed physical condition

This is a residual category for psychoses caused by physical conditions other than those listed earlier. It also includes brain syndromes caused by physical conditions which have not been diagnosed. (In DSM-I this condition was divided between "Acute Brain Syndrome of unknown cause" and "Chronic Brain Syndrome of unknown cause." However, these categories also included the category now called *Psychosis with other [and unspecified] cerebral condition*.)

[294.9 Psychosis with unspecified physical condition]

This is not a diagnosis but is included for use by medical record librarians only.

II. B. NONPSYCHOTIC ORGANIC BRAIN SYNDROMES (309)

309 Nonpsychotic organic brain syndromes ((Mental disorders not specified as psychotic associated with physical conditions))

This category is for patients who have an organic brain syndrome but are not psychotic. If psychoses are present they should be diagnosed as previously indicated. Refer to pages 22–23 [p. 53] for description of organic brain syndromes in adults.

In children mild brain damage often manifests itself by hyperactivity, short attention span, easy distractability, and impulsiveness. Sometimes the child is withdrawn, listless, perseverative, and unresponsive. In exceptional cases there may be great difficulty in initiating action. These characteristics often contribute to a negative interaction between parent and child. If the organic handicap is the major etiological factor and the child is not psychotic, the case should be classified here. If the interactional factors are of major secondary importance, supply a second diagnosis under *Behavior disorders of childhood and adolescence;* if these interactional factors predominate, give only a diagnosis from this latter category.

309.0 *Nonpsychotic OBS with intracranial infection*
309.1 *Nonpsychotic OBS with drug, poison, or systemic intoxication*
   309.13* NONPSYCHOTIC OBS WITH ALCOHOL* (SIMPLE DRUNKENNESS)
   309.14* NONPSYCHOTIC OBS WITH OTHER DRUG, POISON, OR SYSTEMIC INTOXICATION*
309.2 *Nonpsychotic OBS with brain trauma*
309.3 *Nonpsychotic OBS with circulatory disturbance*
309.4 *Nonpsychotic OBS with epilepsy*
309.5 *Nonpsychotic OBS with disturbance of metabolism, growth, or nutrition*
309.6 *Nonpsychotic OBS with senile or presenile brain disease*
309.7 *Nonpsychotic OBS with intracranial neoplasm*
309.8 *Nonpsychotic OBS with degenerative disease of central nervous system*
309.9 *Nonpsychotic OBS with other [and unspecified] physical condition*
   [.91* ACUTE BRAIN SYNDROME, NOT OTHERWISE SPECIFIED*]
   [.92* CHRONIC BRAIN SYNDROME, NOT OTHERWISE SPECIFIED*]

III. PSYCHOSES NOT ATTRIBUTED TO PHYSICAL CONDITIONS LISTED PREVIOUSLY (295–298)

This major category is for patients whose psychosis is not caused by physical conditions listed previously. Nevertheless, some of these patients may show additional signs of an organic condition. If these organic signs are prominent, the patient should receive the appropriate additional diagnosis.

295 Schizophrenia

This large category includes a group of disorders manifested by characteristic disturbances of thinking, mood, and behavior. Disturbances in thinking are marked by alterations of concept formation which may lead to misinterpretation of reality and sometimes to delusions and hallucinations, which frequently appear psychologically self-protective. Corollary mood changes include ambivalent, constricted, and inappropriate emotional responsiveness and loss of empathy with others. Behavior may be withdrawn, regressive, and bizarre. The schizophrenias, in which the mental status is attributable primarily to a *thought* disorder, are to be distinguished from the *Major affective illnesses* (q.v.), which are dominated by a *mood* disorder. The *Paranoid states* (q.v.) are distinguished from schizophrenia by the narrowness of their distortions of reality and by the absence of other psychotic symptoms.

295.0 Schizophrenia, simple type

This psychosis is characterized chiefly by a slow and insidious reduction of external attachments and interests and by apathy and indifference leading to impoverishment of interpersonal relations, mental deterioration, and adjustment on a lower level of functioning. In general, the condition is less dramatically psychotic than are the hebephrenic, catatonic, and paranoid types of schizophrenia. Also, it contrasts with schizoid personality, in which there is little or no progression of the disorder.

295.1 Schizophrenia, hebephrenic type

This psychosis is characterized by disorganized thinking, shallow and inappropriate affect, unpredictable giggling, silly and regressive behavior and mannerisms, and frequent hypochondriacal complaints. Delusions and hallucinations, if present, are transient and not well organized.

295.2 Schizophrenia, catatonic type

295.23* SCHIZOPHRENIA, CATATONIC TYPE, EXCITED*
295.24* SCHIZOPHRENIA, CATATONIC TYPE, WITHDRAWN*

It is frequently possible and useful to distinguish two subtypes of catatonic schizophrenia. One is marked by excessive and sometimes violent motor activity and excitement and the other by generalized inhibition manifested by stupor, mutism, negativism, or waxy flexibility. In time, some cases deteriorate to a vegetative state.

295.3 Schizophrenia, paranoid type

This type of schizophrenia is characterized primarily by the presence of persecutory or grandiose delusions, often associated with hallucinations. Excessive religiosity is sometimes seen. The patient's attitude is frequently hostile and aggressive, and his behavior tends to be consistent with his delusions. In general the disorder does not manifest the gross personality disorganization of the hebephrenic and catatonic types, perhaps because the patient uses the mechanism of projection, which ascribes to others characteristics he cannot accept in himself. Three subtypes of the disorder may sometimes be differentiated, depending on the predominant symptoms: hostile, grandiose, and hallucinatory.

295.4 Acute schizophrenic episode
This diagnosis does not apply to acute episodes of schizophrenic disorders described elsewhere. This condition is distinguished by the acute onset of schizophrenic symptoms, often associated with confusion, perplexity, ideas of reference, emotional turmoil, dreamlike dissociation, and excitement, depression, or fear. The acute onset distinguishes this condition from simple schizophrenia. In time these patients may take on the characteristics of catatonic, hebephrenic, or paranoid schizophrenia, in which case their diagnosis should be changed accordingly. In many cases the patient recovers within weeks, but sometimes his disorganization becomes progressive. More frequently remission is followed by recurrence. (In DSM-I this condition was listed as "Schizophrenia, acute undifferentiated type.")

295.5 Schizophrenia, latent type
This category is for patients having clear symptoms of schizophrenia but no history of a psychotic schizophrenic episode. Disorders sometimes designated as incipient, prepsychotic, pseudoneurotic, pseudopsychopathic, or borderline schizophrenia are categorized here. (This category includes some patients who were diagnosed in DSM-I under "Schizophrenic reaction, chronic undifferentiated type." Others formerly included in that DSM-I category are now classified under *Schizophrenia, other [and unspecified] types* (q.v.).)

295.6 Schizophrenia, residual type
This category is for patients showing signs of schizophrenia but who, following a psychotic schizophrenic episode, are no longer psychotic.

295.7 Schizophrenia, schizo-affective type
This category is for patients showing a mixture of schizophrenic symptoms and pronounced elation or depression. Within this category it may be useful to distinguish excited from depressed types as follows:

295.73* SCHIZOPHRENIA, SCHIZO-AFFECTIVE TYPE, EXCITED*
295.74* SCHIZOPHRENIA, SCHIZO-AFFECTIVE TYPE, DEPRESSED*

295.8* Schizophrenia, childhood type*
This category is for cases in which schizophrenic symptoms appear before puberty. The condition may be manifested by autistic, atypical, and withdrawn behavior; failure to develop identity separate from the mother's; and general unevenness, gross immaturity, and inadequacy in development. These developmental defects may result in mental re-

tardation, which should also be diagnosed. (This category is for use in the United States and does not appear in ICD-8. It is equivalent to "Schizophrenic reaction, childhood type" in DSM-I.)

295.90* Schizophrenia, chronic undifferentiated type*
This category is for patients who show mixed schizophrenic symptoms and who present definite schizophrenic thought, affect and behavior not classifiable under the other types of schizophrenia. It is distinguished from *Schizoid personality* (q.v.). (This category is equivalent to "Schizophrenic reaction, chronic undifferentiated type" in DSM-I except that it does not include cases now diagnosed as *Schizophrenia, latent type* and *Schizophrenia, other [and unspecified] types.*)

295.99* Schizophrenia, other [and unspecified] types*
This category is for any type of schizophrenia not previously described. (In DSM-I "Schizophrenic reaction, chronic undifferentiated type" included this category and also what is now called *Schizophrenia, latent type* and *Schizophrenia, chronic undifferentiated type.*)

296 Major affective disorders ((Affective psychoses))

This group of psychoses is characterized by a single disorder of mood, either extreme depression or elation, that dominates the mental life of the patient and is responsible for whatever loss of contact he has with his environment. The onset of the mood does not seem to be related directly to a precipitating life experience and therefore is distinguishable from *Psychotic depressive reaction* and *Depressive neurosis.* (This category is not equivalent to the DSM-I heading "Affective reactions," which included "Psychotic depressive reaction.")

296.0 Involutional melancholia
This is a disorder occurring in the involutional period and characterized by worry, anxiety, agitation, and severe insomnia. Feelings of guilt and somatic preoccupations are frequently present and may be of delusional proportions. This disorder is distinguishable from *Manic-depressive illness* (q.v.) by the absence of previous episodes; it is distinguished from *Schizophrenia* (q.v.) in that impaired reality testing is due to a disorder of mood; and it is distinguished from *Psychotic depressive reaction* (q.v.) in that the depression is not due to some life experience. Opinion is divided as to whether this psychosis can be distinguished from the other affective disorders. It is, therefore, recommended that involutional patients not be given this diagnosis unless all other affective disorders have been ruled out. (In DSM-I this disorder was considered one of two subtypes of "Involutional Psychotic Reaction.")

MANIC-DEPRESSIVE ILLNESSES (MANIC-DEPRESSIVE PSYCHOSES)
These disorders are marked by severe mood swings and a tendency to remission and recurrence. Patients may be given this diagnosis in the absence of a previous history of affective psychosis if there is no obvi-

ous precipitating event. This disorder is divided into three major subtypes: manic type, depressed type, and circular type.

296.1 Manic-depressive illness, manic type ((Manic-depressive psychosis, manic type))

This disorder consists exclusively of manic episodes. These episodes are characterized by excessive elation, irritability, talkativeness, flight of ideas, and accelerated speech and motor activity. Brief periods of depression sometimes occur, but they are never true depressive episodes.

296.2 Manic-depressive illness, depressed type ((Manic-depressive psychosis, depressed type))

This disorder consists exclusively of depressive episodes. These episodes are characterized by severely depressed mood and by mental and motor retardation progressing occasionally to stupor. Uneasiness, apprehension, perplexity, and agitation may also be present. When illusions, hallucinations, and delusions (usually of guilt or of hypochondriacal or paranoid ideas) occur, they are attributable to the dominant mood disorder. Because it is a primary mood disorder, this psychosis differs from the *Psychotic depressive reaction*, which is more easily attributable to precipitating stress. Cases incompletely labeled as "psychotic depression" should be classified here rather than under *Psychotic depressive reaction*.

296.3 Manic-depressive illness, circular type ((Manic-depressive psychosis, circular type))

This disorder is distinguished by at least one attack of both a depressive episode *and* a manic episode. This phenomenon makes clear why manic and depressed types are combined into a single category. (In DSM-I these cases were diagnosed under "Manic-depressive reaction, other.") The current episode should be specified and coded as one of the following:

296.33* MANIC-DEPRESSIVE ILLNESS, CIRCULAR TYPE, MANIC*

296.34* MANIC-DEPRESSIVE ILLNESS, CIRCULAR TYPE, DEPRESSED*

296.8 Other major affective disorder ((Affective psychosis, other))

Major affective disorders for which a more specific diagnosis has not been made are included here. It is also for "mixed" manic-depressive illness, in which manic and depressive symptoms appear almost simultaneously. It does not include *Psychotic depressive reaction* (q.v.) or *Depressive neurosis* (q.v.). (In DSM-I this category was included under "Manic depressive reaction, other.")

[**296.9 Unspecified major affective disorder**]

[AFFECTIVE DISORDER NOT OTHERWISE SPECIFIED]

[MANIC-DEPRESSIVE ILLNESS NOT OTHERWISE SPECIFIED]

297 Paranoid states

These are psychotic disorders in which a delusion, generally persecutory or grandiose, is the essential abnormality. Disturbances in mood, behavior, and thinking (including hallucinations) are derived from this delusion. This distinguishes paranoid states from the affective psychoses and schizophrenias, in which mood and thought disorders, respectively, are the central abnormalities. Most authorities, however, question whether disorders in this group are distinct clinical entities and not merely variants of schizophrenia or paranoid personality.

297.0 *Paranoia*

This extremely rare condition is characterized by gradual development of an intricate, complex, and elaborate paranoid system based on and often proceeding logically from misinterpretation of an actual event. Frequently the patient considers himself endowed with unique and superior ability. In spite of a chronic course the condition does not seem to interfere with the rest of the patient's thinking and personality.

297.1 *Involutional paranoid state* ((Involutional paraphrenia))

This paranoid psychosis is characterized by delusion formation with onset in the involutional period. Formerly it was classified as a paranoid variety of involutional psychotic reaction. The absence of conspicuous thought disorders typical of schizophrenia distinguishes it from that group.

297.9 *Other paranoid state*

This is a residual category for paranoid psychotic reactions not classified earlier.

298 Other psychoses

298.0 *Psychotic depressive reaction* ((Reactive depressive psychosis))

This psychosis is distinguished by a depressive mood attributable to some experience. Ordinarily the individual has no history of repeated depressions or cyclothymic mood swings. The differentiation between this condition and *Depressive neurosis* (q.v.) depends on whether the reaction impairs reality testing or functional adequacy enough to be considered a psychosis. (In DSM-I this condition was included with the affective psychoses.)

[298.1 *Reactive excitation*]

[298.2 *Reactive confusion*]

    [ACUTE OR SUBACUTE CONFUSIONAL STATE]

[298.3 *Acute paranoid reaction*]

[298.9 *Reactive psychosis, unspecified*]

[299 Unspecified psychosis]

    [DEMENTIA, INSANITY, OR PSYCHOSIS NOT OTHERWISE SPECIFIED]

This is not a diagnosis but is listed here for librarians and statisticians to use in coding incomplete diagnoses. Clinicians are expected to complete a differential diagnosis for patients who manifest features of several psychoses.

IV. NEUROSES (300)

300 Neuroses

Anxiety is the chief characteristic of the neuroses. It may be felt and expressed directly, or it may be controlled unconsciously and automatically by conversion, displacement, and various other psychological mechanisms. Generally, these mechanisms produce symptoms experienced as subjective distress from which the patient desires relief.

The neuroses, as contrasted to the psychoses, manifest neither gross distortion or misinterpretation of external reality nor gross personality disorganization. A possible exception to this is hysterical neurosis, which some believe may occasionally be accompanied by hallucinations and other symptoms encountered in psychoses.

Traditionally, neurotic patients, however severely handicapped by their symptoms, are not classified as psychotic because they are aware that their mental functioning is disturbed.

300.0 *Anxiety neurosis*

This neurosis is characterized by anxious over-concern extending to panic and frequently associated with somatic symptoms. Unlike *Phobic neurosis* (q.v.), anxiety may occur under any circumstances and is not restricted to specific situations or objects. This disorder must be distinguished from normal apprehension or fear, which occurs in realistically dangerous situations.

300.1 *Hysterical neurosis*

This neurosis is characterized by an involuntary psychogenic loss or disorder of function. Symptoms characteristically begin and end suddenly in emotionally charged situations and are symbolic of the underlying conflicts. Often they can be modified by suggestion alone. This is a new diagnosis that encompasses the former diagnoses "Conversion reaction" and "Dissociative reaction" in DSM-I. This distinction between conversion and dissociative reactions should be preserved by using one of the following diagnoses whenever possible.

300.13* HYSTERICAL NEUROSIS, CONVERSION TYPE*

In the conversion type, the special senses or voluntary nervous system are affected, causing such symptoms as blindness, deafness, anosmia, anaesthesias, paraesthesias, paralyses, ataxias, akinesias, and dyskinesias. Often the patient shows an inappropriate lack of concern or *belle indifférence* about these symptoms, which may actually provide secondary gains by winning him sympathy or relieving him of unpleasant responsibilities. This type of hysterical neurosis must be distinguished from psychophysiologic disorders, which are mediated by the autonomic nervous system; from malingering, which is done consciously; and from neurological lesions, which cause anatomically circumscribed symptoms.

300.14* HYSTERICAL NEUROSIS, DISSOCIATIVE TYPE*

In the dissociative type, alterations may occur in the patient's state of consciousness or in his identity, to produce such symptoms as amnesia, somnambulism, fugue, and multiple personality.

300.2 Phobic neurosis

This condition is characterized by intense fear of an object or situation which the patient consciously recognizes as no real danger to him. His apprehension may be experienced as faintness, fatigue, palpitations, perspiration, nausea, tremor, and even panic. Phobias are generally attributed to fears displaced to the phobic object or situation from some other object of which the patient is unaware. A wide range of phobias has been described.

300.3 Obsessive compulsive neurosis

This disorder is characterized by the persistent intrusion of unwanted thoughts, urges, or actions that the patient is unable to stop. The thoughts may consist of single words or ideas, ruminations, or trains of thought often perceived by the patient as nonsensical. The actions vary from simple movements to complex rituals such as repeated handwashing. Anxiety and distress are often present either if the patient is prevented from completing his compulsive ritual or if he is concerned about being unable to control it himself.

300.4 Depressive neurosis

This disorder is manifested by an excessive reaction of depression due to an internal conflict or to an identifiable event such as the loss of a love object or cherished possession. It is to be distinguished from Involutional melancholia (q.v.) and Manic-depressive illness (q.v.). Reactive depressions or Depressive reactions are to be classified here.

300.5 Neurasthenic neurosis ((Neurasthenia))

This condition is characterized by complaints of chronic weakness, easy fatigability, and sometimes exhaustion. Unlike hysterical neurosis the patient's complaints are genuinely distressing to him and there is no evidence of secondary gain. It differs from Anxiety neurosis (q.v.) and from the Psychophysiologic disorders (q.v.) in the nature of the predominant complaint. It differs from Depressive neurosis (q.v.) in the moderateness of the depression and in the chronicity of its course. (In DSM-I this condition was called "Psychophysiologic nervous system reaction.")

300.6 Depersonalization neurosis ((Depersonalization syndrome))

This syndrome is dominated by a feeling of unreality and of estrangement from the self, body, or surroundings. This diagnosis should not be used if the condition is part of some other mental disorder, such as an acute situational reaction. A brief experience of depersonalization is not necessarily a symptom of illness.

300.7 Hypochondriacal neurosis

This condition is dominated by preoccupation with the body and with fear of presumed diseases of various organs. Though the fears are not of delusional quality, as in psychotic depressions, they persist despite reassurance. The condition differs from hysterical neurosis in that there are no actual losses or distortions of function.

300.8 Other neurosis

This classification includes specific psychoneurotic disorders not classified elsewhere, such as "writer's cramp" and other occupational neuroses. Clinicians should not use this category for patients with "mixed" neuroses, which should be diagnosed according to the predominant symptom.

[300.9 Unspecified neurosis]

This category is not a diagnosis. It is for the use of record librarians and statisticians to code incomplete diagnoses.

V. PERSONALITY DISORDERS AND CERTAIN OTHER NONPSYCHOTIC MENTAL DISORDERS (301–304)

301 Personality disorders

This group of disorders is characterized by deeply ingrained maladaptive patterns of behavior that are perceptibly different in quality from psychotic and neurotic symptoms. Generally, these are life-long patterns, often recognizable by the time of adolescence or earlier. Sometimes the pattern is determined primarily by malfunctioning of the brain, but such cases should be classified under one of the nonpsychotic organic brain syndromes rather than here. (In DSM-I "Personality Disorders" also included disorders now classified under *Sexual deviation, Alcoholism,* and *Drug dependence.*)

301.0 Paranoid personality

This behavioral pattern is characterized by hypersensitivity, rigidity, unwarranted suspicion, jealousy, envy, excessive self-importance, and a tendency to blame others and ascribe evil motives to them. These characteristics often interfere with the patient's ability to maintain satisfactory interpersonal relations. Of course, the presence of suspicion of itself does not justify this diagnosis, since the suspicion may be warranted in some instances.

301.1 Cyclothymic personality ((Affective personality))

This behavior pattern is manifested by recurring and alternating periods of depression and elation. Periods of elation may be marked by ambition, warmth, enthusiasm, optimism, and high energy. Periods of depression may be marked by worry, pessimism, low energy, and a sense of futility. These mood variations are not readily attributable to external circumstances. If possible, the diagnosis should specify whether the mood is characteristically depressed, hypomanic, or alternating.

301.2 Schizoid personality

This behavior pattern manifests shyness, oversensitivity, seclusiveness, avoidance of close or competitive relationships, and often eccentricity. Autistic thinking without loss of capacity to recognize reality is common, as is daydreaming and the inability to express hostility and ordinary aggressive feelings. These patients react to disturbing experiences and conflicts with apparent detachment.

301.3 Explosive personality (Epileptoid personality disorder)

This behavior pattern is characterized by gross outbursts of rage or of verbal or physical aggressiveness. These outbursts are strikingly different from the patient's usual behavior, and he may be regretful and repentant for them. These patients are generally considered excitable, aggressive, and overresponsive to environmental pressures. It is the intensity of the outbursts and the individual's inability to control them which distinguishes this group. Cases diagnosed as "aggressive personality" are classified here. If the patient is amnesic for the outbursts, the diagnosis of *Hysterical neurosis, Nonpsychotic OBS with epilepsy,* or *Psychosis with epilepsy* should be considered.

301.4 Obsessive compulsive personality ((Anankastic personality))

This behavior pattern is characterized by excessive concern with conformity and adherence to standards of conscience. Consequently, individuals in this group may be rigid, overinhibited, overconscientious, overdutiful, and unable to relax easily. This disorder may lead to an *Obsessive compulsive neurosis* (q.v.), from which it must be distinguished.

301.5 Hysterical personality (Histrionic personality disorder)

These behavior patterns are characterized by excitability, emotional instability, overreactivity, and self-dramatization. This self-dramatization is always attention-seeking and often seductive, whether or not the patient is aware of its purpose. These personalities are also immature, self-centered, often vain, and usually dependent on others. This disorder must be differentiated from *Hysterical neurosis* (q.v.).

301.6 Asthenic personality

This behavior pattern is characterized by easy fatigability, low energy level, lack of enthusiasm, marked incapacity for enjoyment, and oversensitivity to physical and emotional stress. This disorder must be differentiated from *Neurasthenic neurosis* (q.v.).

301.7 Antisocial personality

This term is reserved for individuals who are basically unsocialized and whose behavior pattern brings them repeatedly into conflict with society. They are incapable of significant loyalty to individuals, groups, or social values. They are grossly selfish, callous, irresponsible, impulsive, and unable to feel guilt or to learn from experience and punishment. Frustration tolerance is low. They tend to blame others or offer plausible rationalizations for their behavior. A mere history of repeated legal or social offenses is not sufficient to justify this diagnosis. *Group delinquent reaction of childhood (or adolescence)* (q.v.), and *Social maladjustment without manifest psychiatric disorder* (q.v.) should be ruled out before making this diagnosis.

301.81* *Passive-aggressive personality**

This behavior pattern is characterized by both passivity and aggressiveness. The aggressiveness may be expressed passively, for example by obstructionism, pouting, procrastination, intentional inefficiency, or stubbornness. This behavior commonly reflects hostility which the individual feels he dare not express openly. Often the behavior is one expression of the patient's resentment at failing to find gratification in a relationship with an individual or institution upon which he is overdependent.

301.82* *Inadequate personality**

This behavior pattern is characterized by ineffectual responses to emotional, social, intellectual, and physical demands. While the patient seems neither physically nor mentally deficient, he does manifest inadaptability, ineptness, poor judgment, social instability, and lack of physical and emotional stamina.

301.89* *Other personality disorders of specified types* (*Immature personality, Passive-dependent personality, etc.*)*

301.9 [*Unspecified personality disorder*]

302 Sexual deviations

This category is for individuals whose sexual interests are directed primarily toward objects other than people of the opposite sex, toward sexual acts not usually associated with coitus, or toward coitus performed under bizarre circumstances, as in necrophilia, pedophilia, sexual sadism, and fetishism. Even though many find their practices distasteful, they remain unable to substitute normal sexual behavior for them. This diagnosis is not appropriate for individuals who perform deviant sexual acts because normal sexual objects are not available to them.

302.0 *Homosexuality*

302.1 *Fetishism*

302.2 *Pedophilia*

302.3 *Transvestitism*

302.4 *Exhibitionism*

302.5* *Voyeurism**

302.6* *Sadism**

302.7* *Masochism**

302.8 *Other sexual deviation*

[**302.9** *Unspecified sexual deviation*]

303 Alcoholism

This category is for patients whose alcohol intake is great enough to damage their physical health or their personal or social functioning, or when it has become a prerequisite to normal functioning. If the alcoholism is due to another mental disorder, both diagnoses should be made.

The following types of alcoholism are recognized:

303.0 Episodic excessive drinking

If alcoholism is present and the individual becomes intoxicated as frequently as four times a year, the condition should be classified here. Intoxication is defined as a state in which the individual's coordination or speech is definitely impaired or his behavior is clearly altered.

303.1 Habitual excessive drinking

This diagnosis is given to persons who are alcoholic and who either become intoxicated more than twelve times a year or are recognizably under the influence of alcohol more than once a week, even though not intoxicated.

303.2 Alcohol addiction

This condition should be diagnosed when there is direct or strong presumptive evidence that the patient is dependent on alcohol. If available, the best direct evidence of such dependence is the appearance of withdrawal symptoms. The inability of the patient to go one day without drinking is presumptive evidence. When heavy drinking continues for three months or more, it is reasonable to presume addiction to alcohol has been established.

303.9 Other [and unspecified] alcoholism

304 Drug dependence

This category is for patients who are addicted to or dependent on drugs other than alcohol, tobacco, and ordinary caffeine-containing beverages. Dependence on medically prescribed drugs is also excluded so long as the drug is medically indicated and the intake is proportionate to the medical need. The diagnosis requires evidence of habitual use or a clear sense of need for the drug. Withdrawal symptoms are not the only evidence of dependence; while always present when opium derivatives are withdrawn, they may be entirely absent when cocaine or marihuana are withdrawn. The diagnosis may stand alone or be coupled with any other diagnosis.

304.0 Drug dependence, opium, opium alkaloids and their derivatives

304.1 Drug dependence, synthetic analgesics with morphinelike effects

304.2 Drug dependence, barbiturates

304.3 Drug dependence, other hypnotics and sedatives or "tranquilizers"

304.4 Drug dependence, cocaine

304.5 Drug dependence, Cannabis sativa (hashish, marihuana)

304.6 Drug dependence, other psycho-stimulants (amphetamines, etc.)

304.7 Drug dependence, hallucinogens

304.8 Other drug dependence

[304.9 Unspecified drug dependence]

VI. PSYCHOPHYSIOLOGIC DISORDERS (305)

305 Psychophysiologic disorders ((Physical disorders of presumably psychogenic origin))

This group of disorders is characterized by physical symptoms that are caused by emotional factors and involve a single organ system, usually under autonomic nervous system innervation. The physiological changes involved are those that normally accompany certain emotional states, but in these disorders the changes are more intense and sustained. The individual may not be consciously aware of his emotional state. If there is an additional psychiatric disorder, it should be diagnosed separately, whether or not it is presumed to contribute to the physical disorder. The specific physical disorder should be named and classified in one of the following categories.

305.0 *Psychophysiologic skin disorder*
This diagnosis applies to skin reactions such as neurodermatosis, pruritis, atopic dermatitis, and hyperhydrosis in which emotional factors play a causative role.

305.1 *Psychophysiologic musculoskeletal disorder*
This diagnosis applies to musculoskeletal disorders such as backache, muscle cramps, and myalgias, and tension headaches in which emotional factors play a causative role. Differentiation from hysterical neurosis is of prime importance and at times extremely difficult.

305.2 *Psychophysiologic respiratory disorder*
This diagnosis applies to respiratory disorders such as bronchial asthma, hyperventilation syndromes, sighing, and hiccoughs in which emotional factors play a causative role.

305.3 *Psychophysiologic cardiovascular disorder*
This diagnosis applies to cardiovascular disorders such as paroxysmal tachycardia, hypertension, vascular spasms, and migraine in which emotional factors play a causative role.

305.4 *Psychophysiologic hemic and lymphatic disorder*
Here may be included any disturbances in the hemic and lymphatic system in which emotional factors are found to play a causative role. ICD-8 has included this category so that all organ systems will be covered.

305.5 *Psychophysiologic gastrointestinal disorder*
This diagnosis applies to specific types of gastrointestinal disorders such as peptic ulcer, chronic gastritis, ulcerative or mucous colitis, constipation, hyperacidity, pylorospasm, "heartburn," and "irritable colon" in which emotional factors play a causative role.

305.6 *Psychophysiologic genito-urinary disorder*
This diagnosis applies to genito-urinary disorders such as disturbances in menstruation and micturition, dyspareunia, and impotence in which emotional factors play a causative role.

305.7 Psychophysiologic endocrine disorder

This diagnosis applies to endocrine disorders in which emotional factors play a causative role. The disturbance should be specified.

305.8 Psychophysiologic disorder of organ of special sense

This diagnosis applies to any disturbance in the organs of special sense in which emotional factors play a causative role. Conversion reactions are excluded.

305.9 Psychophysiologic disorder of other type

VII. SPECIAL SYMPTOMS (306)

306 Special symptoms not elsewhere classified

This category is for the occasional patient whose psychopathology is manifested by a single specific symptom. An example might be anorexia nervosa under *Feeding disturbance* as listed below. It does not apply, however, if the symptom is the result of an organic illness or defect or other mental disorder. For example, anorexia nervosa due to schizophrenia would not be included here.

306.0 Speech disturbance
306.1 Specific learning disturbance
306.2 Tic
306.3 Other psychomotor disorder
306.4 Disorder of sleep
306.5 Feeding disturbance
306.6 Enuresis
306.7 Encopresis
306.8 Cephalalgia
306.9 Other special symptom

VIII. TRANSIENT SITUATIONAL DISTURBANCES (307)

307* Transient situational disturbances[7]

This major category is reserved for more or less transient disorders of any severity (including those of psychotic proportions) that occur in individuals without any apparent underlying mental disorders and that represent an acute reaction to overwhelming environmental stress. A diagnosis in this category should specify the cause and manifestations of the disturbance so far as possible. If the patient has good adaptive capacity, his symptoms usually recede as the stress diminishes. If, how-

---

[7] The terms included under DSM-II Category 307*, "Transient situational disturbances," differ from those in Category 307 of the ICD. DSM-II Category 307*, "Transient situational disturbances,* contains adjustment reactions of infancy (307.0*), childhood (307.1*), adolescence (307.2*), adult life (307.3*), and late life (307.4*). ICD Category 307, "Transient situational disturbances," includes only the adjustment reactions of adolescence, adult life, and late life. ICD 308, "Behavioral disorders of children," contains the reactions of infancy and childhood. These differences must be taken into account in preparing statistical tabulations to conform to ICD categories.

ever, the symptoms persist after the stress is removed, the diagnosis of another mental disorder is indicated. Disorders in this category are classified according to the patient's developmental stage as follows:

307.0* *Adjustment reaction of infancy**

Example: A grief reaction associated with separation from patient's mother, manifested by crying spells, loss of appetite, and severe social withdrawal.

307.1* *Adjustment reaction of childhood**

Example: Jealousy associated with birth of patient's younger brother and manifested by nocturnal enuresis, attention-getting behavior, and fear of being abandoned.

307.2* *Adjustment reaction of adolescence**

Example: Irritability and depression associated with school failure and manifested by temper outbursts, brooding, and discouragement.

307.3* *Adjustment reaction of adult life**

Example: Resentment with depressive tone associated with an unwanted pregnancy and manifested by hostile complaints and suicidal gestures.

Example: Fear associated with military combat and manifested by trembling, running, and hiding.

Example: A Ganser syndrome associated with death sentence and manifested by incorrect but approximate answers to questions.

307.4* *Adjustment reaction of late life**

Example: Feelings of rejection associated with forced retirement and manifested by social withdrawal.

IX. BEHAVIOR DISORDERS OF CHILDHOOD AND ADOLESCENCE (308)

308* Behavior disorders of childhood and adolescence ((Behavior disorders of childhood)) [8]

This major category is reserved for disorders occurring in childhood and adolescence that are more stable, internalized, and resistant to treatment than *Transient situational disturbance* (q.v.) but less so than *Psychoses, Neuroses,* and *Personality disorders* (q.v). This intermediate stability is attributed to the greater fluidity of all behavior at this age. Characteristic manifestations include such symptoms as overactivity, inattentiveness, shyness, feeling of rejection, overaggressiveness, timidity,

[8] The terms included under DSM-II Category 308*, "Behavioral disorders of childhood and adolescence," differ from those in Category 308 of the ICD. DSM-II Category 308* includes "Behavioral disorders of childhood and adolescence," whereas ICD Category 308 includes only "Behavioral disorders of childhood." DSM-II Category 308* *does not* include "Adjustment reactions of infancy and childhood," whereas ICD Category 308 does. In the DSM-II classification, "Adjustment reactions of infancy and childhood" are allocated to 307* (Transitional situational disturbances). These differences should be taken into account in preparing statistical tabulations to conform to the ICD categories.

and delinquency.

308.0* Hyperkinetic reaction of childhood (or adolescence)*

This disorder is characterized by overactivity, restlessness, distractibility, and short attention span, especially in young children; the
behavior usually diminishes in adolescence.

If this behavior is caused by organic brain damage, it should be
diagnosed under the appropriate nonpsychotic *organic brain syndrome*
(q.v.).

308.1* Withdrawing reaction of childhood (or adolescence)*

This disorder is characterized by seclusiveness, detachment, sensitivity, shyness, timidity, and general inability to form close interpersonal relationships. This diagnosis should be reserved for those
who cannot be classified as having *Schizophrenia* (q.v.) and whose
tendencies toward withdrawal have not yet stabilized enough to
justify the diagnosis of *Schizoid personality* (q.v.).

308.2* Overanxious reaction of childhood (or adolescence)*

This disorder is characterized by chronic anxiety, excessive and unrealistic fears, sleeplessness, nightmares, and exaggerated autonomic
responses. The patient tends to be immature, self-conscious, grossly
lacking in self-confidence, conforming, inhibited, dutiful, approval-
seeking, and apprehensive in new situations and unfamiliar surroundings. It is to be distinguished from *Neuroses* (q.v.).

308.3* Runaway reaction of childhood (or adolescence)*

Individuals with this disorder characteristically escape from threatening situations by running away from home for a day or more without
permission. Typically they are immature and timid, and feel rejected
at home, inadequate, and friendless. They often steal furtively.

**308.4* Unsocialized aggressive reaction of childhood (or adoles-
cence)***

This disorder is characterized by overt or covert hostile disobedience,
quarrelsomeness, physical and verbal aggressiveness, vengefulness, and
destructiveness. Temper tantrums, solitary stealing, lying, and hostile
teasing of other children are common. These patients usually have no
consistent parental acceptance and discipline. This diagnosis should
be distinguished from *Antisocial personality* (q.v.), *Runaway reaction
of childhood (or adolescence)* (q.v.), and *Group delinquent reaction
of childhood (or adolescence)* (q.v.).

308.5* Group delinquent reaction of childhood (or adolescence)*

Individuals with this disorder have acquired the values, behavior,
and skills of a delinquent peer group or gang to whom they are loyal
and with whom they characteristically steal, skip school, and stay out
late at night. The condition is more common in boys than girls. When
group delinquency occurs with girls, it usually involves sexual delinquency, although shoplifting is also common.

308.9* Other reaction of childhood (or adolescence)*

Here are to be classified children and adolescents having disorders not described in this group but which are nevertheless more serious than transient situational disturbances and less serious than psychoses, neuroses, and personality disorders. The particular disorder should be specified.

X. CONDITIONS WITHOUT MANIFEST PSYCHIATRIC DISORDER AND NONSPECIFIC CONDITIONS (316*–318*)

316* Social maladjustments without manifest psychiatric disorder

This category is for recording the conditions of individuals who are psychiatrically normal but who nevertheless have severe enough problems to warrant examination by a psychiatrist. These conditions may either become or precipitate a diagnosable mental disorder.

316.0* *Marital maladjustment**

This category is for individuals who are psychiatrically normal but who have significant conflicts or maladjustments in marriage.

316.1* *Social maladjustment**

This category is for individuals thrown into an unfamiliar culture (culture shock) or into a conflict arising from divided loyalties to two cultures.

316.2* *Occupational maladjustment**

This category is for psychiatrically normal individuals who are grossly maladjusted in their work.

316.3* *Dyssocial behavior**

This category is for individuals who are not classifiable as antisocial personalities but who are predatory and follow more or less criminal pursuits, such as racketeers, dishonest gamblers, prostitutes, and dope peddlers. (DSM-I classified this condition as "Sociopathic personality disorder, dyssocial type.")

316.9* *Other social maladjustment**

317* Nonspecific conditions*

This category is for conditions that cannot be classified under any of the previous categories, even after all facts bearing on the case have been investigated. This category is not for "Diagnosis deferred" (q.v.).

318* No mental disorder*

This term is used when, following psychiatric examination, none of the previous disorders is found. It is not to be used for patients whose disorders are in remission.

XI. NONDIAGNOSTIC TERMS FOR ADMINISTRATIVE USE (319*)

319* Nondiagnostic terms for administrative use*

319.0* *Diagnosis deferred**

319.1* *Boarder**

319.2* *Experiment only**

319.9* *Other**

TABLE II

Comparative Listing of Psychiatric Classifications in DSM-I and DSM-II

DSM-I Code Numbers and Titles	DSM-II Code Numbers and Titles
01–09 ACUTE BRAIN DISORDERS	
01 Acute Brain Syndrome associated with infection	
01.0 Intracranial infection (except epidemic encephalitis)	292.91 Psychosis with other [and unspecified][1] intracranial infection. Specify infection with additional code.
01.1 Epidemic encephalitis	292.21 Psychosis with epidemic encephalitis
01.2 With systemic infection, NEC	294.21 Psychosis with systemic infection. **Specify infection with additional code.**
02 Acute Brain Syndrome associated with intoxication	291.01 Delirium tremens
	291.21 Other alcoholic hallucinosis
02.1 Alcohol intoxication	291.41 Acute alcohol intoxication. **Excludes simple drunkenness.**
	291.61 Pathological intoxication
02.2 Drug or poison intoxication (except alcohol)	294.31 Psychosis with drug or poison intoxication. Specify drug or poison. Excludes alcoholic psychosis (291).[2]
03 Acute Brain Syndrome associated with trauma	293.51 Psychosis with brain trauma. Specify type of trauma with additional code (800–804; 850–854; 998).
04 Acute Brain Syndrome associated with circulatory disturbance	293.11 Psychosis with other cerebrovascular disturbance. Specify disturbance with additional code (430–436; 438).
	294.81 Psychosis with other and undiagnosed physical condition. Specify circulatory disturbance with additional code (393–429; 440–458).

Reprinted with permission from the second edition of *Diagnostic and Statistical Manual of Mental Disorders* (DSM-II), published by the American Psychiatric Association, 1968.

[1] Brackets indicate ICD-8 categories to be avoided in the United States or used by record librarians only.

[2] Additional ICD codes are indicated in parentheses for use when detail is desired regarding the specific condition with which a mental disorder is associated.

TABLE II (continued)
Comparative Listing of Psychiatric Classifications in DSM-I and DSM-II

DSM-I Code Numbers and Titles		DSM-II Code Numbers and Titles	
05	Acute Brain Syndrome associated with convulsive disorder	293.21	Psychosis with epilepsy
06	Acute Brain Syndrome associated with metabolic disturbance	294.11	Psychosis with metabolic or nutritional disorder. **Specify disorder with additional code (240–279).**
07	Acute Brain Syndrome associated with intracranial neoplasm	293.31	Psychosis with intracranial neoplasm. **Specify type of neoplasm with additional code.**
08	Acute Brain Syndrome with disease of unknown or uncertain cause	293.41	Psychosis with degenerative disease of the central nervous system. **Specify disease with additional code.**
		294.81	Psychosis with other and undiagnosed physical condition. **Specify condition with additional code.**
09	Acute Brain Syndrome of unknown cause	[294.91	Psychosis with unspecified physical condition]
10–19	**CHRONIC BRAIN DISORDERS**		
10	Chronic Brain Syndrome associated with diseases and conditions due to prenatal (constitutional) influence		
	10.0 With congenital cranial anomaly		
	10.00 Without qualifying phrase	309.92	Non-psychotic OBS with other [and unspecified] physical condition. **Specify type of congenital cranial anomaly with additional code (740–743).**
	10.01 With psychotic reaction	294.82	Psychosis with other and undiagnosed physical condition. **Specify type of congenital cranial anomaly with additional code (740–743).**
	10.02 With neurotic reaction 10.03 With behavioral reaction	309.92	See above.
10.1	With congenital spastic paraplegia		
	10.10 Without qualifying phrase	309.22	Non-psychotic OBS with brain trauma. **Specify congenital spastic paraplegia with additional code (343).**

Table II (continued)

Comparative Listing of Psychiatric Classifications in DSM-I and DSM-II

DSM-I Code Numbers and Titles		DSM-II Code Numbers and Titles
10.11	With psychotic reaction	293.52	Psychosis with brain trauma. **Specify congenital spastic paraplegia with additional code (343).**
10.12	With neurotic reaction	309.22	See above.
10.13	With behavioral reaction		
10.2	With mongolism		
10.20	Without qualifying phrase	309.92	Non-psychotic OBS with other [and unspecified] physical condition. **Specify mongolism and degree of retardation with an additional code (310.52, 311.52, 312.52, 313.52, 314.52, 315.52).**
10.21	With psychotic reaction	294.82	Psychosis with other and undiagnosed physical condition. **Specify mongolism and degree of retardation with an additional code (310.52, 311.52, 312.52, 313.52, 314.52, 315.52).**
10.22	With neurotic reaction	309.92	See above.
10.23	With behavioral reaction		
10.3	Due to prenatal maternal infectious diseases		
10.30	Without qualifying phrase	309.02	Non-psychotic OBS with intracranial infection. **Specify maternal infection with additional code (761).**
10.31	With psychotic reaction	292.92	Psychosis with other [and unspecified] intracranial infection. **Specify maternal infection with additional code (761).**
10.32	With neurotic reaction	309.02	See above.
10.33	With behavioral reaction		
11	Chronic Brain Syndrome associated with central nervous system syphilis		
11.0	Meningoencephalitic		
11.00	Without qualifying phrase	309.02	Non-psychotic OBS with intracranial infection. **Specify syphilis of CNS with additional code (094.1).**
11.01	With psychotic reaction	292.02	Psychosis with general paralysis

TABLE II (continued)
Comparative Listing of Psychiatric Classifications in DSM-I and DSM-II

DSM-I Code Numbers and Titles	DSM-II Code Numbers and Titles
11.02 With neurotic reaction ⎫ 11.03 With behavioral reaction ⎭	309.02 See above.
11.1 Meningovascular	
11.10 Without qualifying phrase	309.02 Non-psychotic OBS with intracranial infection. Specify other syphilis of CNS with additional code (094.9).
11.11 With psychotic reaction	292.12 Psychosis with other syphilis of central nervous system. Specify other syphilis of CNS with additional code (094.9).
11.12 With neurotic reaction ⎫ 11.13 With behavioral reaction ⎭	309.02 See above.
11.2 Other central nervous system syphilis	
11.20 Without qualifying phrase	309.02 Non-psychotic OBS with intracranial infection. Specify other syphilis of CNS with additional code (094.9).
11.21 With psychotic reaction	292.12 Psychosis with other syphilis of central nervous system. Specify other syphilis of CNS with additional code (094.9).
11.22 With neurotic reaction ⎫ 11.23 With behavioral reaction ⎭	309.02 See above.
12 Chronic Brain Syndrome associated with intracranial infection other than syphilis	
12.0 Epidemic encephalitis	
12.00 Without qualifying phrase	309.02 Non-psychotic OBS with intracranial infection. Specify encephalitis with additional code (062–065).
12.01 With psychotic reaction	292.22 Psychosis with epidemic encephalitis.
12.02 With neurotic reaction ⎫ 12.03 With behavioral reaction ⎭	309.02 See above.
12.1 Other intracranial infections	
12.10 Without qualifying phrase	309.02 Non-psychotic OBS with intracranial infection. Specify infection with additional code.
12.11 With psychotic reaction	292.92 Psychosis with other [and unspecified] intracranial infection. Specify infection with additional code.

TABLE II (continued)

Comparative Listing of Psychiatric Classifications in DSM-I and DSM-II

DSM-I Code Numbers and Titles		DSM-II Code Numbers and Titles
12.12 With neurotic reaction 12.13 With behavioral reaction	}	309.02 See above.
Chronic Brain Syndrome associated with intoxication		
13.0 Alcohol intoxication		
13.00 Without qualifying phrase		No exact counterpart in DSM-II. Closest approximation is 291.52 (Alcohol deterioration).
13.01 With psychotic reaction	{	291.12 Korsakov's psychosis (alcoholic) 291.32 Alcohol paranoid state 291.52 Alcoholic deterioration
13.02 With neurotic reaction 13.03 With behavioral reaction	}	No exact counterpart in DSM-II. Closest approximation is 291.52 (Alcohol deterioration).
13.1 Drug or poison intoxication, except alcohol		
13.10 Without qualifying phrase		309.14 Non-psychotic OBS with other drug, poison, or systemic intoxication. Excludes drug dependence (304). This code and title are used for both the acute and chronic forms of the disorder. Specify drug or poison with additional code (960–979; 981–989).
13.11 With psychotic reaction		294.32 Psychosis with drug or poison intoxication. Excludes alcoholic psychosis (291). Specify drug or poison with additional code (960–979; 981–989).
13.12 With neurotic reaction 13.13 With behavioral reaction	}	309.14 See above.
Chronic Brain Syndrome associated with trauma		
14.0 Birth trauma		
14.00 Without qualifying phrase		309.22 Non-psychotic OBS with brain trauma. Specify type of birth

TABLE II (continued)
Comparative Listing of Psychiatric Classifications in DSM-I and DSM-II

DSM-I Code Numbers and Titles		DSM-II Code Numbers and Titles	
			trauma with additional code (764.0, 765.0, 766.0, 767.0, 768.0, 772.0).
14.01	With psychotic reaction	293.52	Psychosis with brain trauma. Specify type of birth trauma with additional code (764.0, 765.0, 766.0, 767.0, 768.0, 772.0).
14.02	With neurotic reaction }	309.22	See above.
14.03	With behavioral reaction }		
14.1	Brain Trauma, gross force		
14.10	Without qualifying phrase	309.22	Non-psychotic OBS with brain trauma. Specify type of trauma with additional code (800–804; 850–854).
14.11	With psychotic reaction	293.52	Psychosis with brain trauma. Specify type of trauma with additional code (800–804; 850–854).
14.12	With neurotic reaction }	309.22	See above.
14.13	With behavioral reaction }		
14.2	Following brain operation		
14.20	Without qualifying phrase	309.22	Non-psychotic OBS with brain trauma. Specify brain operation with additional code (998).
14.21	With psychotic reaction	293.52	Psychosis with brain trauma. Specify brain operation with additional code (998).
14.22	With neurotic reaction }	309.22	See above.
14.23	With behavioral reaction }		
14.3	Following electrical brain trauma		
14.30	Without qualifying phrase	309.22	See above. Specify type of trauma with additional code (994.8).
14.31	With psychotic reaction	293.52	Psychosis with brain trauma. Specify type of trauma with additional code (994.8).
14.32	With neurotic reaction }	309.22	See above.
14.33	With behavioral reaction }		
14.4	Following irradiational brain trauma		
14.40	Without qualifying phrase	309.22	Non-psychotic OBS with brain trauma. Specify type of trauma

TABLE II (continued)
Comparative Listing of Psychiatric Classifications in DSM-I and DSM-II

DSM-I Code Numbers and Titles		DSM-II Code Numbers and Titles	
			with additional code (990).
14.41	With psychotic reaction	293.52	Psychosis with brain trauma. Specify type of trauma with additional code (990).
14.42	With neurotic reaction ⎫	309.22	See above.
14.43	With behavioral reaction ⎭		
14.5	Following other trauma		
14.50	Without qualifying phrase	309.22	Non-psychotic OBS with brain trauma. Specify type of trauma with additional code.
14.51	With psychotic reaction	293.52	Psychosis with brain trauma. Specify type of trauma with additional code.
14.52	With neurotic reaction ⎫	309.22	See above.
14.53	With behavioral reaction ⎭		
15	Chronic Brain Syndrome associated with circulatory disturbance		
15.0	With cerebral arteriosclerosis		
15.00	Without qualifying phrase	309.32	Non-psychotic OBS with circulatory disturbance. Specify cerebral arteriosclerosis with additional code (437).
15.01	With psychotic reaction	293.02	Psychosis with cerebral arteriosclerosis.
15.02	With neurotic reaction ⎫	309.32	See above.
15.03	With behavioral reaction ⎭		
15.1	With circulatory disturbance other than cerebral arteriosclerosis		
15.10	Without qualifying phrase	309.32	See above. Specify other circulatory disturbance with additional code (393–436; 438–458).
15.11	With psychotic reaction	293.12	Psychosis with other cerebrovascular disturbance. Specify disturbance with additional code (393–436; 438–458).
15.12	With neurotic reaction ⎫	309.32	See above.
15.13	With behavioral reaction ⎭		

TABLE II (continued)
Comparative Listing of Psychiatric Classifications in DSM-I and DSM-II

DSM-I Code Numbers and Titles	DSM-II Code Numbers and Titles	
16 Chronic Brain Syndrome associated with convulsive disorder		
16.00 Without qualifying phrase	309.42	Non-psychotic OBS with epilepsy
16.01 With psychotic reaction	293.22	Psychosis with epilepsy
16.02 With neurotic reaction ⎫	309.42	See above.
16.03 With behavioral reaction ⎭		
17 Chronic Brain Syndrome associated with disturbance of metabolism, growth, or nutrition		
17.1 With senile brain disease		
17.10 Without qualifying phrase	309.62	Non-psychotic OBS with senile or presenile brain disease
17.11 With psychotic reaction	290.02	Senile dementia
17.12 With neurotic reaction ⎫	309.62	See above.
17.13 With behavioral reaction ⎭		
17.2 Presenile brain disease		
17.20 Without qualifying phrase	309.62	Non-psychotic OBS with senile or presenile brain disease
17.21 With psychotic reaction	290.12	Presenile dementia
17.22 With neurotic reaction ⎫	309.62	See above.
17.23 With behavioral reaction ⎭		
17.3 With other disturbance of metabolism, etc., except presenile brain disease		
17.30 Without qualifying phrase	309.52	Non-psychotic OBS with disturbance of metabolism, growth, or nutrition. **Specify disturbance with additional code (240–279).**
	294.02	Psychosis with endocrine disorder. **Specify disorder with additional code (240–258).**
17.31 With neurotic reaction	294.12	Psychosis with metabolic or nutritional disorder. **Specify disorder with additional code (260–279).**

TABLE II (continued)

Comparative Listing of Psychiatric Classifications in DSM-I and DSM-II

	DSM-I Code Numbers and Titles	DSM-II Code Numbers and Titles
18	17.32 With neurotic reaction } 17.33 With behavioral reaction } → 309.52	See above.
	Chronic Brain Syndrome associated with new growth	
	18.0 With intracranial neoplasm	
	18.00 Without qualifying phrase → 309.72	Non-psychotic OBS with intracranial neoplasm
	18.01 With psychotic reaction → 293.32	Psychosis with intracranial neoplasm
	18.02 With neurotic reaction } 18.03 With behavioral reaction } → 309.72	See above.
19	Chronic Brain Syndrome associated with diseases of unknown or uncertain cause; chronic brain syndrome of unknown or unspecified cause	
	19.0 Multiple sclerosis	
	19.00 Without qualifying phrase → 309.82	Non-psychotic OBS with degenerative disease of CNS. Specify multiple sclerosis with additional code (340).
	19.01 With psychotic reaction → 293.42	Psychosis with degenerative disease of CNS. Specify multiple sclerosis with additional code (340).
	19.02 With neurotic reaction } 19.03 With behavioral reaction } → 309.82	See above.
19.1	Huntington's chorea	
	19.10 Without qualifying phrase → 309.82	Non-psychotic OBS with degenerative disease of CNS. Specify Huntington's chorea as additional code (331.0).
	19.11 With psychotic reaction → 293.42	Psychosis with degenerative disease of the CNS. Specify Huntington's chorea as additional code (331.0).
	19.12 With neurotic reaction } 19.13 With behavioral reaction } → 309.82	See above.
19.2	Pick's disease	
	19.20 Without qualifying phrase → 309.62	Non-psychotic OBS with senile or presenile brain disease

TABLE II (continued)
Comparative Listing of Psychiatric Classifications in DSM-I and DSM-II

DSM-I Code Numbers and Titles		DSM-II Code Numbers and Titles
19.21	With psychotic reaction	290.12 Presenile dementia
19.22	With neurotic reaction	
19.23	Without qualifying reaction	309.62 See above.
19.3	Other diseases of unknown or uncertain cause	
19.30	Without qualifying phrase	309.92 Non-psychotic OBS with other [and unspecified] physical condition. **Specify condition when known.**
19.31	With psychotic reaction	294.82 Psychosis associated with other and undiagnosed physical condition. **Specify condition when known.**
19.32	With neurotic reaction	
19.33	With behavioral reaction	309.92 See above.
19.4	Chronic brain syndrome of unknown or unspecified cause	
19.40	Without qualifying phrase	309.92 See above.
19.41	With psychotic reaction	293.92 Psychosis with other [and unspecified] cerebral condition 294.82 Psychosis with other and undiagnosed physical condition
19.42	With neurotic reaction	
19.43	With behavioral reaction	309.92 See above.
20–24	PSYCHOTIC DISORDERS	295–298 Psychoses not attributed to physical conditions listed previously
20	Involutional Psychotic Reaction	296.00 Involutional melancholia 297.10 Involutional paranoid state
21	Affective Reactions	
21.0	Manic depressive reaction, manic type	296.10 Manic-depressive illness, manic type
21.1	Manic depressive reaction, depressed type	296.20 Manic-depressive illness, depressed type. **Includes** "Endogenous depression."
21.2	Manic depressive reaction, other	296.30 Manic-depressive illness, circular type 296.80 Other major affective disorder [296.90 Unspecified major affective disorder]

Table II (continued)

Comparative Listing of Psychiatric Classifications in DSM-I and DSM-II

DSM-I Code Numbers and Titles		DSM-II Code Numbers and Titles	
		298.00	Psychotic depressive reaction
21.3	Psychotic depressive reaction		
22	Schizophrenic Reactions	295	Schizophrenia
22.0	Schizophrenic reaction, simple type	295.00	Schizophrenia, simple type
22.1	Schizophrenic reaction, hebephrenic type	295.10	Schizophrenia, hebephrenic type
22.2	Schizophrenic reaction, catatonic type	295.20	Schizophrenia, catatonic type
22.3	Schizophrenic reaction, paranoid type	295.30	Schizophrenia, paranoid type
22.4	Schizophrenic reaction, acute undifferentiated type	295.40	Acute schizophrenic episode. Excludes acute schizophrenia of types listed above.
22.5	Schizophrenic reaction, chronic undifferentiated type	295.90	Schizophrenia, chronic undifferentiated type
		295.50	Schizophrenia, latent type
22.6	Schizophrenic reaction, schizo-affective type	295.70	Schizophrenia, schizo-affective type
22.7	Schizophrenic reaction, childhood type	295.80	Schizophrenia, childhood type[3]
22.8	Schizophrenic reaction, residual type	295.60	Schizophrenia, residual type
22.9	Other and unspecified	295.99	Schizophrenia, other [and unspecified] types
23	Paranoid Reactions	297	Paranoid states
23.1	Paranoia	297.00	Paranoia
23.2	Paranoid state	297.90	Other paranoid state
24	Psychotic Reaction Without Clearly Defined Structural Change Other Than Above	[299	Unspecified psychosis]
		298.10	Reactive excitation]
		298.20	Reactive confusion]
	No Matching Codes and Titles	298.30	Acute paranoid reaction]
		298.90	Reactive psychosis, unspecified]
30–39	PSYCHOPHYSIOLOGIC AUTONOMIC AND VISCERAL DISORDERS	305	Psychophysiologic disorders

[3] The code designated as "Schizophrenia, childhood type" is for use in the U.S.A. only. ICD code 295.8 is "Schizophrenia, other."

Table II (continued)
Comparative Listing of Psychiatric Classifications in DSM-I and DSM-II

DSM-I Code Numbers and Titles	DSM-II Code Numbers and Titles
30 Psychophysiologic Skin Reaction	305.00 Psychophysiologic skin disorder
31 Psychophysiologic Musculo-skeletal Reaction	305.10 Psychophysiologic musculo-skeletal disorder
32 Psychophysiologic Respiratory Reaction	305.20 Psychophysiologic respiratory disorder
33 Psychophysiologic Cardiovascular Reaction	305.30 Psychophysiologic cardiovascular disorder
34 Psychophysiologic Hemic and Lymphatic Reaction	305.40 Psychophysiologic hemic and lymphatic disorder
35 Psychophysiologic Gastro-intestinal Reaction	305.50 Psychophysiologic gastro-intestinal disorder
36 Psychophysiologic Genito-urinary Reaction	305.60 Psychophysiologic genito-urinary disorder
37 Psychophysiologic Endocrine Reaction	305.70 Psychophysiologic endocrine disorder
38 Psychophysiologic Nervous System Reaction	300.50 Neurasthenic neurosis
39 Psychophysiologic Reaction of Organs of special sense	305.80 Psychophysiologic disorder of organ of special sense
PSYCHONEUROTIC DISORDERS	
40 Psychoneurotic Reactions	300 Neuroses
40.0 Anxiety reaction	300.00 Anxiety neurosis
40.1 Dissociative reaction	300.14 Hysterical neurosis, dissociative type
40.2 Conversion reaction	300.13 Hysterical neurosis, conversion type
40.3 Phobic reaction	300.20 Phobic neurosis
40.4 Obsessive compulsive reaction	300.30 Obsessive compulsive neurosis
40.5 Depressive reaction	300.40 Depressive neurosis
	300.50 Neurasthenic neurosis
	300.60 Depersonalization neurosis
40.6 Psychoneurotic reaction, other	300.70 Hypochondriacal neurosis
	300.80 Other neurosis
	[300.90 Unspecified neurosis]
50-53 PERSONALITY DISORDERS	301 Personality disorders
50 Personality Pattern Disturbance	
50.0 Inadequate personality	301.82 Inadequate personality

Table II (continued)

Comparative Listing of Psychiatric Classifications in DSM-I and DSM-II

DSM-I Code Numbers and Titles		DSM-II Code Numbers and Titles	
50.1	Schizoid personality	301.20	Schizoid personality
50.2	Cyclothymic personality	301.10	Cyclothymic personality
50.3	Paranoid personality	301.00	Paranoid personality
50.4	Personality pattern disturbance, other	301.89	Other personality disorders of specified types
51	Personality Trait Disturbance		
51.0	Emotionally unstable personality	301.50	Hysterical personality
51.1	Passive-aggressive personality	301.81	Passive-aggressive personality
51.2	Compulsive personality	301.40	Obsessive-compulsive personality
51.3	Personality trait disturbance, other	301.89	Other personality disorders of specified types
52	Sociopathic Personality Disturbance		
52.0	Antisocial reaction	301.70	Antisocial personality
52.1	Dyssocial reaction	316.30	Dyssocial behavior
52.2	Sexual deviation	[302.90	Unspecified sexual deviation]
		302.00	Homosexuality
		302.10	Fetishism
		302.20	Pedophilia
	Detailed subdivisions not contained in DSM-I	302.30	Transvestitism
		302.40	Exhibitionism
		302.50	Voyeurism
		302.60	Sadism
		302.70	Masochism
		302.80	Other sexual deviation
52.3	Alcoholism (addiction)	303.90	Other [and unspecified] Alcoholism. Excludes alcoholic psychosis (291); acute poisoning by alcohol (980, E860).
	Detailed subdivisions not contained in DSM-I	303.00	Episodic excessive drinking
		303.10	Habitual excessive drinking
		303.20	Alcoholic addiction
		303.90	Other [and unspecified] alcoholism

TABLE II (continued)
Comparative Listing of Psychiatric Classifications in DSM-I and DSM-II

DSM-I Code Numbers and Titles	DSM-II Code Numbers and Titles
52.4 Drug addiction	[304.90 Unspecified drug dependence]
	304.00 Drug dependence, opium, opium alkaloids and their derivatives
	304.10 Drug dependence, synthetic analgesics with morphine-like effects
	304.20 Drug dependence, barbiturates
Detailed subdivisions not contained in DSM-I	304.30 Drug dependence, other hypnotics and sedatives or "tranquilizers"
	304.40 Drug dependence, cocaine
	304.50 Drug dependence, Cannabis sativa (hashish, marihuana)
	304.60 Drug dependence, other psycho-stimulants
	304.70 Drug dependence, hallucinogens
	304.80 Other drug dependence
53 Special Symptom Reaction	306 Special symptoms not elsewhere classified
53.0 Learning disturbance	306.10 Specific learning disturbance
53.1 Speech disturbance	306.00 Speech disturbance
53.2 Enuresis	306.60 Enuresis
53.3 Somnambulism	306.40 Disorder of sleep
	306.20 Tic
	306.30 Other psychomotor disorder
53.4 Other	306.50 Feeding disturbance
	306.70 Encopresis
	306.80 Cephalalgia
	306.90 Other special symptom
54 TRANSIENT SITUATIONAL PERSONALITY DISORDERS	307 Transient situational disturbances
54.0 Gross stress reaction	307.30 Adjustment reaction of adult life
54.1 Adult situational reaction	307.30 Adjustment reaction of adult life
54.2 Adjustment reaction of infancy	307.00 Adjustment reaction of infancy
54.3 Adjustment reaction of childhood	307.10 Adjustment reaction of childhood

Table II (continued)

Comparative Listing of Psychiatric Classifications in DSM-I and DSM-II

DSM-I Code Numbers and Titles		DSM-II Code Numbers and Titles
54.4	Adjustment reaction of adolescence	307.20 Adjustment reaction of adolescence
54.5	Adjustment reaction of late life	307.40 Adjustment reaction of late life
54.6	Other transient situational personality disturbance	No corresponding diagnosis (Assign another diagnosis in 307 category based upon patient's age.)
60-62	MENTAL DEFICIENCY	310-315 Mental retardation
60	Mental Deficiency (Familial or Hereditary)	
60.0	Mild (I.Q. 70-85)	310.80 Borderline mental retardation (I.Q. 70-85)
		310.80 Borderline mental retardation (I.Q. 68-69)
60.1	Moderate (I.Q. 50-69)	311.80 Mild mental retardation (I.Q. 52-67)
		312.80 Moderate mental retardation (I.Q. 50-51)
60.2	Severe (I.Q. below 50)	312.80 Moderate mental retardation (I.Q. 36-49)
		313.80 Severe mental retardation (I.Q. 20-35)
		314.80 Profound mental retardation (I.Q. Below 20)
60.3	Severity not specified	315.80 Unspecified mental retardation
61	Mental Deficiency, Idiopathic	
61.0	Mild (I.Q. 70-85)	310.90 Borderline mental retardation (I.Q. 70-85)
		310.90 Borderline mental retardation (I.Q. 68-69)
61.1	Moderate (I.Q. 50-69)	311.90 Mild mental retardation (I.Q. 52-67)
		312.90 Moderate mental retardation (I.Q. 50-51)
61.2	Severe (I.Q. below 50)	312.90 Moderate mental retardation (I.Q. 36-49)
		313.90 Severe mental retardation (I.Q. 20-35)
		314.90 Profound mental retardation (I.Q. Below 20)
61.3	Severity not specified	315.90 Unspecified mental retardation

Table III

Proposed Classification of Child Psychiatric Disorders by
Group for the Advancement of Psychiatry

The following major categories are proposed:

1. Healthy Responses
2. Reactive Disorders
3. Developmental Deviations
4. Psychoneurotic Disorders
5. Personality Disorders
6. Psychotic Disorders
7. Psychophysiologic Disorders
8. Brain Syndromes
9. Mental Retardation
10. Other Disorders

These categories are arranged rather arbitrarily and roughly in a hierarchy ranging from healthy responses, through milder to more severe psychological disorders, to syndromes in which somatic factors predominate. The placing of the healthier or the less disturbed groups at the top of this hierarchical arrangement reflects in general the degree of optimism of the Committee regarding the prognostic outlook in childhood, with significant exceptions. The considerations mentioned earlier regarding total personality responses, contrasted with end-organ patterns or specific etiological influences, also apply. A list of the major categories and the proposed subcategories follows.

1. Healthy Responses
   a. Developmental crisis
   b. Situational crisis
   c. Other responses
2. Reactive Disorders
3. Developmental Deviations
   a. Deviations in maturational patterns
   b. Deviations in specific dimensions of development
      1) Motor
      2) Sensory
      3) Speech
      4) Cognitive functions
      5) Social development
      6) Psychosexual
      7) Affective
      8) Integrative
   c. Other developmental deviation
4. Psychoneurotic Disorders
   a. Anxiety type
   b. Phobic type
   c. Conversion type
   d. Dissociative type
   e. Obsessive-compulsive type
   f. Depressive type
   g. Other psychoneurotic disorder

Reprinted with permission from *Psychopathological Disorders of Childhood: Theoretical Considerations and a Proposed Classification*, published by Group for the Advancement of Psychiatry, 1966.

TABLE III (*continued*)

Proposed Classification of Child Psychiatric Disorders by Group for the Advancement of Psychiatry

5. Personality Disorders
   a. Compulsive personality
   b. Hysterical
   c. Anxious
   d. Overly dependent
   e. Oppositional
   f. Overly inhibited
   g. Overly independent
   h. Isolated
   i. Mistrustful
   j. Tension-discharge disorders
      1) Impulse-ridden personality
      2) Neurotic personality disorder
   k. Sociosyntonic personality disorder
   l. Sexual deviation
   m. Other personality disorder
6. Psychotic Disorders
   a. Psychoses of infancy and early childhood
      1) Early infantile autism
      2) Interactional psychotic disorder
      3) Other psychosis of infancy and early childhood
   b. Psychoses of later childhood
      1) Schizophreniform psychotic disorder
      2) Other psychosis of later childhood
   c. Psychoses of adolescence
      1) Acute confusional state
      2) Schizophrenic disorder, adult type
      3) Other psychosis of adolescence
7. Psychophysiologic Disorders
   a. Skin
   b. Musculoskeletal
   c. Respiratory
   d. Cardiovascular
   e. Hemic and lymphatic
   f. Gastrointestinal
   g. Genitourinary
   h. Endocrine
   i. Of nervous system
   j. Of organs of special sense
   k. Other psychophysiologic disorders
8. Brain Syndromes
   a. Acute
   b. Chronic
9. Mental Retardation
10. Other Disorders

CHAPTER FOUR

Limitations of the New Nomenclature for Children's Disorders

BARBARA FISH, M.D.

A DIAGNOSTIC CLASSIFICATION is not an end in itself. It must provide a common frame of reference within which we can formulate the most urgent questions of our field. It is an essential instrument for the study of the epidemiology of psychiatric disorders, essential for developing priorities for research and treatment and for evaluating the efficacy of our programs.

If epidemiology, treatment, and etiology are to be studied on a national or international scale, a common language must be developed. If we are to make any sense to our colleagues, and even if we differ violently in our underlying concepts and assumptions, we must be able to use the same terms to refer to the same patients. Anyone who has tried to get agreement on the use of psychiatric diagnoses must recognize the enormous difficulties involved in reaching consensus on a revised nomenclature.

In addition, there are very special problems in developing adequate nomenclature for diagnosing childhood psychiatric disorders which are inherent in the nature of childhood itself. Children's disorders are seen while personality is still developing; the manifestations of disorder are more undifferentiated than in adults and the clinical picture changes markedly with the child's age. Furthermore, since the functioning of the growing organism is more vulnerable than the more crystallized functioning of mature individuals, psychiatric disorders in children are much more frequently associated with other deviations in development.

Reprinted with permission from *International Journal of Psychiatry*, 7: 6, 1969.

THE ADDITION OF "BEHAVIOR DISORDERS IN CHILDHOOD AND ADOLESCENCE" TO THE NOMENCLATURE

The original APA nomenclature made no provision for the vast majority of children's disorders which lie between transient adjustment reactions on the one hand and the more crystallized personality disorders and neurotic reactions on the other. That the new nomenclature has added a category for "Behavior Disorders of Childhood and Adolescence" expressly to provide for "this intermediate stability . . . attributed to the greater fluidity of all behavior at this age" represents a major advance.

The terms within this category, however, provide only an inadequate range of disorders and include some inappropriate and confusing items. Only three of the terms provide necessary and reliable diagnoses which belong in this category: the "withdrawing," "overanxious," and "unsocialized aggressive" reactions. The "withdrawing reaction," to be distinguished from schizophrenia and schizoid personality, describes the same group of children called "isolated personality" in the GAP *Classification*. The "overanxious reaction," to be distinguished from neuroses, corresponds to the "anxious personality" in the GAP *Classification*.

The "unsocialized aggressive reaction" must be distinguished from its adult counterpart, "explosive personality" (which includes "aggressive personality") and "antisocial personality." The mention of the absence of "consistent parental acceptance and discipline" adds an unnecessary qualification to its description. However, the definition of the "unsocialized aggressive reaction" is more straightforward than the comparable category in the GAP *Classification*—"tension-discharge disorder." The latter includes much philosophical discussion of the meaning of aggression and its relationship to neurotic conflict, but it provides inadequate descriptive guidelines for diagnosing its two subgroups, the "impulse-ridden personality" and the "neurotic personality disorder." As a psychiatrist, one may ask why the appearance of impulsivity and aggression in children—phenomena which are developmentally earlier and more "childish"—required so much more discussion and explaining away than neurotic conflict.

OMISSION OF IMPORTANT DISORDERS UNDER "BEHAVIOR DISORDERS OF CHILDHOOD AND ADOLESCENCE"

In the interests of international professional collaboration, the new APA nomenclature wisely "attempts to provide a middle ground to satisfy the needs of psychiatrists of different schools of theoretical orientation" (*DSM-II*, page 15). The GAP *Classification* admittedly "has drawn most heavily upon psychoanalytic theory" (page 191). Despite this difference in approach, the authors of the APA category of "Behavior Disorders" would have enriched the list of subgroups and made the classification more useful for diagnosing children's disorders if they had drawn from the GAP list of personality disorders in children. This could easily be done without incorporating GAP's theoretical assumptions.

The GAP *Classification* includes childhood variants of some of the adult personality disorders which occur at least as frequently as the "withdrawing reaction." For instance, "oppositional personality" (to be distinguished from "passive-aggressive personality"), "overly dependent personality" (to be distinguished from the old "passive-dependent" type of "passive-aggressive" personality), and "mistrustful personality" (to be distinguished from "paranoid personality"). Some might also wish to include a childhood variant of "compulsive personality" and "hysterical personality," but the GAP definitions barely distinguish these better organized personality types from their adult counterparts. GAP's "overly inhibited personality" includes features of both the "isolated" and "anxious personality" types and may be an unnecessary duplication, or severe variant, of the latter.

In our own typology of children's psychiatric disorders, which classifies children according to four major types of current behavior patterns, we found it necessary to include a category of "immature-labile" ("Type II"), a childhood variant of the "inadequate personality." "These children are characterized by immature and poorly integrated functioning in all areas . . . uneven but generally inadequate abilities . . . impaired by constricted or impulsive behavior . . . may be clinging and demanding at one moment and negativistic the next. . . . Paranoid or neurotic traits, if present, are poorly defined. . . ." The authors of the APA section "Behavior Disorders" probably intended the "hyperkinetic reaction" to refer to the same group of children we described, but the APA definition is limited to a few symptoms and is so nonspecific that it does not differentiate these children from either psychotic children or those with other behavior disorders or even those with transient adjustment reactions who also may be hyperkinetic. GAP's category of "impulse-ridden personality" probably refers to some of the children in our "immature-labile" group, but the GAP term could apply equally well to some better organized children with an "unsocialized aggressive reaction," and the GAP definition is so confused by theoretical assumptions and other features that it will be difficult to apply in any reliable or consistent fashion.

TERMS INAPPROPRIATELY PLACED UNDER "BEHAVIOR DISORDERS OF CHILDHOOD AND ADOLESCENCE"

The new nomenclature has included several terms under the category "Behavior Disorders" that appear to this reviewer to fit more appropriately elsewhere. "Group delinquent reaction," as it is defined, seems to belong to the category of "social maladjustment without manifest psychiatric disorder." Placing these delinquent reactions under "Behavior Disorders" implied that they represent more psychiatric disorder than their adult counterpart of "dyssocial reaction." This is illogical and was probably not the authors' intention.

"Runaway reaction" does not characterize personality or mental disorder at the same level of generalization as the "withdrawing," "overanxious," and "unsocialized aggressive" reactions. There is no more merit in including this particular symptom cluster than there is in including a host of other acts such as lying, stealing, fire-setting, and so on when these acts are performed by children who feel "timid . . . rejected . . . and inadequate" (as distinguished from any of these acts when they are part of the "unsocialized aggressive reaction"). Such partial responses belong to a list of symptoms which could be added to the primary psychiatric diagnosis.

The inclusion of "hyperkinetic reaction" as a discrete behavior disorder may create less of an outcry among child psychiatrists than "runaway reaction," but it will cause much more confusion in the long run in collecting statistics about epidemiology, outcome, or treatment. It must be defined much more specifically at the level of total personality disorder and not in terms of a few symptoms. Overactivity, restlessness, and distractibility occur normally in the infant and young preschool child and are considered to be signs of "immaturity" when they persist or are excessive in degree. Even then, this behavior is a nonspecific response that may appear in a child with a mild adjustment reaction or in one with severe brain damage or schizophrenia, or it may accompany any disturbance of intermediate severity. The symptoms may occur in the "overanxious" and in the "unsocialized aggressive" reactions and in the less well-organized children we have called "immature-labile" (see above). The primary mental disorder must be diagnosed so as to indicate the type and severity of personality disorder in the child, just as one must diagnose adults who manifest depression or anxiety. Such symptoms as hyperactivity or distractibility should be added to the primary diagnosis of mental disorder in order to reflect major manifestations that are not necessarily implied by the primary diagnosis.

If the terms which are used in a diagnostic classification are too nonspecific, each diagnostician will revert to his own idiosyncratic interpretation and no meaningful communication or statistical summary will be possible. I am concerned that "hyperkinetic reaction," as it is now defined, will become the wastebasket in the DSM-II for a very heterogeneous collection of uncertain diagnoses in children, just as was "passive-aggressive personality" in the DSM-I.

THE DIAGNOSIS OF DEVELOPMENTAL DEVIATIONS

Minor or major mental disorders in children are often associated with deviations in development. The new nomenclature has made it only slightly easier to include these deviations in the diagnosis. The major advance here is the increased flexibility in diagnosing mental retardation "whenever present and from all causes," which puts the diagnosis into perspective as a major developmental impairment which may result from organic or other causes. The official recognition that mental retardation may follow major psychiatric disorder and that the developmental defects of early childhood schizophrenia "may result in mental retardation, which should also be diagnosed" avoids the outmoded dichotomy that a child was schizophrenic *or* retarded.

It should be possible to diagnose the other significant developmental deviations "whenever present and from all causes," just as one can now do for mental retardation. For example, speech and specific learning disturbances are important enough to warrant specific diagnostic terms and code numbers. However, they may occur in children with transient adjustment reactions, severe personality disorders, psychoses, or with gross manifestations of an organic brain syndrome. It should be possible to diagnose the primary mental disorder and also the significant developmental symptoms. In some instances the mental disorder may be considered to be a reaction to the developmental handicap. When developmental symptoms occur as the only manifestation of mental disorder, as they may in very young children, this could be noted.

The *DSM-II* does not permit one to add the diagnosis of a developmental (or other) symptom to the diagnosis of a mental disorder, mild or otherwise. Although multiple diagnoses are encouraged, the "Special Symptoms" are left as the single exception to this rule, and these terms are specifically prohibited when other disorders are present. The only rationale for this seems to be that it was the practice of the old *DSM-I*. If the clinician is limited to diagnosing only a symptom *or* a mental disorder, it sets up a false dichotomy which will lead to a wide variability in diagnostic practices and consequently to misleading statistics regarding epidemiology and the evaluation of treatments.

The separate category of "developmental deviations" in the GAP *Classification* highlights the importance of this area for children's psychiatric disorders. GAP allows these deviations to stand as the primary diagnosis or to be combined with an accompanying personality diagnosis, permitting the type of flexibility needed in the *DSM-II*.

The list of "Special Symptoms" from the *DSM-I* has been slightly expanded in the *DSM-II*, but the appendix of supplementary terms, which included a wide variety of symptoms in the *DSM-I*, has been dropped. It would improve the accuracy and comprehensiveness of reporting if terms from a list of symptoms could be added to the primary diagnosis of mental disorders. This need not be as voluminous and minutely detailed as the list of symptoms in the GAP *Classification*, but as a minimum there should be provision for the major categories and terms listed under the GAP category of "developmental deviations" if we are to gather adequate statistics about children.

SCHIZOPHRENIA, CHILDHOOD TYPE, REDEFINED

The revised definition of this disorder in the new nomenclature has improved on the *DSM-I* by describing more explicitly some of the major manifestations of disordered development which may occur. It is broad enough to encompass the criteria for the "schizophrenic syndrome in childhood" listed by the British child psychiatrists, the cases of "early infantile autism" which are schizophrenic (as distinguished from autistic behavior with retardation and/or sensory handicaps which is secondary to severe brain damage), the "symbiotic psychosis" described by Mahler, and the many schizophrenic children described by Bender, in whose study the diagnosis has been confirmed upon follow-up into adulthood.

We will neither facilitate agreement on a definition for this disorder nor will we magically improve the prognosis of these children by the simple expedient of eliminating the classical term (as in the *ICD-8*) or by creating new euphemisms (as in GAP's "interactional psychotic disorder," "schizophreniform psychotic disorder," etc.).

GENERAL COMMENTS ON THE ORGANIZATION OF THE NEW NOMENCLATURE

The *DSM-II* retains many of the internal inconsistencies which are rooted in our past history and our current ignorance. Only in the organic brain syndromes do we have diagnoses based on etiology. For the remaining disorders, where the etiology is unknown we must rely on descriptions of current functioning, symptomatology, course, and prognosis, as in the rest of medicine. Such definitions are understandably clearer for the major psychoses than they are for the milder disorders.

However, some of the inconsistencies from our past could easily be eliminated. The *DSM-II* and *ICD-8* continue to diagnose some disorders according to their major symptoms, although these symptoms can occur over a wide range of mental and personality disorders. It may be historically understandable, but it is nevertheless illogical to diagnose the whole personality in terms of a partial phenomenon. The criticisms made above of "hyperkinetic" and "runaway reactions" and the "special symptoms" apply equally well to the separate diagnostic categories for sexual deviations, alcoholism, drug dependence, and psychophysiologic disorders. We need to record and treat these important symptoms, but our terms should be added to a diagnosis of the total personality disorder if our statistics are to reflect clinical reality. Whether a symptom occurs in a neurotic or psychotic patient affects treatment and outcome. Multiple diagnoses can correct for this, but individual and local practices will vary unless the nomenclature specifies that a primary personality diagnosis as well as its major symptomatic manifestation are to be recorded.

CONCLUSION

The primary aim in creating the new nomenclature was to make it compatible with the *International Classification of Diseases* and to update it without violating established patterns of use. This goal has been achieved. It is easy to see how the need to retain a common language makes for conservatism and permits only the most gradual reorganization and revisions of our terminology. This has given us a nomenclature which is awkward, though not impossible to use. However, it will still provide inadequate recording of children's disorders, although it is better than the *DSM-I*.

A number of important changes could easily be made within the framework of the *DSM-II* to make it a more useful diagnostic instrument for children's disorders. The category of "Behavior Disorders" needs to be revised and expanded. The "hyperkinetic reaction" should be redefined so that it differentiates a group of children whom we have called "immature-labile" from the many other types of hyperkinetic children. At least three of the personality types from the GAP *Classification* ("oppositional," "overly dependent," and "mistrustful") should be added to expand the range of disorders covered.

The critical dimension of developmental disorders could be included if these symptoms could be added to the primary diagnosis of mental disorder. The list of "special symptoms" could be expanded, or a supplemental list of symptoms could be appended, using terms from GAP's "developmental deviations" and some of the major items in GAP's appendix of symptoms. The practice of encouraging multiple diagnoses in the new nomenclature should be extended to developmental disorders in children.

If agreement could be reached on these relatively simple revisions, the *DSM-II* would provide categories for more adequate reporting of children's psychiatric disorders. These recommendations for a less restrictive nomenclature should also make it easier for child psychiatrists to agree on a common set of definitions. This is essential if we are to evaluate the new mental health programs for children which have recently begun and which are being planned for the future.

REFERENCES

Bender, L. A twenty-five year view of therapeutic results. In *The Evaluation of Psychiatric Treatments*, P. Hoch and J. Zubin, editors. Grune & Stratton, New York, 1964.

Creak, M., et al. Schizophrenic syndrome in childhood: progress report (April, 1961) of a working party. British Medical Journal, 2: 889, 1961.

Fish, B. The study of motor development in infancy and its relationship to

psychological functioning. American Journal of Psychiatry, 1:17 1113, 1961.
Fish, B. Problems of diagnosis and the definition of comparable groups: a
neglected issue in drug research with children. American Journal of Psychiatry,
125: 900, 1969.
Fish, B., et al. A classification of schizophrenic children under five years. American Journal of Psychiatry, 124: 1415, 1968.
Fish, B., and Shapiro, T. A typology of children's behavior disorders. Journal
of the American Academy of Child Psychiatry, 4: 32, 1965.
Group for the Advancement of Psychiatry Report No. 62. *Psychopathological
Disorders in Childhood: Theoretical Considerations and a Proposed Classification.*
Group for the Advancement of Psychiatry, New York, 1966.
Mahler, M., Ross, J. R., and DeFries, Z. Clinical studies in benign and malignant cases of childhood psychosis (schizophrenic-like). American Journal of Orthopsychiatry, 19: 295, 1949.

AREA C

Major Psychiatric Disorders of Childhood

CHAPTER FIVE

Neuroses of Children

E. JAMES ANTHONY, M.D.

INTRODUCTION

IT SEEMED PARADOXICAL to Malamud, considering the widespread incidence of psychoneurosis in the population and the glib use of the word "neurotic" not only in academic vocabulary but in everyday conversation, that there was "a surprising lack of unanimity and clarity" as to what was meant by the concept of psychoneurosis.

This lack of unanimity and clarity is even more striking with regard to children, so that prevalence figures are well nigh impossible to obtain. Specific reasons for this have been ascribed to the antidiagnostic attitude of the child guidance movement as a whole, to resistance against using nosological entities derived from adult classifications (rather in the way of hand-me-downs), and to a repugnance to the categorizing of a child permanently during years of development and change. In addition, in many clinics there appeared to be an implicit concept of children as more reactive than introversive, leading to a prepossession in favor of such nondescript categories as "behavior," "conduct," "habit," and "situation." In the few surveys that have been carried out, psychoneurotic reactions have shown a frequency ranging between 5 and 20 per cent of all cases, the figure reflecting the orientation of particular clinics rather than an actual indication of incidence. It seems possible that a potent reason for the relative neglect in the use of this particular category of disorder might be attributable to the absence of a systematic delineation in terms pertaining to childhood.

The failure to recognize psychoneurosis in preadault life is also part of the age-old scotoma for serious emotional disturbances in children. For example, in 1798, in his classification of mental disorders, the philosopher

Kant found it possible to state categorically that there was no such thing as a disturbed child. The view was generally accepted for the next hundred years against all evidence of experience, and it was not until Freud that the question was reopened.

In a brilliant series of logically linked clinical and theoretical inquiries, Freud gradually demonstrated the scientific validity of the poetic truth that the child was father to the man, and the neurotic child father to the neurotic man. In the first instance he found that adult neurotic patients almost invariably gave a history of having undergone a similar type of disturbance at some time during their childhood. At this period the behavior was more likely to be referred to as "naughtiness" and, as he put it, to be "shouted down in the nursery." As he came to scrutinize the childhood situation retrospectively and then directly, he began to recognize the disturbance for what it was, an authentic psychoneurotic reaction. As a result of still further investigation, this clinical neurosis of childhood was seen to be an exaggeration of an underlying developmental conflict that was less discernible. Freud called this disturbance the Oedipus complex and looked on it as crucial in the development of both childhood and adult neurosis.

This concept of infantile neurosis has since occupied a central position in the psychoanalytic theory of neurosis, but, as Hartmann has pointed out, it is not so easy to specify its actual nature. It was Hartmann's view that the pendulum has swung in the opposite direction from there being no recognizable neurosis of childhood to the point where "every naughtiness, actually every behavior of the child that does not conform to the textbook model, every development step that is not according to plan, is considered as neurotic," as a result of which "the broad range of normal variations of behavior is not recognized, and the specific features of . . . a neurosis get lost." He was also of the opinion that many of the very early neuroses were really different from what occurred in the adult and were usually limited to a single functional disturbance. "The way from conflict to symptom seems often to be shorter than in adult neurosis."

CAUSES OF PSYCHONEUROTIC REACTIONS

The normal developmental conflict is at first largely external, stemming from incompatibilities between the child's needs and the external demands of the environment. Gradually, the external demand is internalized, and the developmental conflict disappears, since the balance has shifted from the need to gratify pleasurable impulses to the need to comply with the new internal representatives of the external order. With each resolution of conflict in the child, there is a further step toward the formation of the normal adult personality; but when the conflict is unresolved two forms of neurotic disturbance tend to occur. The first is circumscribed and restricted to the phase of the conflict—that is, the premorbid history seems relatively peaceful, the parents are more helpful than harmful, constitutional factors are slight, and the prognosis fairly good. The second and more common form is a diffuse neurotic disturbance that presents itself as a polymorphous mixture of two or more neuroses. The clinical picture lacks definition, and the pathological processes seem potentially capable of developing in several different directions that are difficult to predict. There is often gross familial pathology with a plethora of constitutional dispositions. In contrast to the first form, the defense mechanisms employed tend to be more various and primitive. As a result of the multiple fixation points, a sequence of different psychoneurotic reactions appears during the course of development.

CLINICAL FEATURES OF FOUR TYPES OF CHILDHOOD NEUROSIS

In his classical studies, Freud described four different types of childhood neurosis, three of which had later neurotic developments in adult life. This well-known series of cases is shown in tabulated form in Table I, exemplifying some of Freud's important conclusions that: (1) psychoneurotic reactions in the adult are associated frequently with psychoneurotic reactions in his childhood, (2) the connection is sometimes continuous but more often separated by a latent period of nonneurosis, (3) infantile sexuality (both fantasied and real) occupies a memorable place in the early history of the patient.

There are certain differences worth noting in the four cases shown in Table I. First, the phobic reactions tend to start at about 4 or 5, the obsessional reactions between 6 and 7, and the conversion reactions at 8. The amount of background disturbance is greatest in the conversion reaction and the mixed neurosis, and it seems only slight in the phobic and obsessional reactions. The course of the phobic reaction seems little influenced by severe traumatic factors, whereas traumatic factors, such as sexual seductions, play an important role in the three other subgroups. It was during this period that Freud had elaborated his seduction hypothesis for the cause of the neuroses in terms of which the obsessive-compulsive and hysterical reactions were alleged to originate in active and passive sexual experiences.

CLASSIFICATIONS OF NEUROTIC REACTIONS

Since these classical descriptions were made, clinicians working directly with children have made many attempts to classify the psychoneurotic reactions of childhood in accordance with their experience, and Table II summarizes the more significant attempts at this. It will be noted that the classification tends to vary with both *time* and *country*. The diagnoses of neurasthenia and psychasthenia have given place to anxiety and obsessive-compulsive reactions. Phobias are the most commonly represented, and

TABLE I

Classical Psychoneurotic Reactions of Childhood[a]

	Conversion Reaction (Dora)	Phobic Reaction (Hans)	Obsessive-Compulsive Reaction (Rat Man)	Mixed Psychoneurotic Reaction (Wolf Man)
Family history	Striking family history of psychiatric and physical illness	Both parents treated for neurotic conflict but not severe	No family history of mental illness	Striking family history of psychiatric and physical illness
Symptoms	Enuresis and masturbation 6–8 yrs. Onset of neurosis at 8. Migraine, nervous cough, and hoarseness at 12. Aphonia at 16. "Appendicitis" at 16. Convulsions at 16. Facial neuralgia at 19. Change of personality at 8 from "wild creature" to quiet child	Compulsive questions at 3–3½ yrs., regard to sex difference. Jealous reaction to sibling birth at 3½. Overt castration threat. Overt masturbation at 3½. Overeating and constipation at 4–5. Phobic reaction at 4–5. Attack of flu at 5 worsens phobia. Tonsillectomy at 5 worsens phobia	Naughty period at 3–4 yrs. Marked timidity following beating by father at 4. Recognizing people by their smells as a child ("Renifleur"). Precocious ego development. Onset of obsessive ideas at 6–7.	Tractable and quiet up to 3¼ yrs. "Naughty" period at 3¼–4 yrs. Phobias at 4–5 yrs. Phobias at 4–5 with nightmares. Obsessional reaction at 6–7 (pious ceremonials). Disappearance of neuroses at 8
Causes	Seduction by older man. Father's illness. Father's affair	Seductive care by mother. Sibling birth at 3½	Seduction by governess at 4. Death of sibling at 4. Beating by father at 4	Seduction by older sister at 3¼. Mother's illness. Conflict between maid and governess

[a] Adapted from Freud.

hysterias are sometimes excluded. Such labels as "hypochondriasis," "tics," "psychosomatic states," and "depression" are peculiar to certain authors. The inclusion of depressive reactions appears to be gaining ground.

In the report by the Group for the Advancement of Psychiatry (GAP) on the classification of psychopathological disorders in childhood, an attempt has been made to define the psychoneurotic reactions in childhood in terms acceptable to anyone working broadly within the psychoanalytic frame of reference. According to the definition offered by the committee, *psychoneurosis in childhood* is said to occur as a result of unconscious conflicts over the handling of sexual and aggressive impulses that, although repressed, remain active and unresolved. These conflicts derive from the relationship of the child to significant family members and belong almost exclusively to the preschool years. During early childhood such conflicts may be expressed in various symptomatic reactions, but in older children they become internalized and relatively encapsulated and tend to be chronic. Many of the milder reactions may resolve spontaneously as the child reworks the conflicts at a later stage of development and higher level of maturation. The response to treatment is also generally good. The symptomatology is composed of both positive and negative phenomena—the former including such reactions as obsessions, conversions, dissociations, and depressions; and the latter being manifested by the absence of a demonstrable organic pathology, a consistent and lasting deterioration in intellectual function, a primary disturbance of mood, and a persistent distortion of external reality. The differential diagnosis includes reactive disorders, developmental deviations, crises within healthy development, and certain predominantly physical disorders that have a symptomatic resemblance to the psychoneurotic picture. These various conditions may also act as precursors in the development of a full psychoneurosis, depending on an intensification and internalization of the conflict. In certain instances, the precipitating situational stress may be so overwhelming and unexpected to the child as to produce a traumatic neurosis, which may be either a severe reactive disorder or a sudden crystallization of a latent or subclinical psychoneurotic state. In certain cases, for reasons not completely clear, symptom formation may not occur. Instead, the personality structure of the child may be affected by neurotic conflicts, altering the patterns of reaction to internal demands and adaptations to the environment, and these may assume the character of personality traits that cause little or no conscious (ego-syntonic) anxiety. When these seeming personality traits become fully crystallized, they coalesce to form a personality disorder.

In the milder cases the differentiation of abnormal from normal reactions presents some degree of difficulty, since various investigations have shown that almost every child manifests various symptom constellations at different stages of his development and that these include neurotic traits

TABLE II

Various Classifications of the Psychoneurotic Reactions of Childhood

Year	Author	Classification
1920	Pearson (U.S.A.)	Disturbances of sociopsychological adjustment due to emotional conflicts. (1) Anxiety, acute and chronic. (2) Psychoneurosis: gastrointestinal dysfunction, upper and lower; urinary dysfunction
1932	Henderson and Gillespie (Britain)	Anxiety psychoneurosis, hysterias, phobias, obsessions, compulsions, tics (some)
1933	Krasnogorski (Russia)	Subcortical type: neurasthenia, psychasthenia. Hypodynamic (anergic) type: hysteria
1936	Miller (Britain)	Subjective disorders: overt anxiety, phobias, compulsions, nocturnal disturbances
1937	Brown (U.S.A.)	Hysterical, psychasthenia, neurasthenia, and anxiety types
1937	English	Acute diurnal and nocturnal anxiety attacks. Chronic anxiety states and phobias
1947	Gerard (U.S.A.)	Nocturnal anxiety, phobias, compulsions, depression, chronic anxiety states
1948	Pacella (U.S.A.)	Acute and chronic anxiety states, phobias, compulsions, conversion phenomena, tics, psychosomatic states
1955	Cameron (Britain)	Anxiety or phobic states, obsessive-compulsive state, hysterical state, alternations in mood
1966	GAP Report (U.S.A.)	Anxiety, phobic, dissociative, obsessive-compulsive, conversion and depressive types

that, if transient, do not require treatment. For example, sleep disturbances may occur in the second and third year, phobias in the fourth and fifth year, obsessional games from the sixth to the eighth year, and a large assortment of anxieties involving disease, disfigurement, disability, and death from the ninth year on.

ROLE OF ANXIETY

There have been more recent attempts to base an understanding of psychoneurotic reactions on the modes of adaptation of the individual to such primary disturbing affects as anxiety and depression. Adaptation has been viewed from various theoretical positions in terms of defense, avoidance, and problem-solving techniques. Freud himself came to regard anxiety as playing a primary role in the development of all other types of disordered behavior, the elements of which could be regarded basically as techniques for reducing or avoiding anxiety. In the second of his theories concerning anxiety, it was anxiety that led to repression and not the reverse. Freud also began to see the intimate connection between special forms of defense and particular types of psychoneuroses as, for instance, between repression and hysteria.

The vicissitudes arising from the emergence of anxiety may result in a variety of counteractions on the part of the individual. For example, the anxiety may remain undefended, without an object, and experienced both psychologically and physically, as in the typical anxiety reaction; or it may be displaced onto some symbolic object or situation, as in the phobic reaction. It may be converted into various somatic symptoms, as in conversion reactions; or it may overwhelm the individual and cause aimless activity or freezing, as in dissociative reactions. It may be transposed by means of various repetitions, rituals, and reactions, as in the obsessive-compulsive reactions; or it may allay itself by self-depreciation, as in the depressive reaction. These techniques are all available to children from a very early phase, and clinically one may see the reaction in relatively pure form or accompanied by one or more of the other neurotic reactions.

ROLE OF DEPRESSION

There has been a more recent tendency to treat another basic psychobiological affective reaction, depression, in a similar style. Both anxiety and depression are appropriate reactions under normal conditions of danger and desertion, but both can become abnormal when they occur in inappropriate circumstances, when they persist for an undue length of time, or when the child is unable to make a developmentally appropriate adaptation to them. In this context, Rado interpreted many of the symptoms of neurosis as a misuse of emergency mechanisms.

Depression can be viewed as an affect, as can anxiety, and allotted a similar conceptual state. As with anxiety, the individual develops various mechanisms for dealing with depression. Whereas *repression* is one of the psychoneurotic's main modes of defense with anxiety, in the case of depression, with its core feelings of unworthiness and helplessness, *regression* is often the mechanism of choice. The other defenses mobilized against the danger of its emergence include obsessive-compulsive reactions, which magically compensate for loss of self-esteem; reversal of affect, characterized by excitement and clowning; identification with idealized objects; acting out in the form of delinquency; and the development of psychosomatic states. All these defenses are means of averting the passive experience of helplessness in the face of frustration or disappointment.

RELATIONSHIP BETWEEN ANXIETY AND DEPRESSION

The fundamental relationship between depression and anxiety is not perfectly clear. Freud had postulated that, whereas anxiety occurs as a reaction to the prospective danger of losing the object, depression develops with actual or fantasied loss. In the situation of separation, the anxiety reaction is evoked by any threatened removal of the mother; but, once she leaves, the child, who cannot as yet distinguish between temporary absence and permanent loss, behaves as if he were never going to see her again until he eventually learns that her disappearance is inevitably followed by her reappearance. The separation syndrome, therefore, contains elements of both anxiety and depression in varying mixture. At an early stage, loss may be felt in terms of need, and the situation is, therefore, a traumatic rather than a dangerous one. Later on, experience teaches the child that the mother can be present but angry with him, and then loss of love becomes a new and much more enduring determinant of anxiety and depression.

ANXIETY REACTION

Definition

Anxiety is a form of fear reaction that is different from normal object fear in the following ways: (1) It is diffuse or free-floating and not restricted to definite situations or objects; (2) it is not accompanied by any degree of insight into its immediate cause; (3) it tends to be experienced in terms of its physical manifestations, but these are not recognized as such by the individual concerned; (4) it is prompted by anticipation of future threats, against which current avoidance responses would not be effective; (5) it is not controlled by any specific psychological defense mechanisms, as are the other psychoneurotic reactions.

The term "anxiety" is synonymous with the earlier phrase "anxiety state," and the more recent phrase "stress reaction." The still older term is "neurasthenia," in which the emphasis was on the functional disorders of various organ systems and the hypochondriacal preoccupations associated with them. The chief symptoms were irritability, fatigue, and exhaustion. Hypochondriasis is now regarded as a symptom that can accompany almost any psychiatric disorder.

Epidemiology

Anxiety and fear, varying in degree and nature, are encountered in all young children. Anxiety neurosis has been referred to not only as *the* neurosis of childhood but also as the form of neurosis that is most commonly reactivated in adult life.

Most of the fears of small children can be traced directly to fears expressed by their mothers, and it is only the occasional fear that seems derived from personal experience. The same was found to be true of fear reactions under conditions of severe external danger, such as bombing raids in London. In situations where the parents felt safe or were not frightened, the children remained equally calm.

With regard to chronic anxiety, apprehensiveness on the part of the mother is often clinically correlated with anxiety in the child—sometimes objectless, sometimes well-defended, and sometimes wholly denied. The communication of anxiety within families proceeds on both verbal and nonverbal levels, but there is a tendency for anxiety to obtain overt expression at the upper and more articulate levels of social class and for the bound forms to affect the lower echelons. Certain autonomic and endocrine measures, acceptable as indices of anxiety, have shown significantly higher mean values for neurotic as compared with control families. Anxiety-prone individuals (overreactors) have been roughly estimated to make up between 5 and 10 per cent of a general population. At the level of the child, this would make up the small percentage of vulnerable children who respond to the challenge of ordinary experience—sibling birth, illness, hospitalization—with anxiety and regression rather than with growth and maturation.

Causes

In ontogenetic studies of anxiety, it has been found that the majority of anxious children start as early as the first month of life to show behavior patterns that later develop into frank expressions of anxiety. The children show stress sensitivity from the very beginning, overreacting to both internal and external stimuli. They are easily startled and take poorly to change.

The anxious child in a family is often regarded as different from his siblings, and the parents usually insist that this quality has been present since birth. Infantile reactions considered indicative of anxiety—apathy, motor excitement, sleeplessness, refusal to eat, and autonomic disturbances—have been related to gross rejection and neglect on the part of the mother. There is also some suggestion that prenatal maternal anxieties, translated into muscular tensions involving the birth canal, may increase the frequency of abnormal birth conditions, which, in turn, enhance the disposition to anxiety in the child. The anxiety proneness has been followed into the preschool and early school years. This constitutional factor could play a part in determining the clinical picture in later neurotic conflicts.

In addition to physical birth trauma, the tendency to surplus anxiety has also been linked to the physiological economy and psychological meaning of the birth process. It has been suggested, for example, that the sensorimotor imbalance involved in parturition may be also implicated in the genesis of the later anxiety, but these views are speculative and controversial. Freud at his most pragmatic felt that there were many anxieties without a prototype in birth and that, in general, the birth trauma assumption was entirely unproved and very improbable, since it was hardly credible that the child had preserved, from the act of birth, any other than tactile and general sensations. He did allow, however, that birth might be responsible for a certain predisposition to anxiety and that this might persist over the period of childhood. The neurotic anxieties originating from this predisposition did not seem to be clearly or closely related to the developmental neuroses of later childhood stemming from the lack of resolution of the

Oedipus complex.

The predisposition is further evident in the amplification of the so-called universal anxieties—separation anxiety, stranger anxiety, and nocturnal anxiety—normally associated with the early anaclitic relationships.

At the later stage of development, the clinical reaction becomes more complex, the anxiety being generated from three different sources. First, there is contagious anxiety, which is communicated to the child by any neurotically fearful adult with whom he is in close contact. Second, there is traumatic anxiety, resulting from some unexpected fright that overwhelms the child's defenses. Third, there is conflict anxiety, which arises out of the intrapsychic sphere and is the most important source of neurotic anxiety. The three types of anxiety intertwine with one another in a series of relationships or syndromes. There are still unanswered questions as to why only certain anxieties get communicated to the child, why some traumata prove so upsetting and persistent while others have only a minimal and short-lived effect, and why conflict anxiety is often able to resolve itself with the passage of time without treatment.

The transmission of contagious anxiety is governed by such factors as the age of the child, the degree of dependency and suggestibility, the sex in relation to that of the anxious parent, and the closeness of identification. The onerousness of a trauma depends on its intensity, unexpectedness, and significance relative to current conflicts. For a traumatic disturbance to resolve itself, four conditions must be fulfilled: (1) The environment should not overreact; (2) the frightening experience should not dovetail into some basic conflict in progress; (3) the secondary gains in the way of solicitude and concern should not be excessive; and (4) the child should be in a state of relative stability in his development.

The resolution of conflict anxiety depends on a more complex set of factors, especially on the backlog of disturbance built up during the whole course of psychosexual development. There is some evidence that conflict anxiety, insurmountable at one stage of development, may be more easily relieved by more competent ego functioning at the next stage of maturing.

The average neurotic anxiety in children contains elements from all three sources (contagious anxiety, traumatic anxiety, and conflict anxiety), the external factors often having lasting determining effects on the configuration of the basic neurotic conflicts.

CLINICAL DESCRIPTION

The symptomatology of the anxiety reaction includes both psychological and physiological symptoms. The principal psychological symptom is a diffuse and vague feeling of apprehension, as if something terrible was going to happen. The anxiety attacks sometimes begin after some manifest trauma, but this is found to be a relative latecomer in the causal chain of events, serving the purpose of externalizing an accumulation of latent but already existing anxieties. The trigger events are various and may include a bout of illness, a surgical operation, an exposure to death, or a failure at school. Having their hair washed is apparently a sufficient stimulus for some sensitive young girls.

In addition to the anxious expectation, the children are generally irritable, worried about their health, and prone to episodes of acute anxiety. During these acute attacks, physical symptoms may come to the fore and dominate the clinical picture. These may include disturbances of the heart's action (palpitation, precordial pain, and cardiac symptoms on effort); disturbances of respiration (nervous dyspnea, pseudoasthma, and hyperventilation); gastrointestinal disturbances (nausea, biliousness, diarrhea, and abdominal pain); and attacks of giddiness, trembling, sweating, and paresthesias. Urinary urgency and frequency are also usually present.

Against this background of hypersensitivity and apprehensiveness, it is possible to differentiate three symptomatic groups.

Nocturnal and diurnal anxiety attacks. These attacks are localized at various points on the sleep-waking cycle and are all characterized by acute terror or panic with cataleptic features, profuse sweating, disorientation, and visual hallucinations. A waking terror may be brought about by visual illusions elaborated in the dark; a half-waking terror is often triggered by hypnagogic or hypnopompic hallucinations occurring during the twilight phase between sleeping and waking; a sleeping terror is brought about during light to moderate sleep, when anxiety dreams have their greatest incidence; a sleep-waking terror, the classical night terror, occurs when the predisposed individual is roused from very deep sleep into half-wakefulness; and, at apparently no specific point in the waking portion of the cycle, a day terror can occur—this is typically very similar to the night terror in its clinical picture and may even alternate with it.

The anxiety attacks in these cases are associated with such factors as interparental aggression, mental illness in the family, sleeping in the parental bedroom, undue parental pressures, traumatic experiences, and phobic, anxious mothers who constantly generate an atmosphere of pervasive anxiety in the household by their hyperalertness to threat from any quarter. These sensitive, suggestible, and imaginative children tend to resonate sympathetically in tune with the mother's anxieties.

Chronic anxiety reaction. In certain immature children there is a permanent attitude of apprehensiveness and an overreaction to almost every unexpected environmental stimulus. This combination of a lowered stimulus threshold, a tendency to generalize responses, and a protracted lability of affect, causing the child to reverberate for long periods after a disturbing experience, produces a clinical picture of a timid, undecided, withdrawing child who has always been afraid of everything and who, through the course of development, has been overwhelmed in turn by separation anxieties, stranger reactions, animal fears, dread of going to school, and general social anxiety. There are no specific attacks of any kind, nor do they confine themselves to any particular object or situation.

Darkness, being alone, people, storms, insects, noises are all included in the apprehensions of the child who is sometimes so afraid that he cannot talk above a whisper. Cimbal referred to this reaction as *lebensfeigheit*, meaning cowardliness with regard to living. Nightmares are frequent, enuresis not uncommon, and anxious preoccupation with bodily functioning almost the rule. The child tends to be delicate and finicky about food, to the constant concern of his equally nervous mother.

Hypochondriacal reaction. A chronic hypochondriacal attitude in the child is made up of current complaints of vague ill health and anxious anticipation of future illness. A variety of factors in the child, the family, and the caring physician may contribute to the genesis of hypochondriasis. Factors in the child include identification with ill parents and siblings and the adoption of familial somatization techniques for dealing with stress; self-mothering in the absence of parental figures; attention-seeking aimed at obtaining a greater acceptance and approval within the family; a flight into sickness to avoid threatening situations or pressures; reactivation of the sickness role that once obtained for the child a suspension from regular routine and the loving solicitude of the parents; a compensation for social and educational failure linked to a lowering of self-esteem; a need to ward off indefinite formless anxiety by the adoption of a definite form of sickness that might be cured; the effect of naive infantile theories of disease that "logically" systematize bodily discomforts; and, above all, the atonement for guilt feelings in relation to hostile and sexual impulses and acts.

The parents of such children, particularly the mothers, may be grossly hypochondriacal themselves and may treat the child as a somatic extension of themselves. Their oversolicitude and protectiveness may thinly veil strong feelings of rejection, but, more frequently, the dislike and hostility is relatively unmasked. From time to time, the overprotective mother may decompensate, giving the child a glimpse of her real attitudes and feelings, and these exposures may in turn set off a reaction of invalidism. Where there is much family history of disease, the anxious anticipation of the parents may fill the child with foreboding about his inheritance. There is no doubt that some mothers, not necessarily nurses by profession, are at their best in the sick room and enjoy the acts of ministration. The child's sickness then becomes an essential part in the relationship with the mother, and he literally becomes her patient. A sick room atmosphere is created around him almost from birth, and he may never have seen himself as a healthy child. The children vary in their reactions; they look and act worried. Hypochondriasis is very much a family disturbance, and the various members seem to understand unconsciously the child's need to be surrounded by as much somatic anxiety as possible. The family may react, in fact, calmly and unconcernedly in the presence of actual illness.

Differential Diagnosis

In the child an anxiety neurosis sooner or later tends to crystallize into one of the anxiety-bound neurotic reactions. The diffuse reaction needs to be distinguished from the reactive disorders and the psychophysiological disturbances. Although physiological concomitants of anxiety are commonly present in varying degrees, they do not ordinarily lead to structural changes in the organ systems involved. Various habit disorders are often associated with anxiety reactions, and these include sleep disturbances, eating problems, temper tantrums, enuresis, nail-biting, masturbation, and stuttering.

Prognosis

The prognosis is related to the stress sensitivity and the predisposition to anxiety accompanying it. Where the development of anxiety has been late, the constitutional factors slight or absent, the birth history uneventful, and the first two or three years relatively peaceful, the anxiety reaction can be treated as a developmental neurotic conflict with relatively favorable prognosis. On the other hand, where chronic insecurity dates from infancy and one or both parents are chronically anxious themselves, the possibility of frequent relapses throughout development must be borne in mind, even though the prognosis for the current attack may be good.

Management

A careful physical examination may be reassuring to some anxious and hypochondriacal children, but the dangers of iatrogenesis must be constantly kept in mind if new complaints and new anxieties are to be avoided. The physical examination is undertaken to assure the doctor that he is not dealing with organic disease and to assure the child that his body is, in fact, a well-functioning entity that might be best left alone to its own wisdom. Like many other psychiatric disorders of childhood, the conflicts of the child are often maintained and magnified by the anxious intrusions of the parents. Psychotherapy with the child should, therefore, be coupled with guidance for the parents and, if necessary, psychiatric treatment when anxious concerns have reached neurotic proportions. The parents particularly need help when the repressed hostility of the anxious child comes to the surface with psychotherapy and is carried back into the home. With hypochondriacal children, a necessary maneuver, early in treatment, entails a cutting down on medication. This should be done gradually and carefully, since the child has come to rely on its magical efficacy and the support should not be removed too hastily. When anxiety is acute and disruptive and sleep much disturbed, the tranquilizing group of drugs may tide the child over a rough period before psychotherapy is able or available to control his anxieties.

PHOBIC REACTION

DEFINITION

In this category the child displaces the content of his original conflict onto an object or situation in the external environment that has some symbolic significance for him. Among the feared external objects or situations frequently chosen by children are animals, school, dirt, disease, high places, elevators, and dying. This condition was formerly classified as anxiety hysteria.

EPIDEMIOLOGY

It is difficult to assess the incidence of phobic reactions because they are so often confused in clinics with the presence of fears. Fears occur regularly during the development of a normal child, and certain types of fears are characteristic of certain stages of development. The infant is frightened by any intense, abrupt stimulus and loss of support; between 5 and 9 months, he shows fear of the unfamiliar in terms of persons, things, and situations; between the ages of 2 and 3 years, animal fears are predominant; fear of the dark does not usually begin until the third year, and, as the child grows older, darkness becomes a contributing factor, if not the main cause, in a great many fears. Since a state of darkness is often equivalent to a state of being alone, regardless of the presence or absence of others, darkness makes the child feel more vulnerable and less able to cope and thereby stimulates his basic anxiety with respect to separation from the mother. According to Gesell, between the ages of 3½ and 4½ years, the child wakes in fear from an animal dream, especially of wolves, as in the case of the Wolf Man. During the preschool years, there is a gradual increase in animal fears, first of eating and biting animals and later of overpowering and destructive animals. Many of the fears of children at this age also pertain to possible injury through drowning, fire, and traffic accidents. As the child grows older and is increasingly able to take account of the past and anticipate the future, his fears are formulated increasingly in terms of remote or imaginary dangers or in terms of misfortunes that do not immediately threaten him but might befall him at a future time. Finally, during the adolescent period, fears and anxieties relating to physical inadequacies and asymmetries, intellectual inadequacies, and sexual functioning may arise.

The problem of differentiating fears from phobias or healthy from morbid fears becomes increasingly difficult as one finds that many of the normal developmental fears of children have never been experienced and are often quite irrational. In addition, the reaction of the child to a simple fear often seems to be disproportionate, persisting for long periods of time. It would, therefore, seem as if many of the simple fears of the preschool child may actually represent phobias in which an apparent neurotic anxiety is hidden behind an apparent object anxiety, the internal danger being transformed into an external one. If this is true, phobic reactions are probably much commoner than would be supposed from examination of clinical records. As transient reactions, they may never be referred beyond the pediatrician. In guidance clinics the phobic reaction is seen most frequently between the ages of 4 and 7 years and equally in boys and girls.

CAUSES

In the normal process of development, children outgrow their susceptibility to the anxiety-producing situations of being alone, of being in the dark, and of encountering strangers. Later the animal phobias also gradually disappear. It is, therefore, the *persistence* of this infantile phobic tendency that characterizes the neurotic in the making.

In the immediate premorbid history of the phobic child, one frequently encounters a period of objectless anxiety marked by restlessness, irritability, and naughtiness. Then comes an incident—for example, the horse falling down in the case of Little Hans—and almost immediately there is a restructuring of internal forces, leading to a diminution of general anxiety and to the formation of a phobia. In Freud's account, the boy's anxiety begins as a free-floating disturbance. Gradually, this diffuse anxiety focuses around questions involving differences between the sexes. Even after the outbreak of the street phobia, Hans is unable to say what it is that he fears. He only admits that in the street he misses his mother and does not want to be away from her. However, when he goes with her for his next walk, he still suffers from generalized anxiety, making his explanation manifestly inadequate.

The next thing, as Freud put it, is "for his anxiety to find an object," and this happens when he later confides to his mother his fear that a horse would bite him. Still later, in the evening, he expresses his further fear that a horse would come into the room. At this point, the average parent might have justifiably become impatient with such foolish fears, but, as Freud remarks, "a neurosis never says foolish things." The clarification of this very meaningful nonsense occupies the next few months. It is possible that the choice of phobia has some relation to a frightening, infantile experience, but, more often than not, the connection between phobia and the primary fear has been lost. Relations between the inner conflict and the specific content of the phobia are also obscure and complex but may be discovered after prolonged clinical study.

In a quite different frame of reference, that of avoidance learning theory, a noxious object or event may acquire aversive properties (fear arousal), and responses that appear in an attempt to avoid the stimuli are reinforced by fear reduction. The anxiety-provoking stimuli associated with the particular stimulus can become generalized to other stimuli in the patient's everyday life and result in a general emotional instability.

CLINICAL DESCRIPTION

The clinical picture presented by the phobic child is markedly different from that of the fearful child. Constitutional and hereditary factors are generally insignificant. The children are described as physically well, cheerful, amiable, active-minded, with a suggestion of emotional and social precocity.

Three phobic states that frequently present themselves to the clinician as demarcated entities are the following.

Animal phobia. This has been described in various parts of this chapter in relation to Hans and the Wolf Man. As previously pointed out, animal fears and anxiety dreams about animals are frequent between the ages of 3 and 5, and it may also be true that frightening experiences with animal pets are not unusual in this age group. It would, therefore, seem natural that in the search for an external object on which to displace internal danger, the animal is a first choice.

In his discussion of animism and totemism, Freud observed that a sense of kinship existed between children and animals, as if they were not too far apart in their thinking and feeling, except for the fact, as noted by the child, that animals seemed much freer in their sexual and aggressive behavior and much less hampered by social restrictions. Animals could, therefore, serve admirably for the projection of unacceptable feelings. Occasionally, the animal phobia may give place to a different type of phobia and in some cases (the Wolf Man) may be replaced by obsessive-compulsive reactions.

School phobia. Many of the circumstances affecting a child's self-esteem arise in connection with his life at school. Here the child is exposed to failure or threat of failure in both the academic and social spheres. With its traditional focus on competition, the school becomes the situation in which children try themselves out in many different ways, realizing both their strengths and their weaknesses. The organism of the school, as with animals, offers an appropriate and convenient symbol for displacement.

The school phobia proper represents only one type of response within the general category of the child's refusal to attend school. At one extreme there is truancy, which can be regarded as more a psychosocial than a neurotic problem. The school phobia proper is now regarded as a variant of the separation problem, based on neurotic conflicts originating within the home but sometimes precipitated by something happening in the school, which then serves as a transference situation. It has been said that "all of a child's worries, fears, anxieties, self-consciousness, feelings of inadequacy, his relation to his parents, to his siblings, to himself tend to gain reflection in the school situation." This would also be an apt statement of the therapeutic situation, and it is not unusual for treatment phobias to develop, leading to drop-outs. The crucial psychopathology in cases of school phobia has been attributed to an anxiety over separation from the mother and to a concomitant anxiety on the part of the mother with regard to separation from her child, with the establishment of a symbiotic relationship in which the two partners are dependent on, demanding of, and dominating each other in turn. At first sight, this would appear to be a pregenital syndrome in psychoanalytic terms, but a more careful analysis of some of the cases leads to the suspicion that behind the anxiety of separation from the mother lies, in Freud's terms, "the next transformation of anxiety," castration anxiety, which involves a danger of separation from the genital that is "tantamount to a second separation from the mother" because possession of the genital organ contains a guarantee of reunion with the mother, and the loss of the organ would mean a loss of this guarantee. In this context, it will be recalled that the first explanation put forward by Hans for his street phobia was a fear of separation from his mother, and it was only subsequently in the course of his treatment that the underlying castration anxiety was revealed.

From an examination of a large number of such cases, it becomes apparent that these cases do represent a heterogeneous group and that the school phobias that begin early are different clinical entities from those beginning, for instance, at puberty or in early adolescence. The latter group tends to comprise severe character disorders and borderline psychoses, and there is often an associated family pathology of some severity, particularly depression in the mother. There is some suggestion, too, that the more external types of precipitating factors—involving disapproving teachers, poor grades, bullying, or shameful incidents in which the child loses face—may all carry a more favorable prognosis than those connected with home and family, such as illness in the child, illness or death in the family, an accident involving the parents, or the development of mental illness in some crucial figure, such as the mother. Often, as if to supplement the phobia, the child may show psychophysiological reactions as well, such as abdominal pain, diarrhea, vomiting, and headache.

Death phobia. This might be referred to as "8-year anxiety," since it tends to occur very regularly at about that age. In his earlier work, Freud referred to the "eight-year boundary line" that seemed to divide childhood. For a while he believed that anyone who had not been subjected to seductive sexual experiences before 8 years could not develop hysteria. In his case of Dora, neurosis began in her eighth year, and in the case of the Wolf Man his infantile neurosis ended abruptly around the eighth year. In the early studies of Piaget, the eighth year also formed a boundary line between the egocentric child with his magical, animistic, realistic tendencies associated with a precausal, prelogical mode of thinking and the operational child who sees the world logically and rationally. In many children, at about this time, there occurs what can be described loosely as an existential crisis. The child becomes preoccupied with ideas of death and dying either about himself or about his parents. Once again, separation anxiety is brought to the forefront; the main presenting fear is that the mother will die; but, again, there is more to the phobia than just this. The child's concept of death, like many of his other concepts, develops gradually during the whole period of childhood. At an early stage, death is thought of mostly in animistic terms in which the dead see, hear, and feel. Later it is viewed as separation or, rather, desertion, and, still later, death becomes personified as a dreaded figure removing the loved person. Before the age of 7, death is reversible. At about 8 years, death for many children becomes irreversible; and, therefore, death wishes, both conscious and unconscious, take on a new emotional coloring. At the time of the crisis, the child becomes aware of a peculiar kind of helplessness in the face of the inevitability of death, with the additional feeling that no one can help, since everyone else is in the same predicament. An experience of death sometimes precipitates the crisis or brings it out at an earlier age, but on closer analysis, it soon becomes clear that the emotional conflicts have been growing uninterruptedly since preschool days and that the fear of death is frequently a fear of punishment and retaliation. A coexistence of death wishes with an experience of actual death, coupled with the sudden realization of the irreversibility of the death process, proceeds to a state of acute panic that leaves the child for a while poorly organized in his defenses and prone to extremely primitive behavior. In fact, at times this panic may take on the appearance of a traumatic neurosis. As the condition improves, the sense of personal immunity to death reasserts itself, and what existentialists refer to as the nonauthentic position becomes reestablished.

DIFFERENTIAL DIAGNOSIS

Developmental crises involving separation anxiety, with concern for the whereabouts of the mother, should be distinguished from phobic disorders, with their internalized and structured character. The mild fears and transient phobias of the healthy preschool child and the fears of specific stressful experiences in reactive disorders should also be recognized as distinct from neurotic phobic disorders.

PROGNOSIS

Freud referred to the phobic neurosis of childhood as the model for all repressive disturbances. He was not certain as to the prognosis without treatment. To quote from his *Collected Papers*, vol. 3:

> phobias are well known to be quite extraordinarily frequent, even in children the strictness of whose upbringing has left nothing to be desired. In later life, these children either become neurotic or remain healthy. Their phobias are shouted down in the nursery because they are inaccessible to treatment and are decidedly inconvenient. In the course of months or years, they diminish, and the child seems to

recover; but no one can tell what psychological changes are necessitated by such a recovery, or what alterations in character are involved in it.

He goes on to point out that, in the adult neurotic patient, one frequently finds a residue of the childhood phobic reaction, as if there were a continuous, undisturbed thread of mental activity stretching between the two neurotic disturbances. The symptom is, therefore, transient, but one cannot say the same for the neurotic substratum.

MANAGEMENT

Phobic children are often a pleasure to treat in that, like Hans, they are generally alert, inquisitive, and resourceful in the therapeutic situation and make full use of all the symbolic equations in play, both consciously and unconsciously. In the classical phobic reaction, one is often able to follow the line of displacement back into the central neurotic anxiety that is, in part, related to troublesome, aggressive wishes and, in part, to erotic impulses most often revealed in the dream material and in masturbatory fantasies. For the analytic therapist, Freud's dictum still holds true: "Sexuality is the key to the problem of the psychoneuroses . . . no one who disdains the key will ever be able to unlock the door."

The child's phobia, especially his school phobia, may create serious problems for the family as a whole. The parents are often understandably concerned as to how far they may proceed with the child in his avoidance behavior and to what extent they can allow the household to be dominated by the restrictions imposed by the phobia. In most of the phobias other than the later school phobias, the prognosis for symptomatic cure is reasonably good within a short period of time, and the parents can, therefore, be prevailed on to resist forceful and punitive measures during the period of therapy. In instances of the later school phobias, the mother may often be as disturbed as the child, and her disturbance may be aggravated by her knowledge that the child is missing out on schooling. In all cases of school phobia, the parents form an integral part of the treatment program. The current practice is to try to return the child as rapidly as possible to the school environment, since the longer he is away, the more difficult it will be to get him back.

In the case of the death phobia, a tranquilizing agent may relieve the panic that besets the child prior to sleep in the acute stage. This period of time is especially troublesome for children with neurotic problems, since sleep may represent the threat of frightening dreams and possible bedwetting, and being alone in the dark may stimulate conflicts around masturbation. For the child with a fear of dying, falling asleep has special problems in itself, since sleep may both consciously and unconsciously be associated with separation and death. With some acute phobias of recent onset and a clear-cut precipitating trauma, Levy's release therapy may be highly effective, especially if this is followed up by more traditional psychotherapy. More recently, Wolpe's method of systematic desensitization has been employed in the treatment of child phobic patients with good reported success.

CONVERSION REACTION

DEFINITION AND HISTORY

Freud first introduced the concept of conversion as a mechanism for transforming anxiety into a dysfunction of bodily structures or organs supplied by the voluntary portion of the central nervous system, involving the striated musculature and the somatosensory apparatus. The symptoms serve to lessen conscious anxiety and to symbolize the underlying mental conflict. Since they also meet the immediate needs of the patients, they serve as a source of secondary gain. The term "conversion reaction" is synonymous with "conversion hysteria."

Toward the end of the nineteenth century, the work of Charcot stimulated a great deal of interest in hysteria, and the Nancy school fostered this interest through its work on hypnosis. Freud was in touch with both groups, which prepared him for his subsquent collaboration with Breuer, culminating in the publication of "Studies in Hysteria" in 1893. This contained Breuer's theory of hypnoidal states and his method of abreaction, whereby the original psychic trauma was reproduced in *statu nascendi* under hypnosis. Both theory and method were later disavowed by Freud, who preferred the talking out of reminiscences. He also rejected Janet's theory that dissociation was the primary mechanism, maintaining that it was effect not cause.

At this stage Freud still believed that the causal trauma was of recent origin and that, once the treatment was applied, the hysterical symptoms disappeared forever. He mentioned, for example, the case of a little girl with attacks of general convulsions who had an immediate convulsive attack under hypnosis when she "saw" a dog coming at her. It seemed that her first attack had occurred soon after she was chased by a mad dog. The abreaction was followed by the disappearance of the symptom, confirming its hysterical nature. That dog was a prelude to many theoretical shifts in the years to follow, but at this stage Freud seemed satisfied with its immediate and manifest significance as a causal agent.

In 1894 Freud stated that the crucial mechanisms at work in hysteria included the presence of an unbearable idea, the capacity for conversion, and the readiness to dissociate.

In 1896 he felt that the *character* of the traumatic event helped to shape the quality and intensity of the symptom that followed, but his vision was now focused beyond the traumatic incident and led him to memories that antedated the abreacted trauma and linked it to a series of disturbing events not strung together simply like the pearls on a necklace but much more like a genealogical tree containing ramifications of memory chains branching at nodal points. As he followed the chains, he made two discoveries: (1) that it led him back to the time of puberty; and (2) that the original experience turned out to be a sexual one.

In continuing this investigation, Freud soon found himself looking beyond puberty into the dark period of childhood. Now he was confronted by a dilemma. Since children at this time in history were by definition asexual, it seemed that he must either abandon his sexual hypothesis or his childhood hypothesis. He decided to abandon neither but rather to incorporate both in a fresh theory that attributed the development of hysteria to the occurrence of actual sexual experiences in childhood below the age of 8 years, which coincided, he noted, with the development of the second dentition. He was now convinced that hysterical symptoms began almost without exception in the eighth year and had to be preceded by a passively endured, unpleasant seduction experience.

He was soon faced with another critical decision when he found that many of the seduction stories told him by patients had never, in fact, taken place and that he had to either sacrifice his theory of neurosis based on childhood sexual experience or take a closer look at the lies. It was at this historical point that he reached his Copernican conclusion that fantasies were as potent as facts in generating the psychoneurotic reaction and had their own psychic reality. In his final etiological step, he brought the infantile sexual fantasies into the over-all framework of the Oedipus complex and traced the development of hysteria to the repression of unresolved oedipal wishes. He decided that the wishful fantasies occurred during the early phase of masturbation, and, in conjunction with this, he made the important clinical observation that the onset of neurosis coincided with the cessation of masturbation, as in the case of Dora.

Childhood hysteria as a clinical condition was first mentioned by Lepois in 1618. From 1873 until 1915, there were thirty-six publications devoted to the topic; from these it is clear that nearly every conceivable form of disturbed behavior was being included in the concept and that it was used to cover almost any kind of emotional instability. From 1915 the subject almost disappeared from the literature until a special number of *The Nervous Child* was devoted entirely to it. It was apparent that the confusion as to what might be included or excluded from the diagnosis still persisted.

EPIDEMIOLOGY

As Kanner points out, one finds in the literature statements that hysteria is an everyday phenomenon in childhood as well as contrary assertions that it is most unusual. The gross manifestations of hysteria in the adult have considerably diminished in the Western world, although they can still be seen in primitives and adolescents. About three to five cases of hysterical contractures, aphonias, and amblyopias can be expected in the outpatient department of a children's hospital every year. The milder forms of conversion seen today are usually part of a mixed neurotic disturbance with phobic, obsessional, depressive, and sometimes even psychotic elements. Various authors have also suggested that hysteria is not so phase-specific as was once thought and that it might well have its roots in a primary disturbance at the oral level, which furnished it with a paranoid substructure and lent malignant aspects to the hysterical personality.

At one time, it had been thought that hysteria was restricted to upper-class females, but Charcot was able to demonstrate that it also occurred in lower-class men, although the rest of Europe felt that this was true only of France, and the rest of France felt that this was true only for Charcot's cases. Conversion reactions still occur predominantly in adolescent girls, but there is no appreciable sex difference during childhood. The incidence below school age is negligible, although cases have been reported as early as 1 to 3 years of age.

In the course of time, hysteria has evidently undergone a downward mobility through the social classes, since it is now more frequent in working-class children and adults. The fact that very few cases of pure conversion hysterias are encountered in guidance clinics has given rise to the erroneous conclusion that the condition is largely nonexistent; but this is far from being the case, since it now appears to occur in milder and more transient forms that are dealt with by the pediatrician. In a study of childhood hysteria in which the diagnosis was made on the basis of multiple symptoms persisting over long periods of time accompanied by the somatic symptoms of anxiety, pseudoneurological symptoms, and/or abdominal pain and vomiting, it was found that hysteria was unusual before the age of 9 and rare before the age of 5, that there was no occurrence of monosymptomatic hysteria, that no males with hysteria were found at follow-up, and that anxiety was a constant manifestation of the condition, suggesting that conversion was not as highly effective in defense as it was classically made out to be. Whether this study by general psychiatrists without training or experience with children actually dealt with childhood hysteria is open to question.

CAUSES

In the historical development of psychoanalytic theory, as delineated above, the original neurotic conflict was located successively in adult, adolescent, and infantile periods of life, and the unbearable idea was reduced first to a sexual act and then to a sexual fantasy. At every stage of Freud's theorizing, however, the mechanism of conversion was judged to be primary for the hysterias.

For Janet, the primary mechanism was that of dissociation, the dissociated function operating in coexistence with normal consciousness or to the exclusion of other functions. He also called attention to the calm mental attitude, *la belle indifférence*, which is not so common in childhood but makes its appearance in early adolescence.

So-called naive or common-sense psychological theory, as propounded by Heider, might help to explain some of the curious pseudoneurological findings that occur in hysteria. The hysteric behaves symptomatically as if he were totally ignorant of anatomy, and his physical symptoms tend to correspond strikingly to the usual lay concepts of disease. For example, hysterical paralysis shows an exact delimitation and an excessive intensity and is more frequently accompanied by sensory disturbances than organic paralysis. The naive theory of illness would tend to incorporate infantile theories of disease within its framework so that the young child's conception of the body and its relationship to the mind governs the symptomatic picture. In the Ganser syndrome, which may occur occasionally in older children and adolescents, the child's naive concept of insanity is at the basis of the peculiar behavior in which absurd, whimsical, and approximate replies are given to simple factual inquiries. The hysterical attack may be precipitated associatively with the content of the unconscious complex if stirred by a conscious occurrence; organically, if for any reason the emotional investment in a particular part of the body reaches a critical level; in the service of paranosic gain, as a flight into illness when reality becomes too painful or too frightening; and in the service of epinosic gain to achieve some secondary benefit. The choice of the afflicted region is determined by the unconscious sexual fantasies and the corresponding erogeneity of the area, somatic compliance (the point of least resistance), the situation in which the decisive repression occurred, and the ability of the organ to symbolize the unconscious drive in question.

CLINICAL DESCRIPTION

There are no physical symptoms in the conversion reaction that cannot be produced by volition or by emotion, although it may be possible to maintain these symptoms for only a short time. The motor symptoms include paralyses, tics, and tremors; the sensory symptoms include anesthesias, paresthesias, and hyperesthesias (the distribution is not according to anatomical lines, varies at different examinations, and is susceptible to suggestion); and the visceral symptoms include anorexia, vomiting, bulimia, hiccups, respiratory tics, and various abdominal complaints.

Ocular hysteria occurs in children about as frequently as in adults, with peak frequencies in the 9- to 10-year and the 13- to 14-year groups and in a sex ratio of 3 girls to 1 boy. In an experimental sampling of patients, vision varied between 20/70 and 20/200, a few individuals having only light perception. None of the children examined experienced any difficulty in getting about, and all showed the constricted tubular peripheral visual fields pathognomonic of hysterical amblyopia.

Hysterical contractures have been reported as not infrequent in the 10- to 15-year age group, with a female predominance ratio of 5 to 1. Precipitating factors include minor trauma or orthopedic procedures. There is

usually evidence of secondary trophic changes, such as cyanosis and coldness of the part. Psychological factors include disturbed parents and parental relationships, rigid authoritarian attitudes toward the child, and
early feeding and behavior difficulties in the child. A period of severe emotional stress coincides with the onset of the symptoms. There are two
hysterical syndromes encountered fairly frequently in childhood: tic syndrome and hysterical paresis.

Tic syndrome. Like school phobias, the symptom of tics may be
found against several different backgrounds of disturbance. Tics are not
uncommon in the postencephalitic syndrome; they may occur with severe
character disorders, as in the Tourette syndrome; and they may be included in a psychoneurotic reaction. The tic syndrome can be roughly
differentiated into two groups. In the first of these, the tic represents a
conversion symptom in a genital syndrome, and in these cases, tics are
usually single and simply patterned. There is often a history of psychological trauma at the onset, and the psychopathology evoked has an oedipal
configuration with associated castration anxiety. The family history, apart
from mild neurosis, is relatively clear, and there are no conspicuous disturbances in the premorbid history. The child often occupies a special
position in the family, such as being the only boy, and his parents, especially his mother, are inclined to pressure and restrict him. From early life
he has shown a tendency to hyperactivity, and the parents have had difficulty keeping him quiet and still. The EEG is normal. The prognosis with
psychotherapy is favorable, and some of the milder varieties may clear up
spontaneously within weeks or months.

The second type of tic disturbance has a mixed clinical picture and is
generally associated with a neurotic character disorder, sometimes close to
a borderline psychotic state. This disturbance has been referred to as a
pregenital conversion reaction, and the psychopathology displays both oral
and anal features. Anal sadism, exhibitionism, and voyeurism are prominent, and the symptoms may include coprolalia. Attempts have been
made to separate the various parts of the symbolic movement into components representing pantomimes of unconscious, aggressive, and erotic
wishes. Whereas the hysterical convulsion appears to be a gross translation
of the unconscious wish and fear, the hysterical tic is more in the nature of
a compromise movement in which only a fractional part of the impulse
gains expression.

Hysterical paresis. This type of conversion response is not uncommon
at puberty and is sometimes brought about by a strongly worded suggestion from a parental figure indicating possible loss of function or disability. In the female there is often a marked ambivalent attitude toward the
male, alternatively rejecting and inviting. The girl is usually highly con-
temptuous and disparaging of boys, refusing to associate with them, and
her crude and rough demeanor overlies a masculine identification. She is
also outspokenly envious of boys and may list their many unfair advan-

tages. The precipitating factors are often menarche, which serves as a reality and confirmation of her no-longer-deniable femininity, and exposure, even indirectly, to some violent sexual incident, which may weaken the defense of masculine identification and necessitate the conversion of the emerging anxiety. In the boy the background is usually one of a passive, feminine character configuration with a submission to parental expectation. The conversion symptom is usually precipitated by a mobilization of anxiety in reference to guilt and punishment associated with pubertal masturbation and an excessively harsh superego structure, leading to a marked inhibition of any form of aggression. The biological thrusts of puberty resulting from endocrinological changes often upset the neurotic equilibrium, and previously successful defenses, such as masculine identification in the female and feminine identification in the male, are no longer adequate.

DIFFERENTIAL DIAGNOSIS

In adolescents and adults, conversion disorders frequently occur in hysterical personalities, but this is not always the case in childhood. It is also unusual to see a purely hysterical disorder in children, and combined disorders are more common, in which a conversion reaction exists along with other neurotic or sometimes psychotic disturbances. Conversion disorders must be distinguished principally from symptoms of predominantly physical illness and psychophysiological disorders. Occasionally, the psychophysiological disorder and the conversion reaction may be so mixed—as in certain cases of vomiting, encopresis, hyperventilation, and enuresis—that it is difficult to decide to what extent the habit disorder has been drawn into the service of conversion.

PROGNOSIS

The purer the conversion reaction and the freer the personality from character disorder, the better is the prognosis. The absence of gross pathology in the parents is also more conducive to a favorable outcome. In a nine-year follow-up of thirty-seven children diagnosed as having hysteria, hypochondriasis, and mixed psychoneurosis, five cases presented hysteria at the time of follow-up and five anxiety neurosis. The remainder had physical and mental symptoms of various kinds, apart from two patients who seemed to be completely well. However, the terminal comment at the end of the section on epidemiology applies here as well, since both refer to the same study.

MANAGEMENT

Since the time of Charcot, many different treatment procedures have been tried successfully with hysteria, most of them incorporating some mode of suggestion. These have aimed at removing symptoms, but they leave the underlying conflict unresolved. The use of hypnosis with children, especially with girls at puberty or approaching puberty, has iatrogenic dangers attached to it. It is certainly possible to let the child relive hypnotically the episode responsible for the conversion, but it is inevitably treated by some children as a seduction, and they react accordingly. Furthermore, the mere removal of a conversion symptom with all the primary and secondary gains attached to it can bring about resentment at the act of deprivation.

Insight therapy is aimed at uncovering the neurotic conflict that has led to the conversion and at helping the child to reconvert. In the psychoanalytic mode of treatment, the decoding of the unconscious meaning of the conversion symptom through interpretation induces progressive alterations in the transference relationship and in the symptomatology until the work of reconstruction pieces together the historical development of the symptom, making use of dreams and fantasies as an adjunct.

As Kanner has pointed out, environmental manipulation is sometimes more successful with hysterical children than with hysterical adults, and he has even suggested the exploitation of such sublimatory activities as dramatics, so that the child can learn that "exaggerated acting is bad acting!"

DISSOCIATIVE REACTION

Definition

Neurotic anxieties belonging to this category may bring about temporary disorganization of the personality that culminates in such aimless behavior as fugue states, catalepsy, amnesia, twilight states, narcolepsy, and pseudo-delirious and stuporous states. Self-representation may be disturbed, with the development of personality dissociation and multiple personality formation. Formerly, this reaction was classified as a type of conversion hysteria.

Epidemiology

This is perhaps the most dramatic of the group of hysterias. At first sight, it appears to involve a process of decompensation and a failure of defense, but on careful inspection it is seen that the fugue states, dream states, somnambulism, and stupor are fairly structured entities that operate behind a curtain of amnesia so that the conscious ego of the patient is able to state quite blandly that he has no knowledge whatsoever of what he is supposed to have said or done in his other condition. Fugue states have been described in girls around the age of 8 and again at puberty. Somnambulism also is rarely found below the age of 8 and increases in frequency toward the end of childhood. In one series of 193 children, 13 per cent of the cases were diagnosed as having hysteria, 20 per cent showed dissociative reactions, and 80 per cent combined dissociative and conversion reactions. The girls outnumbered the boys about 3 to 1. The incidence appeared higher in children coming from subcultural areas.

CAUSES

Janet's theory of hysteria is especially applicable to the dissociative reaction. He regarded the main factor as a disturbance of the synthesis of the personality, characterized by a restriction of consciousness and a tendency to dissociation. Certain functions and ideas are split off from the conscious personality; the more they have been involved in a major affective experience, the more they are apt to become dissociated. Unlike Freud's theory of the repressed conflict, the theory of dissociation does not help to explain why dissociation takes place. It was possible for Janet to cite heavy neuropathic tainting as predisposing to the disturbance, as this was found in many of the cases, especially the more serious. There is sometimes a dissociative tendency in the family, so that the pattern for the symptom can be copied from observations made within the family. The loss of personal identity entailed in this type of reaction is commonly accompanied by amnesia, which is different from organic amnesia in that it occurs suddenly and without trauma and is usually recoverable spontaneously or with the help of therapy. There is no recorded case of a child demonstrating multiple personalities, but fugue states and somnambulism are not uncommon. The predisposition to gross reactions of the dissociative kind includes heavy constitutional factors (although not neurosyphilis in the parents, as Freud once thought), disturbed family relationships, and unfavorable environments. Mental or physical illness in the family can act as a powerful model for abnormal behavior in a hypersuggestible, predisposed child.

CLINICAL DESCRIPTION

Children with a tendency to dissociation seem fairly well adjusted in their normal states, though somewhat shy and subdued. More than with the other hysterias of childhood, the dissociative type tends to be monosymptomatic, massive, and acute. Janet has attempted to describe two forms of dissociated state, using somnambulism as a model. In one form, the monoideistic, there is a striking poverty of content, and this is the form characteristically found in children. The poverty is, in fact, relative to the depth and intensity of the treatment process. The deeper the process, the richer the clinical content.

Two of the dissociative reactions are among the more frequent in childhood: somnambulism and twilight states.

Somnambulism. This can be defined as a fugue state that begins during sleep and is usually of shorter duration than a fugue. The movements of the somnambulist seem to be in response to the manifest or latent content of the dream, and the meaning may be an escape from the temptation of the bed or a movement toward a particular goal that represents gratification or reassurance. It becomes increasingly common after the age of 8, reaching a peak frequency around middle adolescence. At the

earlier ages, the motivation often appears on the surface, such as the acting out of some unconscious wish. In some cases the approach behavior is
prominent, and in others avoidance, but in the majority of cases there may
be a combination of approach and avoidance. At the point of greatest ambivalence, the patient may wake up. Compared with children who suffer
from night terrors and nightmares, the sleep-walker appears to be less intelligent, less imaginative, less prone to conscious anxiety but more suggestible. It has been referred to as a motor syndrome, sometimes associated
with other motor disturbances, such as tics. The patient tends to express
himself more frequently through activity than in words, and dreaming is
somewhat sparse and poorly recalled.

Twilight states. The typical history of a child, typically a female,
manifesting twilight states is as follows. The early childhood is usually
described as easy and uneventful, with a close relationship with both parents. A sibling is born when the child is about 3 or 4 years of age, and soon
after, the child, almost predictably, undergoes some traumatic sexual experience with an older person, which the child at first keeps secret but about
which there are considerable guilt feelings. At about the fifth or sixth year,
there is a realignment in the family. The child begins to show an exaggerated affection toward her mother and alienates herself from her father; in
one case the alienation was increased to the point of not recognizing him.
The child appears to become increasingly disturbed, and about her eighth
year she begins to suffer from twilight states in which she both reenacts
her sexual seduction and at the same time shows marked hostility to the
mother. As soon as the attack subsides, she once again reverses her behavior and clings affectionately to her mother, pleading for protection. After-
ward, she shows complete amnesia for the whole event.

DIFFERENTIAL DIAGNOSIS

Like conversion disorders, the dissociative reaction often occurs in hysterical personalities but may appear in other psychopathological disorders as
well. In its gross form it needs to be differentiated from psychotic disorders, epileptic equivalents, and analogous symptoms in some other types
of neurotic reactions.

PROGNOSIS

The prognosis for any particular dissociative state may be good, since they
often disappear spontaneously in the course of a few months, to be replaced by some other symptomatic expression, usually from the same reactive group. One occasionally sees alternations of fugue states, somnambulism, and twilight states. The prognosis is less favorable for reactions
beginning in childhood and reactions associated with personality disorders
or with dissociative tendencies within the family. The dictum that hysterical parents have hysterical children is probably truer for this group than
for any other one of the hysterias.

MANAGEMENT

There is a tendency to treat children belonging to this group like psychotics or borderline psychotics and to hospitalize them for long periods of time. When the reaction takes the form of stupor or catalepsy, the need for hospitalization is understandable. The dramatic and unusual symptoms usually obtain a great deal of professional attention and interest for the child, and one of the epinosic gains is to become an interesting case. Once again, psychotherapy should be aimed at the underlying conflict situation rather than the symptom itself. The therapist must strive to remain unimpressed by the symptomatic repertoire of the patient while giving every consideration to the very real problems engendered by the illness. Hypnosis or Amytal abreaction is often successful in relieving the acute symptoms.

OBSESSIVE-COMPULSIVE REACTION

DEFINITION

In these disorders the anxiety aroused by the unconscious conflict is counteracted by the occurrence of thoughts (obsessions), acts or impulses to act (compulsions), or mixtures of both that are all isolated from the original, unacceptable impulse. The child often recognizes his ideas or behavior as unreasonable but is, nevertheless, compelled to repeat his rituals. Often the external behavior represents the opposite of the unconscious wish, as with excessive orderliness and washing compulsions overlying impulses to soil and mess. Counting and touching ceremonials or recurrent thoughts appear frequently, resulting in marked anxiety if these are interfered with by the parents or other persons. This category includes many cases formerly classified as "psychasthenia" (Janet), in which phobias, compulsions, and obsessions were accompanied by doubts, timidity, and depressions. Janet believed that a general lowering of psychological force was the basic cause of the difficulty, and he felt that the condition had some relation to epilepsy, of which it was perhaps a milder form. Early in his studies Freud began to notice connections between hysteria and obsessional neurosis. In the first place, he accorded the anancastic reaction full recognition as an illness entity and then drew it into a grouping with hysteria. In the earlier work he referred to them both as defense neuroses, and later they became the transference neuroses. He regarded the transposition of affects that brought about the clinical picture in obsessional neuroses as equivalent to the conversion of affects that operated in hysteria. He very soon related them both as originating from infantile sex experiences, and in the seduction hypothesis he outlined a schematic relationship in which the premature exposure to sexuality, if passive and unpleasurable, led to the development of hysteria, whereas if active and pleasurable, it gave rise to an obsessional neurosis characterized by self-reproach for the sexual aggressiveness entailed. With his discovery of the Oedipus complex, Freud attributed to the development of hysteria to a direct depression of oedipal wishes and the development of obsessional neurosis to a regression to anal-sadistic levels. Eventually, he delineated the psychopathology of the obsessional neurosis in terms of anal erotism and sadism, which he linked together; bisexuality; defense mechanisms of isolation, undoing, and reaction formation; unusual intellectual drives; and premature ego development.

EPIDEMIOLOGY

About 20 per cent of all cases of obsessional neurosis begin under the age of 15, and 50 to 60 per cent earlier than the age of 20. Of the childhood cases, about half have an acute onset, and the other half develop insidiously. There is a slight preponderance of females, but by no means as marked as in hysteria, and females are more inclined to have an acute onset. About a third of the cases present a mixed clinical picture involving obsessional thoughts, acts, and phobias; about a third are mainly represented by thoughts and acts; a sixth of the cases are predominantly phobic; and another sixth of the cases are atypical in that the obsessional condition is complicated by the presence of other psychopathological states. The condition, in general, tends to occur in the upper brackets of social class, intelligence, and education. An appreciable number of parents of obsessional children also suffer from obsessional illness, about 10 per cent, and between 40 to 60 per cent show obsessional traits. There is a general consensus that obsessional illness is frequent in the family of obsessionals and also that more familial pathology is present than is the case in other psychoneuroses; from 4 to 15 per cent of the parents may be psychotic. None of these findings can be offered as proof of heredity, since the effect may well be the result of social conditioning. No twin control studies have as yet been carried out. In a California survey of obsessive-compulsive reactions in children, it was found that the sample group comprised 1.2 per cent of the total adult and child psychiatric load, that there were equal numbers of boys and girls, and that the average age of onset was 7½ years. The group as a whole showed a better than average intelligence.

CAUSES

Obsessions and compulsions of a minor kind begin early in life and persist through childhood. These disturbances are first seen in the elaborate bedtime and feeding rituals set up by the toddler, without which he cannot function comfortably. Rituals are frequently associated with rigid routines on the part of compulsive parents, who, although not initiating the behavior, often seem to do their best to keep it going. A little later, obsessional fears, often recognized as unreasonable and absurd, lead to the use of magical countermeasures and are continued still later in the form of obsessional games, such as the avoidance of cracks on the pavement ("Step on a crack and break your mother's back!").

According to psychoanalytic theory, obsessions are the consequence of release of repressed instinctual impulses and wishes from their unconscious representation; the released elements are then transferred to the sphere of consciousness in conjunction with some idea or set of ideas that has no presumptive relationship to the unconscious impulse, so that the child is unable to understand why he should be obsessed in this way. The reaction is interpreted as a defense against aggressive and sexual impulses, particularly in relation to the Oedipus complex. The initial defense is by regression to the anal-sadistic level, but the impulses at this level are also intolerable and must be warded off by reaction formation, isolation, and undoing. Because the use of these defenses renders superfluous the use of repression proper, the offensive impulses can exist in consciousness, although, when they do, they are divorced from their affective significance and so remain meaningless to the patient.

Because of the familial tendency, several investigators have assumed a specific constitutional predisposition, and terms such as "ideo-obsessive constitution" and "obsessive psychopathic constitution" are defined as an inherent tendency toward an abnormal persistence of responses in conjunction with autonomic lability. The child-rearing of obsessional parents is rigidly scheduled, and the child is brought up with what Kanner refers to as an "overdose of parental perfectionism." The child learns early that strict adherence to what he is taught is right and to do otherwise is wrong. The child's world is inevitably clean, neat, and orderly, and it is equally inevitable that the child of such an environment develops "just so" attitudes. It is not clear to what extent obsessional neurotic and personality disorders can be related to difficulties in sphincter training, nor are there any conclusive research findings to confirm or refute the connection. An investigation of 5-year-olds showed no behavioral differences in those who had been trained early or punitively, as compared with those trained late and permissively. It is possible that the cause lies not in a particular sphere but in the total training experience given to the child, whereby every aspect of his developmental world becomes infused with inflexible concerns. Sullivan has pointed to preoccupation in childhood as a precursor to later obsessional development.

Children who develop obsessional neurosis in late childhood or adolescence have often exhibited a variety of symptoms during the course of their development. These include phobias (40 per cent), hypersensitivity (35 per cent), anxiety (32 per cent), inhibitions (25 per cent), obsessiveness (22 per cent), shyness (20 per cent). Eighty-three per cent of such children can be regarded as nervous. In contrast to the extroverted personality of the hysteric, introversion is found more commonly, although it is not marked prior to the onset of the illness.

The premorbid personality has been investigated from the psychoanalytical and clinical points of view. Clinicians, describing the obsessional personality, have pointed to the cautious, deliberate, persistent, conscientious, dependable, dogged, austere, and perfectionistic person; whereas psychoanalysts, elaborating on the original anal-erotic triad of Freud— orderliness, frugality, and obstinacy—have emphasized the stubbornness, egocentricity, and inflexibility of the person in general and, in particular, portray such individuals as tyrannical, power-loving, dictatorial, hypercritical, vindictive, avaricious, parsimonious, irritable, malcontented, and hypochondriacal. The positive and negative pictures also seem to depend on the degree of adjustment shown by the obsessional individual, whether his management of his life situation indicated a successful or unsuccessful obsessionality. If the child is doing well at school, his ambitious and intellectual parents will be inclined to treat his obsessional traits with respect, whereas the child with a school problem may be described in similar terms, but the wording of the complaint will be more negatively phrased.

The classical triad may exist in different proportions. In a typical group of obsessional cases, 72 per cent will be orderly, 4 per cent disorderly, and 24 per cent in between; 50 per cent will be frugal, 6 per cent extravagant, and 44 per cent in between; 40 per cent will be obstinate, 20 per cent compliant, and 40 per cent in between. There is a tendency for some children to maintain leakage symptoms, so that they show dirtiness, disorderliness, and compliance in the setting of a perfect obsessional personality. This is especially characteristic of certain cases of encopresis, in which a scrupulously clean child will show a psychological leakage in addition to his physical leakage.

As in the case of the Rat Man, the child begins his obsessional illness with the emergence of unacceptable thoughts—sometimes blasphemous, sometimes sexual, and sometimes aggressive. He may try hard to think of something else and shake off the disturbing thoughts, sometimes even literally by means of ticlike movements. Unlike the adult obsessional, the child usually cannot keep his thoughts or ruminations to himself and may force his parents to participate in his rituals, answer his repetitious questions, and cater to his obsessional wants as punctiliously as he does himself. The mother's compulsions may not fit those of the child, and she consequently tends to become increasingly impatient with his insistence and may attempt to turn him aside from his demands, first by reason and argument and finally by punishment, so that child and mother are soon locked in an interminable sadomasochistic battle. The child finds himself caught between two wrongs: His unconscious wishes are wrong, and his conscious defenses are also wrong. Invariably, anxiety and depression may supervene, together with vague psychosomatic symptoms of various kinds.

DIFFERENTIAL DIAGNOSIS

These disorders must be distinguished from normal, compulsive rituals of the toddler around training situations and from the obsessional games of the early school child carried out in the service of mastering aggressive impulses.

Prognosis

Recent studies of the natural history of obsessional neurosis as it extends through the lifetime of the individual seem to indicate that the prognosis is not as unfavorable as was once thought and that spontaneous remissions are fairly frequent. The factors influencing prognosis in an unfavorable direction are existence of obsessional symptoms in early childhood, the occurrence of a premorbid obsessional personality, the occurrence of obsessional acts, and a severe clinical picture on first admission. Although obsessional symptoms starting at about 6 years of age may clear up spontaneously in one or two years (see Wolf Man), Kanner has stated that he has never known pathological obsessions of children to subside without outside therapeutic help. Sometimes the obsessional symptoms subside, but the background of anxiety, sensitivity, and inhibition may remain, with the result that the child continues to be nervous. Sometimes the child may begin to hide or camouflage his symptomatic acts. The prognosis, with treatment, of childhood obsessional states is fairly good, especially after prolonged, intensive psychotherapy. About 30 to 40 per cent of the cases become completely free, with another 40 to 50 per cent "much improved" or "improved." About 10 to 15 per cent of the cases apparently do not improve. The adult cases do less well if one takes the average of five well-known studies: 27 per cent are free of symptoms, 37 per cent are improved, and about 36 per cent remain static or grow worse.

Management

Therapy with an obsessional child takes place in a series of stages. In stage one, the child is relieved to talk about his peculiar symptoms without being mocked, criticized, or punished; within this therapeutic setting, he is enabled to bring his whole repertoire of symptoms into the open. He can also express his anger at the repercussions his illness brings about in his home environment. In stage two, the child attempts to use the therapist in the same way he uses his mother, as a participant in his ceremonials. When the therapist balks at assuming this particular role, a stormy situation ensues. In stage three, which is often heralded by freer dream material, the child's defenses appear less inflexible, and a greater amount of leakage enters into the treatment. The stage that follows is characterized by messiness and aggression, and the child seems for a while to wallow in his regressions. As this stage abates—to the relief of the parents, who are, at this point, constantly threatening to take the child out of treatment— frank oedipal wishes and thoughts begin to emerge, and from then on the treatment resembles that of other neurotic children.

DEPRESSIVE REACTION

DEFINITION

Psychoneurotic, depressive disorders involve internalized conflicts in relation to deeply ambivalent feelings and are not commonly seen in their fully developed adult form in children, although what have been referred to as "depressive equivalents" may take the place of the depression, varying in their composition with the child's stage of development. The conflict anxiety is said to be mitigated by self-deprecation and the sagging of mood. In older children, as in adults, a loss of self-esteem, associated with feelings of guilt and ambivalence toward loved persons, has been reported. Psychomotor retardation and agitation are occasionally present but are much less marked than in adults.

The fully developed depressive syndrome in the adult psychotic can be said to have three classes of symptoms: primary (sad affect, reduction of drive and productivity, and psychomotor agitation and retardation), secondary (feelings of helplessness, hopelessness, and worthlessness), and tertiary (obsessional reactions, hypochondriacal preoccupations, delusions and hallucinations, suicidal thoughts and tendencies). The neurotic reaction borrows a little from this general picture, although excluding the more malignant tertiary components and adding a neurotic conflict and neurotic personality to the clinical picture. The depressive reaction in children in turn borrows something from the neurotic depression of adults—the sadness, helplessness, loneliness, homesickness, and inadequacy—excluding, to some extent, the structured, internalized conflict in relation to ambivalence and adding phase-characteristic depressive equivalents.

The difference between the child and adult picture can be attributed in part to the inability of the child to verbalize his affective state, to the incomplete development of the superego, and to the absence of consistent self-representation. The difference between neurotic and psychotic depression is that, in the former, the individual attempts to force external objects to replenish his reduced narcissistic supplies and, in the latter, the individual withdraws from and incorporates the unsatisfying object, attempting to reestablish his self-esteem in the intrapsychic sphere. Many psychoanalysts have stressed the fact that the child, by virtue of his indispensable need for an object relationship, is compelled to direct his attention toward external, substitute objects. In addition, his weak superego prevents typical depressive clinging to lost objects in the form of protracted mourning, at the same time permitting replacements and substitutes. It does not encourage assaults on the ego in the form of self-reproach and pervasive pathological guilt. The rapid regressions of childhood also imply quicker restitutions.

The depressed child experiences a feeling of pain over real or supposed deprivation and may resign himself in a helpless, impotent way to the painful situation or react with aggression against the source of pain. The depressive response is always associated with undischarged aggression, and fear of superego sanctions leads to repression or displacement of the aggression onto the self. The defenses against the depressive affect are similar to those used to withstand anxiety.

When depression is carefully defined in adult terms, it is difficult for some investigators to acknowledge its occurrence before puberty. When the investigator is prepared to compromise with the criteria and accept the depressive equivalents in the child equally with depression in the adult, it is possible to regard certain clinical states, such as school phobias, as manifesting depression. It is generally agreed that transient, depressive feelings are frequent in childhood, but this does not represent a psychopathological state, and some clinicians have questioned whether depressive equivalents do not represent a potpourri of childhood psychopathology rather than the syndrome of depression.

Epidemiology

Because of the controversial nature of the evidence offered for the existence of this reaction as an entity, it is almost a hopeless task to attempt to ascertain its prevalence. The few studies in the literature are merely descriptive of a small number of cases.

Causes

From an etiological standpoint, it would seem important to differentiate among psychotic depressions, which do not appear to occur during childhood; reactive depressions in response to loss, seen in anaclitic depressions, grief reactions, and in the rudimentary mourning of older children, and depressive reactions linked to neurotic conflicts. Within the framework of psychoanalytic theory, the nuclear conflict of the psychoneuroses would be expected to operate similarly in the case of the depressive reaction. The crucial question would then be that of the circumstances under which one would expect depression to ensue from the oedipal disturbance. The complex contains within it affects of fear and anxiety as well as reactions of guilt, love, tenderness, hostility, and aggression. It involves the fantasied loss of one or both parents, the renunciation of one or both parents, jealousy, envy, and death wishes. In the face of competition with the adult, the child may experience strong feelings of inadequacy and inferiority.

There seems little doubt that the depressive reaction, when it occurs, must have a close relationship to the aggressive feelings directed toward the loved parent of the same sex, thereby generating a conflict of ambivalence. Even the resolution of that conflict and the preservation of the rival involves some degree of loss in the renunciation of the basic desires. It is not surprising that some children, predisposed to depression, react to the dilemma with depressive feelings, the castration anxiety in such cases remaining relatively mild. Again, whereas many children awake from oedipal dreams containing death wishes in a state of great anxiety, demanding reassurance, these susceptible children continue to lie sadly in their beds, full of remorse and often weeping uncontrollably.

CLINICAL DESCRIPTION

The depressive picture in children between 8 and 11 years includes the following characteristics: weeping bouts, some flatness of affect, fears of death for self or parents, irritability, somatic complaints, loss of appetite and energy, varying degrees of difficulty in school adjustment, and vacillation between clinging to and unreasonable hostility toward their parents. Self-deprecation is often marked. The child may look sad and depressed, talk in a weak voice, turn his head to the wall, cry frequently, and constantly iterate his loneliness. Nothing appears to cheer him up, and he seems to have all the energy drained out of him. The precipitating factors are usually specific events, such as accidents and physical illnesses but not the real loss of either parent.

Instead of depression, a child may present with depressive equivalents, which can include eating and sleeping disturbances, antisocial behavior, accident proneness, running away from home, boredom and restlessness, fatigue, difficulty in concentration, and sexual acting out. These also represent modes of defense adopted to ward off feelings of depression, isolation, loneliness, and emptiness.

The occurrence of depressive feeling and depressive equivalents is not unlike the occurrence of free-floating anxiety and the anxiety equivalents before they have been counteracted by mechanisms of displacement, conversion, dissociation, etc. Objectless depression, like objectless anxiety, occasions a certain degree of perplexity, because the child is not sure why he is depressed when there are no current reasons for the response. With objectless depression, as with objectless anxiety, there exists a feeling that something unpleasant is going to happen in the future, giving rise to a sense of foreboding and doom coupled with pessimism.

The wish to die may stimulate suicidal ruminations, suicidal attempts, and actual suicide. There exists a great deal of untenable statistical data regarding suicide in childhood. The figures are based on notified cases, and there is a growing belief that a number of cases are never reported or are disguised as accidents. It is not surprising that incidence figures not only vary from one report to the next but may be contradictory. Suicide is said to be rare under 10 (only three children reported in this group in 1958), varying between 35 and 60 each year in the age group of 10 to 14 years, and between 250 and 300 each year in the age group of 15 to 19 years. This is out of the total child population of the United States up to 19 years. Girls outnumber boys in attempting suicide 3 to 1, and boys outnumber girls in successful suicide 3 to 1. The proportion of attempted to successful suicide is approximately 100 to 1. In one study of attempted suicide in adolescence, it was found that 15 per cent had a previous history of major accidents, and 6 per cent had made previous suicide attempts. In

8 per cent the father was dead. In half the cases, there was no adult figure in the house at the time of the attempt, but in 29 per cent of the cases the mother was at home. One of the main causes given was the use of disciplinary measures giving rise to emotional upset and depression. The suicidal method most in favor was the use of drugs—aspirins, barbiturates, and tranquilizers. Some of the attempts at suicide seemed to be manifestations of risk-taking behavior.

The core factor in the formation of a suicidal personality in childhood is thought to be a loss of love, real and fantasied. The part played by depression may be relatively small—less than 7 per cent, although this may be related to the difficulty in recognizing depression below the age of puberty. In the adolescent, identity crisis may play the role that depression plays in the adult. The amount of psychosis found varies with the study but is thought to be small. However, in one study at the Payne Whitney Clinic, 23 of 37 attempted suicides between the ages of 13 and 19 were diagnosed as schizophrenic. The same study defines the suicidal adolescent as

an individual who is delusional in varying degrees, withdrawn, spending a considerable amount of time in fantasy activity, with little if any somatic complaints, but constructing a picture of supposed wrongs done to him by associates, parents, or siblings. He may show very little by way of overt anxiety and might or might not have complaints of feelings of depression.

Impulsiveness may, on occasion, lead to suicidal attempts, but these are often ill-conceived and, therefore, likely to be unsuccessful. In the younger group there may be a real physical difficulty in bringing off a successful suicide. Occasionally, a child may imitate a suicide seen on TV.

The psychodynamics underlying suicidal attempts include an appeal component representing a plea for help in dealing with sexual difficulty and hostile impulses aimed at the parents. According to Zilboorg, suicide at puberty is more often a primitive urge resulting from frustration of genital wishes rather than an oral-aggressive one. Both intrapsychic and interpersonal conflicts of a serious nature are present in all suicidal attempts in children, most patients demonstrating long-standing, unrecognized disturbed mental states. These are usually associated with disturbed family relations and, most frequently, rejecting or highly ambivalent mothers. The immediate motives are usually multiple and include anxiety over school work, problems revolving around sexuality and social adaptation, and frequently some experience interpreted in terms of loss.

Differential Diagnosis

Depressive reactions must be differentiated from acute reactive disorders (grief), anaclitic depressions, transient depressive feelings in developmental or situational crises, cyclical mood swings occurring in developmental disturbances, and psychotic depressions seen in adolescents with a schizo-affective disorder.

PROGNOSIS

The predisposition to depression is occasionally so strong that the individual responds to all difficulties—frustrations, deprivations, losses—with depression. Klein has postulated a depressive position in the first year of life and Abrahams a primary parathymia in the preschool child as precursors to later depressive elements. The individual with such a depressive personality tends to face problem-solving situations with the expectation of becoming depressed. This is again equivalent to the anxious or stress-sensitive personality.

Symptomatic treatment, aimed at relieving the child's mood, is usually effective but offers no safeguard against the occurrence of similar reactions in the future, unless the underlying neurotic conflict is also resolved and some measure of insight furnished to the child.

MANAGEMENT

As with the other psychoneurotic conditions, intensive psychotherapy is the treatment of choice for the depressive reaction. Antidepressive drugs, such as amitriptyline (Elavil), may be indicated when the phenomenological picture is similar to the depressions of adult life, with marked loss of self-esteem, withdrawal from social interaction, depressive affect, self-accusation, and self-deprecation. In cases of attempted suicide in children, it is better to hospitalize the patient for a period after the attempt. Tranquilizers and antidepressants can be used as adjuncts, but the therapeutic aim should be insight rather than reassurance, since it is important for the patient to develop some understanding of his unsatisfied needs and the way in which his suicidal attempt relates to the unconscious motivating forces. It has been suggested that, during this critical period, the psychiatrist should make himself more easily available to the child and prescribe the frequency of the therapeutic interviews in relation to the child's needs.

REFERENCES

Agras, S. The relationship of school phobia to childhood depression. Amer. J. Psychiat., 116: 533, 1959.

Anthony, E. J. An experimental approach to the psychopathology of childhood —encopresis. Brit. J. Med. Psychol., 30: 146, 1957.

Anthony, E. J. An experimental approach to the psychopathology of childhood —sleep disturbances. Brit. J. Med. Psychol., 32: 19, 1959.

Bakwin, H. Suicide in children and adults. J. Amer. Med. Wom. Ass., 19: 489, 1964.

Bergman, P. Neurotic anxieties in children and their prevention. Nerv. Child, 5: 37, 1946.

Colm, H. N. Phobias in children. Psychoanal. Rev., 46: 65, 1959.

Dührssen, A. Die problematik der zwangsneurose an hand vonkinderfallen. Prax. Kinderpsychol., 3: 1, 1954.

Eisenberg, L. School phobia: a study in the communication of anxiety. Amer. J. Psychiat., 114: 712, 1958.

Freud, S. *Collected Papers*, vol. 3. Hogarth Press, London. 1959.

Glaser, K. Attempted suicide in children and adolescents: psychodynamic observations. Amer. J. Psychother., 19: 220, 1965.

Gould, R. E. Suicide problems in children and adolescents. Amer. J. Psychother., 19: 228, 1965.

Group for the Advancement of Psychiatry. *A Proposed Classification of Psychopathological Disorders in Childhood*. Group for the Advancement of Psychiatry, New York, 1966.

Hartmann, H. Problems of infantile neurosis: a discussion. Psychoanal. Stud. Child, 9: 16, 1954.

Jacobziner, H. Attempted suicide in children. J. Pediat., 56: 519, 1960.

Jacobziner, H. Attempted suicide in adolescents by poisoning: statistical report. Amer. J. Psychother., 19: 247, 1965.

Judd, L. L. Obsessive compulsive neurosis in children. Arch. Gen. Psychiat., 12: 136, 1965.

Kanner, L. *Child Psychiatry*, ed. 3. Charles C Thomas, Springfield, Ill., 1957.

Klein, E. Psychoanalytic aspects of school problems. Psychoanal. Stud. Child, 3–4: 369, 1949.

Lancet (editorial). Suicide and suicidal attempts in children and adolescents. Lancet, 2: 847, 1964.

Lawler, R. Suicidal attempts in children. Canad. Med. Ass. J., 89: 751, 1963.

Lazarus, A. The use of emotive imagery in the treatment of children's phobias. J. Ment. Sci., 108: 191, 1962.

Malamud, W. The psychoneuroses. In *Personality and the Behavior Disorders*, J. McV. Hunt, editor, vol. 2, p. 833. Ronald Press, New York, 1944.

Müller-Küppers, M. Beiträge zur Kinderpsychologie. III. Selbstmord bei kindern. Psychiat. Neurol. Med. Psychol., 7: 42, 1955.

Proctor, J. T. Hysteria in childhood. Amer. J. Orthopsychiat., 28: 394, 1958.

Robins, E., and O'Neal, P. Clinical features of hysteria in children. Nerv. Child, 10: 246, 1954.

Sandler, J., and Joffe, W. G. Notes on childhood depression. Int. J. Psychoanal., 46: 88, 1965.

Sperling, M. Equivalents in depression in children. J. Hillside Hosp., 8: 138, 1959.

Starr, P. Some observations on the diagnostic aspects of childhood hysteria. Nerv. Child, 10: 214, 1954.

Toolan, J. M. Depression in children and adolescents. Amer. J. Orthopsychiat., 32: 404, 1962.

CHAPTER SIX

Psychophysiological Disorders of Children

STUART M. FINCH, M.D.

DEFINITION

PSYCHOPHYSIOLOGICAL DISORDERS in children, like those in adults, are defined in the American Psychiatric Association standard nomenclature as conditions in which the symptoms "are caused by emotional factors and involve a single organ system, usually under autonomic nervous system innervation." This definition is really an oversimplification of an extremely complex set of disorders. The term "psychophysiological disorder" is best reserved for a diverse group of conditions in which both psychic and biological factors play a role in producing a somatic disorder. Typically, such diseases include obesity, bronchial asthma, eczema, and ulcerative colitis. In these conditions there appears to be a biological factor, often only partially identified, which in combination with certain psychopathological stresses leads to the development of a particular syndrome.

The term "psychophysiological" as used today replaces the older terms of "organ neurosis" and "psychosomatic disorder." This area of medicine, however, remains vague and ill defined, and just how many disease entities can properly be included in this broad term is as yet unclear. Modern research has shown that many illnesses previously thought to be purely infectious or degenerative have emotional aspects. Even vulnerability to the common cold appears to have a relationship to emotional tensions. This chapter discusses only those conditions that have gradually come to be considered typical of the psychophysiological disorder group.

ANOREXIA NERVOSA

DEFINITION

Anorexia nervosa is a serious and sometimes life-endangering condition characterized by a self-imposed, severe dietary limitation, leading to extreme loss of weight, malaise, and other associated symptoms and serious malnutrition.

CLINICAL DESCRIPTION

Although it is most common in young adults, anorexia nervosa can occur at puberty or even before. The most typical history is that of the slightly obese youngster who decides to go on a self-imposed and often severe diet. The decision may be based on some small incident where the youngster was criticized for his obesity or awkwardness. The child and his parents are often pleased with the resulting weight loss until it becomes excessive, at which point efforts to encourage the child into a more reasonable intake are found to be futile. The common-sense approach to the child in terms of the need for a certain number of calories, vitamins, etc., seems useless. The child becomes increasingly malnourished and gaunt but clings to the idea that he is improving his health.

A 12-year-old may begin such a diet at 115 pounds and continue to lose weight until he is perhaps 60 pounds, by which point his entire body physiology is extremely disturbed. He may continue with exercises, again of a self-imposed nature. Restlessness is common in these youngsters, and that intensifies the physiological difficulty.

The diagnosis of anorexia nervosa is made on the basis of the excessive weight loss combined with the history of the peculiar dietary limitations the youngster has imposed on himself. As the malnutrition continues, the youngster becomes increasingly cachectic, but, in spite of his general physical weakness, he often continues with body-building exercises. Body reserves are generally used up. Blood sugar drops, and the youngster may suffer a circulatory collapse. It is essential in making the diagnosis to rule out any other cause of anorexia and subsequent weight loss. An undiscovered malignancy or infection, for example, may simulate anorexia nervosa.

The premorbid personality of the youngster with anorexia nervosa is usually one of a constricted, compulsive, rigid type. Hypersensitivity is a very common characteristic, and some of these children have schizoid traits. Both oral and anal residual qualities are usual. Once the disorder has developed, the child devotes a great deal of time and thought to the whole subject of food. In spite of learning the caloric content of foods and the requisites of an adequate diet, the child continues to eat very little— far below the requirement for normal health. The mechanism of denial is extremely prominent in these youngsters. They will claim to feel physically fine when it is obvious that they are so weak they can hardly stand or walk. They can even look in a mirror and remain oblivious to the fact that they are seriously malnourished. Bribes and threats by family or physician aimed at getting the youngster to eat more are usually fruitless.

It has been postulated that the psychodynamics of the anorexic child involves the entanglement of sexual and aggressive instincts with the concept of food intake. These basically immature youngsters fear growing up. Eating becomes a destructive oral aggressive act, one that also has sexual connotations. Unconsciously, to eat is to grow bigger, more aggressive, and more sexual. In attempting to ward off such dangerous instinctual impulses, the child also wards off eating.

The parents of children with anorexia nervosa present no uniform type of psychopathology. Most of these youngsters have probably been overprotected by one or both parents. As with most other psychosomatic disorders, the child has had a close and markedly ambivalent tie to one parent or the other. The disorder tends to occur somewhat more commonly in girls than in boys, but the close ties exist between either parent and children of either sex. By the time the disorder is well advanced, one parent, if not both, has usually become extremely overconcerned and oversolicitous and may spend long hours bribing, threatening, and otherwise attempting to get the child to eat.

PSYCHOPHYSIOLOGY

Anorexia nervosa is a nonclassic psychophysiological disorder in which it is difficult to postulate the existence of a biological factor. Most of the symptoms of this disorder can be explained on the basis of severe psychological difficulties, which result in a marked limitation of nutritional intake. The subsequent physiological results are those of ordinary malnutrition—loss of weight with all the concomitant secondary factors associated with severe malnutrition. The end result of self-imposed starvation is physically the same as if the child were subjected to involuntary starvation. Once the child begins to eat again, all these physical problems disappear. When a child does recover from anorexia, however, there is apt to be a swing back toward obesity, which probably does include a biological factor.

MANAGEMENT AND PROGNOSIS

As with children suffering from other psychophysiological disorders, the youngster with anorexia nervosa is often not recognized as having a serious psychological difficulty until the physical symptoms are well advanced. They are usually children who have been regarded as well behaved and even well adjusted. They may have done well academically and have presented no management problems to their parents. Only closer observation reveals the past hypersensitivity, marginal social adjustment, and compulsive features. One of the first requirements of the effective management of these children is convincing the parents that there is a large psychological contribution. This may not be particularly difficult during the middle and advanced stages of the disorder, when they see the child's peculiar and distorted view of his food intake and his insistence that he is in good health. Parents can be helped to understand that the youngster is physically healthy in terms of the absence of any organic disease. They need to understand that the child's symptomatology is emotional and the result of his own attitude toward eating.

Enlistment of parental cooperation in the total treatment program is vitally essential, whether the child is to be treated as an outpatient or in a residential center. By the time the disorder is well developed, considerable secondary gain has usually been added. All parental efforts toward enticing or threatening the child into eating must be discontinued, and the child must be convinced that his dietary intake is totally up to him. This attitude must also be developed in any other important adults involved in the treatment process, including the local family physician, relatives, and hospital personnel. The child is in a chronic battle with all those who would make him eat, and it is essential that this battleground be removed.

The treatment approach to the child himself is that of relatively forceful and active interpretation of what is going on and to some extent why. He must be helped to understand not only that his dieting is excessive and harmful to himself but also that it is based on his unwillingness to grow up. The extensive use of denial by the child as a mechanism of defense means, as a rule, that therapy cannot succeed unless this particular mechanism is met head on. Some therapists feel that better results are obtained by granting the child's wishes and allowing him thorough, total oral regression, which is thought by some to underlie this disorder. Others find that this does not work nearly so well as facing the child with reality, challenging his use of denial, and actively pushing him toward acceptance of some of the duties and responsibilities appropriate to his age group. The child's nutritional intake must be detached from his aggressive and sexual struggles while these other problems are dealt with. He should be helped to understand how he is using food in an attempt to find a solution to difficulties he has feared facing.

It sometimes becomes necessary to feed the patient intravenously or by nasal tube. If such measures become necessary, the child must be helped to understand that he himself has caused the situation and that the measures undertaken are not provoked by hostility on the part of the physicians but are practical requirements of the circumstances. When the child begins to face what he is doing, these treatment procedures become unnecessary.

Neither excessive concern about the child's physical health nor a sadistic approach are of value. The general therapeutic approach, at least in the beginning, is a matter-of-fact accounting of what the youngster must have in the way of food intake, plus reassurance that, if other problems are present, they may be discussed. In the meantime, food intake must remain at a specified level, and weight gain must take place, or the involuntary feeding will, of necessity, be introduced. Once the patient has begun to divorce his eating from his other difficulties, his physical status begins to improve, and his emotional problems can be worked on in a more leisurely and classical fashion.

OBESITY

CLINICAL DESCRIPTION

Obesity in childhood is much more difficult to describe accurately than it is in adulthood. The fat baby and the chubby toddler are commonplace and do not necessarily qualify as obese children. In general, obesity in youngsters begins to be diagnosed as a recognized and clearly defined syndrome during the grade school years. At this time, the obese child is one whose weight reveals him to be excessively heavy for his age and his height. The obesity may have been present during infancy and remained throughout grade school and into adolescence. Or it may begin later in childhood or even in early adolescence. The classically obese child has an obvious excess of adipose tissue.

The obesity itself is apt to interfere with the child's participation in normal childhood activities, particularly in athletics. Taunts from other children further isolate the obese child, who turns increasingly to eating and less to ordinary physical activities. Sensitivity about obesity tends to become enhanced at puberty. At this time, many of these youngsters begin to take dieting more seriously. Also, families tend to pay less attention to obesity during prepuberty than at adolescence.

From a statistical standpoint, obesity in children is more prevalent when they have obese parents. It is commonly observed that obese children are jolly on the surface but unhappy inside, but this is not invariably so. Some obese youngsters are reasonably well adjusted, in spite of their obesity. Others are sensitive, selfish, and without friends.

PSYCHOPHYSIOLOGY

Obesity, like most other psychophysiological disorders, is only partially understood. The overeating that results in obesity may arise from any one of several causes or combinations of causes. Certainly, some children become overweight because of purely endocrine difficulties. Such cases are relatively rare and are usually identified by a thorough physical examination. The remaining obese children, the majority of them, are not a homogeneous group. It is often difficult to determine whether the obesity is at least in part genetic or is due primarily to a family pattern of overeating.

The work of Bruch suggested that perhaps a majority of obese youngsters have developed this condition as a result of perpetuated and exaggerated oral needs. The orally oriented individual has great needs and demands much from his environment. He may sometimes have his needs met by excessive love and attention; at other times he may seek to meet them by an increase in caloric intake. Bruch's studies have indicated that many obese children come from families in which food is overvalued. Mothers who themselves are oral in nature tend to feed the infant whenever he is uncomfortable, regardless of the reason for his discomfort. The young child builds a pathway from need to eating. He remains oral, dependent, and insecure; as a result, he is often uncomfortable. He attempts to satiate himself through eating and, as a result, becomes obese. He often has little if any motivation to diet because there are no other routes through which he can meet his oral needs.

It appears that there are genetic, constitutional, biological, and psychological factors contributing to the hyperphagia that results in obesity. Certain children, although obese, are not particularly maladjusted, and their obesity can be kept under control without great difficulty. The overall picture presented by each child requires considerable attention to each of these factors.

MANAGEMENT AND PROGNOSIS

Obesity in a youngster is not generally considered a life-endangering or even a serious disorder. Parents may occasionally bring a child to a physician because of obesity. More often than not, this condition is recognized by the physician, and it becomes his responsibility to suggest a course of treatment. Frequently, the child and his parents have been aware that he is overweight, but they have either accepted this as part of the family pattern or assumed that it would eventually disappear.

Proper management of the obese child involves a thorough study of the family and of the child himself. If the family tends toward overweight and the youngster's obesity is not excessive, few if any therapeutic measures may be necessary. If, on the other hand, the youngster reveals the psychological characteristics typical of many obese children—immaturity, hypersensitivity, and insatiability—more stringent therapeutic measures may be necessary.

BRONCHIAL ASTHMA

DEFINITION

Bronchial asthma is a condition characterized by recurrent episodes of a wheezing type of dyspnea with labored and prolonged expiration. Attacks of asthma may be brief and mild or severe and prolonged, reaching the stage of status asthmaticus. The symptoms are due primarily to a narrowing of the smaller bronchi and bronchioles. Although the condition may occur at almost any time in life, it often originates during the childhood years.

CLINICAL DESCRIPTION

The child with bronchial asthma is subject to recurrent attacks of wheezing dyspnea, which may come on as a result of exposure to a particular allergen, during a period of emotional stress, or without apparent reason. The attacks may last from a few minutes to several days. The labored breathing may be mild or may reach the point where the child needs the assistance of an artificial respirator. The attacks may be seasonal or not.

An attack of bronchial asthma is physically uncomfortable and produces anxiety in the child and the parents. Medical advice is usually sought early, and the diagnosis is relatively easy, based on the characteristic wheezing respirations and the prolonged expiratory phase, with prominent rhonchi and rales. If the condition persists over a number of years, there is a tendency for the youngster to develop emphysema, with a diminished vital capacity.

As soon as the diagnosis is established, the average physician begins to search for the allergic factors that he assumes are responsible for the attacks, scheduling a series of skin tests and taking a careful history in an attempt to narrow down the search. Although it is sometimes possible to find specific allergens that produce the attack whenever the patient is exposed to them, at other times such a search is fruitless.

Physicians have long known that children with bronchial asthma frequently reveal overt emotional difficulties. Some physicians tend to attribute this to the asthma itself, but others feel that it is a contributing cause. Probably both factors are involved. Emotional factors do contribute to asthma in many youngsters, and the child with asthma is also prone to develop additional emotional problems as a result of his condition.

The characteristic course of asthma during childhood is extremely varied. Sometimes it begins very early in life and continues throughout childhood into adult life. At other times it begins late in childhood, lasts a short time, and then becomes quiescent. Serious cases usually start during the preschool years and become increasingly incapacitating as the child grows older.

As a result of repeated asthmatic attacks and the additional limitations imposed by medical management, many of these youngsters lead relatively secluded, quiet lives. They miss the opportunity of mingling freely with their peers. They are often forbidden athletic opportunities. They may be put on limited diets and be subjected to long-term desensitization procedures. Asthmatic children often have other psychosomatic difficulties, such as eczema and other skin problems.

PSYCHOPHYSIOLOGY

Asthmatic children can be broadly divided into two groups. One group contains those youngsters who show a number of neurotic symptoms and relatively few strong allergic reactions. These are children who respond well to residential treatment in special homes for asthmatic children. They do not tend to become steroid-fast, although they may originally react fairly well to steroid treatment. The other group of asthmatic children show fewer neurotic symptoms and less improvement when separated from parents and placed in a residential treatment center. They are prone to remain steroid-fast—that is, they do not tolerate removal of steroids, and, if this is attempted, they redevelop their asthmatic symptoms.

The theories developed over the years regarding the psychological contributions to asthma in children have been numerous and conflicting. They have included the concepts that the asthmatic dyspnea represents a repressed cry of the infant for the mother, the perpetuation of an early mother-child ambivalent tie, the perpetuation of various anal features due to strict toilet-training, and an overall emotionally deprived early infancy and childhood. It seems impossible at this point to present any well-documented, proved, and unchallenged theory as to the psychological role in the production of asthma. It is not even possible to delineate certain types of personality structure in asthmatic children, as some authorities claim is possible in ulcerative colitis, for example. Asthmatic children may and often do have other psychosomatic difficulties, including eczema, ulcerative colitis, rheumatoid arthritis, and migraine. They may be neurotically oriented children or have severe characterological problems. Early in the investigation of the psychological aspects of asthma, it was felt that these youngsters were by and large more intelligent than the average, but subsequent studies by Schneer have proved that this is not so.

At the present time, one can only say that various psychological factors may be involved in the production of asthma. These factors may be more important in some children than in others. It should also be kept in mind that an asthmatic attack is a psychologically traumatic event. Inability to breathe has life-threatening aspects and is bound to produce anxiety. The possibility of a subsequent attack may well reactivate the anxiety and assist in producing a new attack. The surrounding adults who themselves become increasingly anxious only serve to intensify the child's anxiety.

MANAGEMENT AND PROGNOSIS

The child with bronchial asthma deserves, as does any other youngster with a serious chronic disorder, a complete physical and a psychiatric evaluation. Such a total study often gives important clues to the biological and psychological factors involved, thus allowing appropriate therapeutic measures. Some youngsters do not respond well to psychiatric measures and present a lesser amount of psychopathology. The immunological and autoimmunological factors appear to be predominant in these children. In other youngsters the neurotic features are more prominent, and environmental manipulation and psychiatric treatment are more effective. There are, of course, children with combinations of both; for them, total team management is essential.

Residential centers for asthmatic children are located primarily in the West and Southwest parts of the United States, and it was originally assumed that their greatest benefit stemmed from the climate. Although this may be important in certain cases, the concomitant parentectomy may be even more crucial in others, where separation of the child from his family psychopathology leads to marked improvement in the asthma, even without medication or other therapeutic measures. The children most apt to benefit by this environmental manipulation are those with more neurotic features and fewer allergic problems.

The psychiatric treatment of asthmatic children is not particularly unique. It is based on the neurotic or characterological problems the youngster presents. As with most other psychosomatic problems, it is essential to have a good working relationship with the other physicians involved in the treatment of the child. Many nonpsychiatric physicians, although aware that emotions may contribute to asthma, do not have a thorough understanding of the importance of the child's psychodynamics and the family psychological interactions. They may not recognize the importance of the emotional impact of some of their own advice to the family and how this can be distorted by both parents and child. For example, increasing limitations placed on the youngster's food intake, drastic curtailment of activities and socialization, getting rid of all pets, and total revision of household management and cleaning can at times be useful, but they may also produce almost as many problems as they cure. If the nonpsychiatric physician understands family dynamics, he may modify his approach and yet still accomplish his therapeutic goals.

Treatment of the child's parents is essential when the youngster's emotional difficulties are predominant. Also, some therapeutic assistance to parents is usually necessary when the child's asthma is primarily of an allergic nature. In the first instance, the treatment is directed toward the underlying emotional problems of the parents, as they may affect the emotional maturation of the child. In both instances, it is necessary to help the parents deal realistically with the asthmatic child so that they neither overprotect nor reject him. Secondary gain accruing to the child from his asthmatic attacks should be minimized. All possible physical activities should be encouraged whenever they are not contraindicated by the asthma itself. The tendency for parents to infantalize such youngsters is common and must be minimized. It is often a matter of delicate judgment as to what physical or social limitations need to be imposed on these children. Such judgments are best reached by the team of physicians, all of whom should be thoroughly acquainted with all aspects of the child's family and his disease.

FUNCTIONAL CONSTIPATION

DEFINITION

Functional constipation may be defined as a chronic condition due primarily to emotional problems in which the bowel is evacuated only at long intervals and with difficulty. The child with this disorder characteristically has a bowel movement only every several days and, often, only with the help of suppositories, laxatives, or some stool-softening agent.

CLINICAL DESCRIPTION

A typical history of the child with functional constipation reveals that his difficulty began early, usually during his first year and invariably by the second or third year of life. The child seemed, according to his parents, not to have a daily bowel movement as they wished but occasionally to skip a day or two. This was followed by parental manipulations designed to produce a daily movement. Slowly, over a period of months, the child became increasingly recalcitrant about evacuation, and the parents increasingly concerned. They began to take additional measures to produce the bowel movement they thought necessary each day, since the child seemed unable to do so without parental interference.

By the time a youngster has reached school age with this condition, he is often quite constipated; his parents have proved to themselves and to the physician that, if left to his own devices, he will not have a normal bowel movement for three or four days, perhaps even longer. As a result, the parents have often instituted a regimen of suppositories, enemas, or mineral oil. The evacuations the child does produce may, if infrequent, be large and perhaps even painful.

The diagnosis is made on the basis of the history of infrequent bowel movements, a parent-child conflict over the production of bowel movements, and the demonstration of a potentially normal colon. The last includes the ruling out of Hirschsprung's disease, which is a megacolon due to a faulty innervation. The latter condition is relatively rare but may require a colon biopsy in order to confirm the diagnosis. It is, of course, quite possible for a child with Hirschsprung's disease to become involved in a parent-child battle similar to that seen in the child with functional constipation. There is a general atonicity of the bowel in both conditions. The fecal mass tends to build up, and there may be leakage around the main fecal mass, producing mild soiling in the child.

It is safe to say that the majority of cases of chronic constipation in children result from emotional problems rather than neurological problems. A careful history usually elicits early toilet-training difficulties and the fact that at least one parent has been overly stressful about daily bowel movements. Once the child begins to resist parent demands and withhold feces, an atonic colon that performs poorly tends to develop. Such an atonicity is further enhanced by parental use of laxatives, enemas, and suppositories. Too much parent-child interaction begins to focus around the child's habits of elimination. The administration of enemas holds a mixture of fear and pleasure for the child. A child with functional constipation presents a mixture of passive-aggressive rebellion toward parental demands and an atonic and poorly functioning colon.

PSYCHOPHYSIOLOGY

This condition stems for the most part from overly intensified parental attempts toward early bowel-training. Children with functional constipation have literally chosen to resist parental demands by not giving the very thing the parent seems most anxious to receive—a bowel movement every day. The personality of one or the other parent may be predominantly anal in nature, leading the parent to focus on the child's bowel habits in a demanding and forceful way. Such parents are often convinced of the potentially dire results of constipation, thus rationalizing their frequent intervention. The children with functional constipation may present predominantly anal characteristics, being obstinate, ambivalent, and generally passive-aggressive. Some of them present an overtly characterological passive-aggressive attitude; others become, at least by grade school age, predominantly compulsive. In both cases, however, the child's basic orientation is one of resistance—not only in bowel habits but in other areas. Although those who have become compulsive appear less resistant and obstinate, these characteristics are basically present.

Constipation is one of the psychosomatic disorders that have relatively little of a biological nature contributing to the basic cause. It appears that almost any child can be coerced into functional constipation by an overly demanding parent and that preexisting or physiological deficiency need not exist in the lower gastrointestinal tract to result in this condition.

Prognosis and Management

The prognosis of functional constipation in childhood depends both on the age at which it is recognized and treated and on the degree of psychopathology within the parent and child. In general, the earlier the condition is diagnosed, the easier it is to treat. Treatment requires that the parents be helped to understand the degree to which they are preoccupied with the child's regularity of bowel movement. It is usually necessary to support and reassure parents during the early stages of treatment so that they will be able to give up their excessive demands on the child. As soon as the patient becomes convinced that his elimination is not of tremendous importance to his parents, he will become more regular. However, most youngsters with functional constipation also have many other anal characteristics, which may also need treatment.

It may be useful in the beginning of treatment to prescribe regular doses of mineral oil or some other stool-softening agent in order to prevent painful defecation. Both parents, however, must recognize the need for removing their attention from this physiological function and for allowing the child to assume such responsibility himself.

ULCERATIVE COLITIS

Definition

Ulcerative colitis is a serious chronic condition characterized by recurrent episodes of severe, bloody diarrhea. It is accompanied by anorexia, weight loss, and anemia. There are characteristic changes in the mucosa of the lower bowel and occasionally in the terminal ileum.

CLINICAL DESCRIPTION

Ulcerative colitis may occur at any time during the life span and has even been reported in neonates. The disease may develop in a child gradually, with one or more mild attacks that go unrecognized, or it may develop in a fulminating form that is fatal in a period of a month or two. Most characteristically, the patient develops diarrhea, with up to forty stools a day in which there is excessive mucus and varying degrees of blood. He loses his appetite, complains of cramping abdominal pains, and becomes listless and apathetic. An individual attack of ulcerative colitis may last from a few weeks to a few months, after which the symptoms may abate but rarely disappear entirely. Further attacks tend to occur when the child is under some type of emotional tension.

The child with chronic ulcerative colitis usually remains somewhat anemic and underweight. If the condition persists for years, the child's growth may be seriously affected. Acute attacks of colitis carry with them the dangers of exsanguination or bowel perforation. Another complication of long-standing ulcerative colitis in both children and adults is the higher incidence of carcinoma of the bowel.

The diagnosis is made on the basis of the history and of X-ray and sigmoidoscopic examination of the bowel. The colon mucosa is friable and bleeds easily. Ulcerations may or may not be visible on sigmoidoscopy. Pseudopolyposis is common. The disease may affect any or all of the lower bowel and at times extends into the distal portion of the ileum.

It has been suggested that children with ulcerative colitis can be divided into two relatively distinct personality types. By far the most common are those with obsessional personalities. The typical history reveals that the child has been perfectionistic, rigid, and overly conscientious. This pseudomature adjustment has been interrupted occasionally by brief episodes of infantile dependent behavior. Many of these youngsters have a history of peculiar eating habits, with intense dislikes for certain foods based on their consistency or color. There may also be a history of constipation, with occasional periods of mild diarrhea. When the child develops an attack of ulcerative colitis, he characteristically becomes whiney, depressed, and demanding; he generally withdraws from most of his ordinary activities. The depression in these children is quite prominent, and preoccupations with death are not uncommon.

A smaller number of children with ulcerative colitis have a personality quite different from that outlined above. They are querulous, demanding, manipulative children. These youngsters are somewhat less apt to develop acute fulminating attacks of colitis. Their symptoms are somewhat less dramatic but more constant. They often use the colitis in a manipulative fashion to force parents and others to meet their excessive demands.

The parents of children with ulcerative colitis present more than the average amount of psychopathology, but there does not appear to be any single type of family dynamics characteristic of this disorder. One often finds a close, ambivalent, and almost symbiotic tie between the child and one of the parents.

PSYCHOPHYSIOLOGY

Ulcerative colitis, like many other psychophysiological disorders, has been studied more thoroughly in adults than in children. One can probably assume, however, that similar factors operate regardless of the age of the patient. The most promising current research in ulcerative colitis appears to point in the direction of autoimmunological factors. It has been demonstrated that the peripheral circulating blood of the patient with ulcerative colitis contains some as-yet-unidentified substance that is toxic to colon cells. Two basic questions remain unanswered. One has to do with the specific antigen in the blood and its exact location, and the second has to do with the original triggering device that sets off the attack of colitis. One can presume but as yet not prove that emotional tension is the original triggering device. It is often but not always possible to demonstrate some type of emotional crisis surrounding the onset of colitis. It is also presumed but as yet not proved that, once the process begins, the reduction in emotional tension does not necessarily lead to a remission in the disease. Psychiatric improvement may not be followed by a similar improvement in bowel pathology.

MANAGEMENT AND PROGNOSIS

Children with ulcerative colitis have, over the years, been treated by a variety of methods. Whenever this situation prevails, it is a probable indicator that the disease in question is not understood—and this is certainly true with ulcerative colitis. Currently, management of the child with this disease usually involves some dietary restrictions, particularly during an exacerbation of the disease. Iron may be prescribed to combat the anemia, and, if the latter becomes serious, transfusions may be necessary. Some physicians rely on steroids, particularly during acute attacks, but there is always the danger of problems inherent in removing the steroids later. A considerable number of these children eventually come to surgery, where a one-stage or two-stage colectomy is performed. The timing of the surgery is important. Although the fatality rate is much greater than normal in those patients who have suffered severe bleeding or perforation, one is reluctant to remove the colon from a child who seems to be getting along reasonably well. Once extensive, nonreversible changes have taken place in the bowel, it is probable that surgery will eventually have to take place. The incidence of carcinoma in such a diseased bowel increases after the passage of several years. Surgeons sometimes prefer to leave the rectal stump, particularly if it is not seriously diseased, in the hope of reanastomosis, thus ridding the youngster of a permanent ileostomy. Such reanastomoses in children are not frequent; of those that are performed, quite a number are unsuccessful because of a continuation of the disease in the rectal segment.

The most successful management of children with ulcerative colitis is based on a team approach involving a child psychiatrist, surgeon, pediatrician, and social worker. Each child and his parents are seen by all members of the team, and a joint decision is reached on the basis of the findings of each team member. There seems little doubt that psychotherapy for the child and casework for the parents are helpful in this disorder.

GENERAL PRINCIPLES OF TREATMENT OF PSYCHOPHYSIOLOGICAL DISEASE

This extremely complex group of disorders is at best only partly understood, without even general agreement as to which conditions should be properly classified under the category of psychophysiological disorders. Certainly, in order to be considered as a psychophysiological disorder, the condition should have a strong emotional component. Most of these disorders also have a biological factor that may or may not be recognized. A great deal more research is needed to treat them more successfully and more scientifically than at present.

One should bear in mind that growing children are constantly changing, attempting to adapt. In most instances the parents at least consciously desire to have the physical problem eradicated but do not, as a general rule, perceive the emotional component. The majority of them do not see their own contribution to this emotional component and are not ready to accept help for themselves in order to cure what to them seems to be an obviously physical problem. Unfortunately, the viewpoint of many physicians is much like that of the parents. They are so busily engaged in treating the physical disorder that they deny appropriate attention to the psychological problems.

PSYCHOSOMATIC PERSONALITY

If one attempted to describe a psychosomatic personality in children, he would probably picture a relatively brittle, pseudomature youngster who in most instances pleases the adults with whom he comes into contact. He is a good child, a good student, and has not been a problem to anyone except with his occasional physical difficulties. When the psychosomatic disorder becomes really serious, he is apt to continue to be the good child and to impress most physicians as well as other adults as a well-adjusted youngster. He may tolerate physical procedures well, even stoically, and his occasional infantile reactions are apt to be dismissed as normal by the physician. When it is pointed out that he has not adjusted especially well to youngsters of his own age, the parents or even the physician may reply that he has, after all, had some physical problems and, therefore, could not be expected to adjust well.

MANAGEMENT

In general, the management of a psychosomatically ill child may require the services of a team of not only physicians but members of other mental health disciplines as well. This need may be one of the chief barriers to the successful treatment of these children. The various specialists in medicine are not always able to work together in harmonious fashion, and where a psychiatrist is one of the predominant members of the team, continuing cooperation can become even more difficult. Nonpsychiatric physicians may be unfamiliar with and reluctant to work with such disciplines as social work and psychology, even though thorough and total communication between the various disciplines is essential.

A series of steps is necessary if a child with a psychophysiological disorder is to be treated with reasonable effectiveness. Step one is fundamental and involves the conviction of the primary physician that the disorder is psychosomatic. The average general practitioner has relatively little understanding of these disorders, particularly of their emotional psychic elements. It is essential that he recognize the strong psychic component and that he be convinced that it is necessary to deal with this if the treatment is to be successful.

Step two, which follows naturally, is that this primary physician convince the child's parents that there is a large psychic element in the disease and that it must be taken into account in the treatment program. The physician can only do this if he himself is convinced not only of the importance of the psyche but also of the importance of the emotions in the production of this particular disorder.

Step three involves the enlisting of a team able to understand and undertake a therapeutic regimen for the youngster and his family. Such a team—comprised of a psychiatrist, a nurse, a social worker, and other professionals in various disciplines of medicine and outside of medicine—needs to understand the child's total physical situation and his emotional and intellectual status. They should also have a complete knowledge of the family and how their emotional reactions may have played a part in the disorder.

Making such a team operate smoothly is difficult. The time spent treating these youngsters and their families is great. In ulcerative colitis, for example, the surgeon may limit himself to removing the colons of those patients whose colitis has made this a necessary step, but if he is to be involved in the treatment both before and after colectomy, he will have to involve himself with a team of professionals working with the child.

The final step in working with these youngsters is the individual treatment of the child himself and the treatment of the parents. These youngsters should have the opportunity for regular psychotherapy while they are receiving adequate medical and surgical care. The parents often require extensive social casework to understand their own contributions to the child's illness and to alter his emotional environment.

REFERENCES

Alexander, F., and French, T. M. *Studies in Psychosomatic Medicine.* Ronald Press, New York, 1948.

American Psychiatric Association. *Diagnostic and Statistical Manual of Mental Disorders*, ed. 2. American Psychiatric Association, Washington, 1968.

Bruch, H. Psychiatric aspects of obesity in children. Amer. J. Psychiat., 99: 752, 1943.

Dunbar, F. *Psychosomatic Diagnosis.* Hoeber Medical Division, Harper & Row, New York, 1948.

Engel, G. L. Studies of ulcerative colitis: V. Psychological aspects and their implications for treatment. Amer. J. Dig. Dis., 3: 315, 1958.

Finch, S. M., and Hess, J. Ulcerative colitis in children. Amer. J. Psychiat., 118: 819, 1962.

Harms, E., editor. *Somatic and Childhood Aspects of Childhood Allergies.* Macmillan, New York, 1963.

Mirsky, I. A. Physiological, psychological and social determinants in the etiology of duodenal ulcer. Amer. J. Dig. Dis., 3: 285, 1958.

Schneer, H., editor. *The Asthmatic Child.* Harper & Row, New York, 1963.

Weiss, E., and English, O. S. *Psychosomatic Medicine*, ed. 3. W. B. Saunders, Philadelphia, 1957.

CHAPTER SEVEN

Personality Disorders of Children

JOSEPH D. TEICHER, M.D.

CONCEPT OF PERSONALITY

DEFINITION

PERSONALITY OR CHARACTER does not develop independently; nor is it an accidental phenomenon. Rather, it is determined in large measure by the interaction between the instincts and the environment. Personality refers to the individual's habitual patterns of behavior, the nature and design of which are unconsciously determined. These patterns of behavior are the outward manifestation of the individual's inner interests and, in particular, his instinctual impulses.

No two individuals are identical in this regard. First, there are inevitable differences in instinct need and presentation. Second, there are differences in instinctual cathexis, in the intensity of instinctual drives. Clinical psychiatry is dedicated to the identification and description of the patient's unique pattern of instinctual functioning, for these data bring about an understanding of his mode of adapting to life—that is, of his personality.

PERSONALITY FORMATION

Personality formation can best be described as a process of progressive integration. At each maturational stage, different psychological and physiological functions are coordinated to form dynamic patterns of behavior. The organization of primitive faculties and impulses in the infant can best be described as chaotic. Later, as the child learns to adapt needs to external conditions, these impulses and the faculties that permitted their expression and fulfillment are organized to form specific patterns of behavior. Because these patterns assure gratification of the child's basic needs—

theoretically, at least—he is no longer completely dependent on the crucial adults in his environment. At the same time, however, the child's personality structure as a whole reflects his responses to the conscious and unconscious components of his parents' personalities and his perception of their conscious and unconscious attitudes toward him.

Concurrent with the formation of personality, the child develops a typical mode of behavior. Social and cultural factors may, of course, be expected to exert considerable influence on behavior. If this influence is to be a favorable one, the demands imposed on the child by the environment should not exceed realistic limits, and, above all, the environment must provide the child with adequate emotional support.

THE DETERMINANTS OF PERSONALITY

According to psychoanalytic theory, the dynamic forces that operate to produce the elements of personality determine the interaction between the instincts and the environment and, by implication, the regulation of instinctual expression by ego and superego. The concept of instincts is generally accepted, but their classification has long been the subject of controversy; nor is it likely that this dilemma will be resolved in the near future. Under the circumstances, it would seem most useful, for clinical purposes, to center this discussion on the child's uneven efforts in the course of his development to master his sexual and aggressive impulses.

The ego seeks to regulate instinctual expression to conform with the demands of the external world. In the early stages of development, the parents function as auxiliary egos and assist in the control of the instincts. Subsequently, parental dictates with regard to instinctual discharge are internalized to form the child's superego or conscience. The superego imposes further controls on instinctual expression, insofar as violations of internalized parental values give rise to guilt feelings.

As the child develops, the ego and superego continue to mature and to influence his mode of behavior. At successive stages in his development, the nature of the child's instinctual expressions and his capacity to delay discharge, which depend on ego and superego function, determine personality structure. Viewed from this perspective, those factors that may impair personality development emerge clearly. Just as there are individual differences in many constitutional givens, individual children may manifest wide differences in rate of ego development. The rate of ego maturation may also be affected by constitutional nervous system dysfunction. The controls exercised by the superego with regard to instinctual expression may be inappropriate—that is, either too rigid or overpermissive—if the superego represents the distorted values of emotionally disturbed parents. The ability of parents, particularly the mother, to gratify the child's basic needs—and thereby afford him a sense of security and the specific mode of gratification—plays a crucial role in molding his earliest personality traits. As the child grows older, his expanding activities and contact with an increasing number of people color his emotional functioning. At this point, his family, their modes of behavior and emotional expression, his peers, and the cultural milieu all exert an influence on his development. In fact, however, the groundwork has already been laid; the child's potential level of personality organization and function is determined during the earliest stages of development.

ASSESSMENT OF PSYCHOPATHOLOGY IN CHILDHOOD

Nosology

Current diagnostic categories compound the confusing aspects of the clinical picture. The fact that the whole spectrum of psychopathology in childhood has been fitted rather forcibly into diagnostic categories adopted from the fields of adult psychiatry and criminology represents a major source of difficulty. Anna Freud has stated in this connection that this solution to the problems intrinsic to the diagnosis of personality pattern and trait disturbances in childhood has proved to be unsatisfactory as a basis for assessment, prognosis, and the selection of appropriate therapeutic measures.

Many authors have pointed out that, in contrast to later stages of development, it is more difficult to draw a line of demarcation between mental health and illness in childhood. During the early years of life, the relative strength of id and ego is in a constant state of flux; adaptive and defensive mechanisms, normal and pathogenic processes frequently merge. It has also been postulated that the transition from one developmental level to the next constitutes a potential psychological hazard, for it is at this point that major or minor stress is most likely to produce arrest in development, malfunction, fixation, or regression. Particularly when id impulses develop at a more rapid rate than ego functions, various factors may combine to undermine, distort, and deflect the forces on which mental growth is based.

As a general rule, current classifications of emotional disturbances have not contributed to our understanding of the causes of specific disorders to any degree; nor do they facilitate differential diagnosis in a dynamic sense. Yet, unless the clinician is aware of the underlying pathogenesis of an emotional disturbance, he cannot accurately evaluate the patient's presenting symptoms, assign them to the proper dynamic categories, or institute appropriate therapeutic measures. Diagnostic formulations that are primarily descriptive, that derive from superficial observation of overt symptoms, may have disastrous repercussions when they are used as the basis for psychoanalytic inferences. Of particular significance for the classification of emotional disorders in childhood is the fact that current diagnostic procedures neglect such crucial variables as age and stage of development. Nor do they make sufficient allowance for the difference between symptoms due to the delay or failure to acquire and perfect specific personality traits and symptoms caused by the breakdown of previously acquired functions or by regression to a less mature level of functioning.

SYMPTOMS

Symptoms manifested in childhood do not necessarily carry the same significance they do in adult life, where typical symptom complexes lead to specific diagnoses. The presenting symptoms of immature individuals are much too unstable to provide reliable criteria for purposes of assessment; in fact, the child does not maintain a stable level of functioning in any area at any time. Instead, the assessment of child psychopathology hinges on one crucial variable, the child's capacity to move forward in progressive stages until maturation has been achieved, his personality is sufficiently integrated, and he has adapted successfully to the social community. By the same token, emotional upsets become diagnostically and prognostically significant when they exert an adverse effect on the child's overall development—whether it is slowed up, reversed, or brought to a standstill.

Clearly, the assessment of psychopathology in childhood would become more meaningful if developmental norms were developed for all the parameters of the personality and attention were redirected from symptoms to the child's position on the development scale. In that event, concern would center, more appropriately, on drive, ego, and superego development; on the structure of the personality—that is, the stability of the boundaries between id, ego, and superego—and on the child's modes of functioning—that is, evidence that primary thought processes have begun to give way to secondary thought processes, of progress from the pleasure principle to the reality principle. Considered within this frame of reference, it becomes apparent that the pathogenic impact of hereditary factors depends in large measure on the developmental influences with which they interact. Similarly, organic defects, body malformations, may give rise to a wide range of psychological consequences, depending on the child's environmental circumstances and mental equipment. Although any of the elements elicited in the assessment of child psychopathology may be identical by definition, there may be wide differences in the significance attached to such elements in different personality settings. The fact is that indications of possible psychopathology in childhood cannot be properly evaluated if they are viewed in isolation or according to preconceived, rigid standards and criteria. Rather, they must be considered in relation to the child's total functioning and in terms of their potential effect on his development.

PERSONALITY DISORDERS IN CHILDHOOD

DEFINITION

Personality disorders in children represent relatively fixed pathological trends in personality development and functioning that have become a way of life more or less. According to the second edition of the *Diagnostic and Statistical Manual of Mental Disorders* (DSM-II) of the American Psychiatric Association (APA), "This group of disorders is characterized by deeply ingrained maladaptive patterns of behavior that are perceptively different in quality from psychotic and neurotic symptoms." DSM-II further states that most frequently the personality disorders find expression in life-long patterns.

Personality disorders are deep-seated disturbances; as such, their inherent structure can rarely be altered by therapy. At the same time, however, prolonged therapy may lead to an improvement in functioning, even though basic changes in personality structure occur very infrequently.

General Considerations

Clinical features. Children with personality disorders solve their conflicts simply by changing their personality. This does not cause subjective feelings of discomfort unless they are confronted with the harsh realities of life, at which time they are forced to realize that their adaptive capacities are inadequate. On superficial examination, the mode of behavior of children with personality disturbances appear to be appropriate under normal conditions. When these children are under stress, however, they are unable to maintain their emotional equilibrium. Pathological personality traits then emerge as a reflection of their underlying disturbance.

Causes. As pointed out earlier, clinical syndromes in childhood are shaped by age and developmental status, level of personality organization, and the nature and quality of the child's interaction with his environment. Unfortunately, at the present stage of our knowledge, it is impossible to postulate an etiological schema for personality disorders in childhood that take all these variables into account and that are conceptually and theoretically adequate and universally accepted.

A major impediment to efforts in this connection stems from the instability of symptoms and reactions in childhood. It is not difficult to recognize that the child is in conflict with his environment at a given point in his development. However, criteria have not yet been developed that permit us to predict the subsequent fate of this conflict, whether it will develop into an internal conflict or a personality disorder. The personality disorders—those psychopathological problems in children that are neither neurotic nor reactive and that represent relatively fixed trends in personality development and personality functioning—are an area of particular concern and have given rise to considerable speculation. This concern is understandable in light of the fact that these disorders are thought to represent a more or less fixed way of life, largely because of the fact that they are accompanied by minimal subjective anxiety, which obviously has an adverse influence on treatment efforts and prognosis.

INADEQUATE PERSONALITY

Although on examination they do not appear to be grossly deficient physically or mentally, according to the APA definition, adults in this category have an inadequate response to intellectual, emotional, social, and physical demands and display poor adaptability, ineptness, poor judgment, lack of physical and emotional stamina, and social incompatibility. Admittedly, the applicability of a definition as inclusive as this one to personality disorders in childhood is questionable. It is generally agreed that, even if a child does have this syndrome, it has less impact on him than on an adult so classified. More important, however, is the fact that criteria such as inadequate response to intellectual and emotional demands and social incompatibility clearly fail to recognize that the developing child has limited responsibilities and freedom. Under these circumstances, a diagnosis of inadequate personality would be difficult to substantiate; in any event, it is made only rarely.

SCHIZOID PERSONALITY

Isolation is the most prominent symptom of the children in this group. They are further characterized by an inability to form close relationships with others, an inability to express normal feelings of aggression, and a tendency to withdraw emotionally from the environment. Typically, these children are quiet, shy, obedient, sensitive, and retiring. Frequently, they become more withdrawn and introverted at puberty, and sometimes they become eccentric. Many authors have pointed out that children with schizoid personalities show a marked infantilism, so that even their attempts to meet the ordinary problems of childhood evoke feelings of frustration, which give rise to poorly handled hostility. Fantasy becomes a common refuge. Most of these children grow up to be isolated adults; some develop psychotic episodes.

Causes. The specific factors that produce this mode of behavior have not been clearly delineated. However, the available data do permit some generalizations. The histories of these patients point up their life-long isolation from parents, siblings, and others; in addition, there is a strong possibility that this pattern may be constitutionally determined. Almost without exception, the parents of such children are themselves without close relationships, despite a façade of sociability. Uusually, despite vehement protests to the contrary, these parents also manifest a marked ambivalence toward their child; they attach great importance to his physical care but are incapable of providing him with emotional warmth or acceptance.

Treatment. With therapy, such children may develop some warmth and a social façade, but, almost invariably, they return to their solitary activities with relief. The more severe cases may develop a psychotic reaction in adolescence under the stress of phase-specific tasks.

CYCLOTHYMIC PERSONALITY

Adult cyclothymic personalities are characterized by "recurring and alternating periods of depression and elation. . . . These mood variations are not readily attributable to external circumstances." However, this diagnosis is almost never applied to a child. Mood changes in a child are influenced by parental attitudes, the family milieu, and peer relationships. If parents reward or praise the child, he feels happy; if they are chronically critical, he is depressed.

It has been suggested that children who are subjected to the chronic disapproval of their parents may be predisposed to the development of a cyclothymic personality. At first glance they appear mature, happy, and active. In fact, they are extremely sensitive, react with tears or depression when they are punished, and reveal marked mood variations, alternating between happiness and sadness with minimal stimuli. Although these features would seem to provide a foundation for the development of a cyclothymic personality in later life, not all children with these characteristics develop this disorder.

Causes.   The basic pathology stems from a conflict between a severe, punitive superego and powerful primitive unconscious impulses. When the superego is in ascendancy, the child is depressed and preoccupied with thoughts of self-deprecation and self-recrimination. Early childhood traumata, such as desertion, precipitate hostility, which is turned inward and is manifested clinically as depression. As pointed out above, this clinical picture will not emerge with any clarity in the child whose emotional expressions depend on his parents' attitudes toward him. Nor is the presence of such symptoms in childhood a reliable indication of the subsequent development of a cyclothymic personality; the fluidity of developmental processes in childhood prevents such a prediction.

Treatment.   Treatment is necessarily intensive and should involve the parents, whose attitudes and care have much to do with the child's personality development and modes of behavior. Thus, child therapy becomes family therapy; understanding of the dynamics that underlie the child's problem must include an understanding of the family dynamics.

PARANOID PERSONALITY

Many of the elements described above in connection with the schizoid personality are present in this syndrome, coupled with an exquisite sensitivity in interpersonal relations. Suspiciousness, mistrust, envy, extreme jealousy, and stubbornness are characteristic. Most marked is the tendency toward projection, a mechanism of defense by which one's own internal inadequacies and immaturities are attributed to others. This mechanism operates unconsciously and, although it is very common in children, is not so highly systematized in the early stages of development as it is in adults.

Causes.   Projection offers the child a means of ridding himself of uncomfortable feelings of inadequacy. This does not mean that the child who projects is going to develop a paranoid personality—whether he blames his peers for being poor sports because he himself is a bad athlete or a sore loser, blames his teacher for his failing grades, or accuses others of attacks he alone has provoked. The difficulties inherent in the accurate prediction of future psychopathology in the early years of life have been emphasized throughout this chapter. The child's extreme sensitivity may be due, for example, to an unusual constitutional sensitivity of the ego, although it certainly is enhanced by a sense of insecurity and inadequacy and by the turbulent, suspicious, distrustful attitudes of disturbed parents.

Treatment. The goal of treatment is to strengthen the child's confidence, sense of security, and safety; to help him to develop appropriate reality-testing; and to ameliorate family pathology. Treatment is always difficult; it is not always successful.

HYSTERICAL PERSONALITY

Once again, the fluidity of development precludes the use of this diagnosis with children. Nor is it used frequently with reference to adults, primarily because it is defined only vaguely and because the symptoms identified with this syndrome are relatively common. Individuals included in this category react with extreme excitement, albeit ineffectively, in stress situations. Because of strong and poorly controlled hostility, guilt, and anxiety, relationships with other people in the environment are consistently undermined by fluctuating emotional attitudes.

PASSIVE-AGGRESSIVE PERSONALITY

This category includes three types of reaction: passive-dependent, passive-aggressive, and aggressive. The underlying psychopathology is the same for each, and the three syndromes occur interchangeably. An anxiety reaction is almost always a concomitant in the clinical picture.

Passive-dependent type. Dependence on one's parents is normal during early childhood. Thus, this diagnosis is applied to those children whose dependency needs exceed normal limits. Such a child appears helpless and indecisive, clings to others, and obviously is neither autonomous nor independent to the degree considered healthy for his age or stage of development. Typically, these children were overprotected by parents who, however, often have mixed reactions about their child, encourage a helpless and clinging attitude, and inhibit the child's development of independence because of their own guilt feelings. Treatment is designed to facilitate the healthy maturation of the child, but an equally essential goal is the correction of unhealthy parental attitudes toward the child.

Passive-aggressive type. This clinical picture occurs most frequently in children. Passive obstructionism, inefficiency, procrastination, stubbornness, and pouting are hallmarks of this type of aggression. This behavior is seen in many children as an expression of resentment, invoked by excessive parental demands. The normal parent expects the child to resent his demands at times and is prepared to accept some of the child's hostility. On the other hand, if any overt expression of hostility is deemed unacceptable by the parent, the child may develop more subtle rebellious behavior, particularly if the parent expresses his objections to the child's hostility by criticizing or punishing him excessively. A classic reaction to such parental behavior is the child who dawdles endlessly over meals because the child is well aware that this type of passive-aggressive behavior will not elicit the punishment or disapproval he has learned to associate with expressions of open hostility. Not unexpectedly, the goal of treatment is to help the child express his resentments and hostilities openly and in more acceptable ways. At the same time, his parents are made aware of their suppressive, critical attitudes and are helped to correct them.

Aggressive type. Such behavior is not to be confused with delinquent reactions. The underlying dependency of the passive-aggressive child is strong and is enforced by ambivalent parental attitudes, especially on the part of the mother. When such a child is frustrated repeatedly, he may display overt and angry behavior, which incidentally may be antisocial. On the other hand, quite often it seems that the child's excessive demands could not conceivably be satiated, that his frustration is self-inflicted and inevitable. In either case, irritability, temper tantrums, destructive behavior, and, above all, a fierce resentment that leads him to strike out at the environment characterize this syndrome. Here, again, treatment focuses not only on helping the child develop healthier modes of expression and adequate gratifications, but also on correcting the parents' pathological attitudes toward the child.

OBSESSIVE COMPULSIVE PERSONALITY

The pathology manifested by a good, conforming child usually escapes recognition. Excessive rigidity and conformity, overconscientiousness, and inhibition of emotional expression are marked in these children, who are so well behaved they become mature or pseudomature too early. Like adults, these children show an obsessive concern with adherence to standards of conscience or conformity and may have an inordinate capacity for work without the usual capacity for relaxation.

Causes. Such children are fixated at the anal stage of libidinal development. The resulting immaturities are countered by a punitive superego that is so strict that the child appears to be unusually well behaved, worrisome, inhibited, and organized. In light of the fact that the parents of such children are compulsive, driving, perfectionistic individuals with very high standards, it has been speculated that this type of personality is hereditary.

Treatment. Treatment seeks to develop a more balanced intrapsychic relationship between instinctual expressions, coping mechanisms, and the dictates of the superego. Parents' attitudes must be altered as well, for one should not underestimate the influence that the parental expectations and image of a good, well-behaved, conscientious child may have had on the child's personality formation.

GAP CLASSIFICATION OF DISORDERS IN CHILDREN

The Committee on Child Psychiatry of the Group for the Advancement of Psychiatry (GAP) has recommended that the classification of personality disorders in childhood remain descriptive until the whole area of chronic or fixed trends in total personality structure has been defined more clearly. The Committee has thus expressed its awareness of the deficiencies in current classifications and the fact that they are basically unsuited to child psychiatry. The Committee has also suggested other categories, in the hope that they may prove more realistic and have greater clinical validity than the categories listed in the APA manual. The categories recommended by GAP are listed below and are largely self-explanatory. This proposed classification has not been universally accepted; nevertheless, it represents a major step forward. The classification is as follows: (1) anxious personality, (2) compulsive personality, (3) hysterical personality, (4) overly dependent personality, (5) oppositional personality, (6) overinhibited personality, (7) overindependent personality, (8) isolated personality (replacing schizoid personality), (9) mistrustful personality (replacing paranoid personality), (10) tension discharge disorders (a) impulse-ridden personality and (b) neurotic personality disorder, (11) sociosyntonic personality disorder, (12) sexual deviations, (13) other personality disorders.

Anxious personality. These children are chronically tense and apprehensive over new situations. Their anxiety is not so crippling, however, as the anxiety experienced in anxiety neurosis.

Compulsive personality. These children are characterized by excessive orderliness, cleanliness, and conformity. Their personalities are rigid and inflexible, with occasional obsessive thoughts and compulsive rituals.

Hysterical personality. More girls than boys are included in this group which shows tendencies toward overly dramatic, flamboyant, overly labile, overly affective, overly suggestible, coy, and seductive behavior. Symptom formation of conversion or dissociative nature may occur with stress.

Overly dependent personality. Children in this group are chronically helpless, clinging, and overly dependent and have difficulty in achieving independent initiative. Included here are some children formerly classified as passive-aggressive, passive-dependent, immature, or unstable personalities.

Oppositional personality. These children show their aggressiveness by oppositional behavior of a passive character, which often has aggressive implications. Typically, they use negativism, stubbornness, and procrastination and are often quite provocative. These children were previously in the passive-aggressive category.

Overly inhibited personality. On superficial examination, these children manifest passivity, shyness, motor inhibition, and marked constriction of personality functions. They differ from the schizoid (isolated) personalities, however, in that they have a deep desire for warm meaningful relationships.

Overly independent personality. These children show a chronically ebullient, active behavior, with a need to rush toward independence and concomitant difficulty in accepting limits. Their behavior is pseudoprecocious, for, in general, they have a positive attitude.

Isolated personality (replacing schizoid). These children tend to show distant, detached, cold, or withdrawn attitudes. They are frequently isolated, seclusive, and unable to form warm and meaningful attachments.

Mistrustful personality (replacing paranoid). This disorder, rare in childhood and more common during adolescence, is characterized by suspiciousness, intense distrust of others, and rigidity in thinking.

Tension discharge disorder. These children exhibit chronic behavioral patterns involving aggressive and sexual impulses. As a result, they are in constant conflict with society, for they act out these impulses in an antisocial or destructive fashion. Included here are the former designations of antisocial personality, sociopathic personality, and psychopathic personality. In addition, children who were previously diagnosed as acting out or as manifesting conduct disorders and behavior disorders fall into this category. This category includes two major subdivisions:

Impulse-ridden personality. These children have a low frustration tolerance and shallow relationships with adults. They have poor control of their impulses, little anxiety and internalized guilt, and defective superego formation.

Neurotic personality disorder. The behavior of these children is similar to that of the impulse-ridden personalities, described above, with two exceptions: They act out tension resulting from conflict of a neurotic origin, and there is evidence of conscience formation.

Sociosyntonic personality disorder. This category consists of two groups. The first exhibits aggressive antisocial personality trends that, although they deviate from the standards of society, are consonant with their environment (the dyssocial category). The second group includes children from subcultures, such as isolated rural settings, who may have hallucinatory experiences, embrace voodoo beliefs, etc.

Sexual deviations. These children show chronic, relatively fixed sexual deviations. Usually, this classification is used only with adolescents and applies only in those cases where the deviation is pervasive and chronic.

Other personality disorders. Included here are personality disorders not listed under other headings, such as cyclothymic personality.

SUMMARY

When the progressive integration of personality and the establishing of structural boundaries between id, ego, and superego are impaired by the conscious and unconscious parental attitudes toward the child, psychopathology will result. Constitutional givens are an important factor. The particular manifest continuation of specific attitudes singles out personality types. Precipitate reaction formations, related to early infantile stages of development, determine character traits. Treatment is not restricted to the child but involves the parents or family as well. The most effective type of treatment by far for these clinical syndromes is the psychoanalytically oriented approach.

REFERENCES

Ackerman, N. W. Psychiatric disorders in children: diagnosis and etiology in our time. In *Current Problems in Psychiatric Diagnosis*, P. Hoch and J. Zubin, editors, p. 205. Grune & Stratton, New York, 1953.

Allen, F. H. *Psychotherapy with Children.* W. W. Norton, New York, 1942.

American Psychiatric Association. *Diagnostic and Statistical Manual of Mental Disorders*, ed. 2. American Psychiatric Association, Washington, 1968.

American Psychiatric Association. *Diagnostic Classification in Child Psychiatry.* Psychiat. Res. Rep. Amer. Psychiat. Ass., No. 18, 1964.

Erikson, E. H. *Childhood and Society*, ed. 2. W. W. Norton, New York, 1963.

Finch, S. M. *Fundamentals of Child Psychiatry.* W. W. Norton, New York, 1960.

Freud, A. *The Ego and Mechanisms of Defense.* Hogarth Press, London, 1937.

Freud, A. *Normality and Pathology in Childhood.* International Universities Press, New York, 1965.

Group for the Advancement of Psychiatry. *Basic Concepts in Child Psychiatry.* Report No. 12. Group for the Advancement of Psychiatry, New York, 1957.

Group for the Advancement of Psychiatry. *Diagnostic Process in Child Psychiatry.* Report No. 38. Group for the Advancement of Psychiatry, New York, 1957.

Group for the Advancement of Psychiatry. *Psychopathological Disorders in Childhood: Theoretical Considerations and a Proposed Classification.* Report No. 62. Group for the Advancement of Psychiatry, New York, 1966.

Hoch, P. H., and Zubin, J., editors. *Psychopathology of Childhood.* Grune & Stratton, New York, 1955.

Jessner, L., and Pavenstedt, E. *Dynamic Psychopathology in Childhood.* Grune & Stratton, New York, 1959.

Lippman, H. S. *Treatment of the Child in Emotional Conflict.* McGraw-Hill, New York, 1956.

Pearson, G. H. J. *Emotional Disorders of Children.* W. W. Norton, New York, 1949.

Teicher, J. D. *Your Child and His Problems.* Little, Brown, Boston, 1953.

CHAPTER EIGHT

Antisocial Personality and Dyssocial Behavior

ROBERT L. STUBBLEFELD, M.D.

DEFINITIONS

THE CONCEPT of juvenile delinquency has been known to man for many centuries. Socrates in 500 B.C. stated that "children now love luxury. They have bad manners and contempt for authority. They show disrespect to their elders and love to chatter in place of exercise." Shakespeare had a character say in a play, "I would that man could forego the pleasure of life from four and ten to one and twenty, when youth does nothing but fight, drink, and get wench with child."

Modern concepts of delinquency suggest that children who are called delinquent are ill primarily in terms of society, in their inability to conform to the social milieu. Since the social and cultural milieu is influenced by many factors—education, radio, television, socioeconomic levels, minority racial groups, poverty, war and threat of war, civil rights movements, immigration, and many others—it is not possible to give precise definitions of delinquent behavior. In addition, one can view our states and cities as a wide variety of legal systems, attempting to evaluate, modify, and contain individual and group behavior. What is viewed as antisocial behavior in one city may not be viewed identically in another city or may be viewed differently by the same city officials over a period of time. As an illustration, an adolescent Negro boy may be arrested and sent to a reformatory for participating in a restaurant sit-in, and, after the local laws are changed, essentially the same behavior would go unnoticed. Laws tend to reflect current morality to a greater or lesser extent, and children are caught up in intense personal conflicts in our rapidly shifting and changing culture. Clearly, some fail to adapt to the various pressures as well as others. We can speak of two types of sociopathic patterns: (1) antisocial personality, characteristic of children and adolescents who are always in trouble, who seem not to profit from experience or punishment, and who have no loyalties to persons other than themselves, and (2) dyssocial behavior, characteristic of children and adolescents who have been brought up in amoral or immoral families or institutions and who have identified with strong loyalties to a criminal element—for example, children whose parents are gypsies or habitual criminals.

EPIDEMIOLOGY

It is generally accepted that the incidence of antisocial personality varies from about 2 per cent to about 7 per cent of the childhood population. There are more than three thousand juvenile courts in this country, and modern policies of juvenile probation programs permit many officers, after appropriate education and inservice instruction, to make quick decisions in the community, so that many children are not booked and identified by a formal court procedure. The reporting systems must be studied at the probation officer level in order to obtain accurate figures for study.

In boys the major offenses are truancy, stealing, fire-setting, vandalism, and cruelty to animals and humans; in girls the major offenses are stealing, shoplifting, and sexual promiscuity. It is accepted generally that the incidence is higher in males; it is higher in low-income, minority, and culturally deprived groups; and it rises with industrialization and urbanization of a population. Distribution and incidence studies should be done in individual cities and regions to plan reasonable control programs in the classical public health sense of the phrase, since it is difficult to generalize about findings from one city to develop a public crime and delinquency prevention program in another city.

CAUSES AND PATHOLOGY

The general physician and the psychiatrist should consider a number of diagnostic possibilities in evaluating the possible cause of antisocial and dyssocial behavior. He should think in terms of conditions that must be met in order to explain the maladaptive behavior pattern of the individual child. Any illness or defect that contributes to misperception of the external environment or the inability to identify with healthy personalities or the inability to inhibit hyperaggressive or hyperlibidinal behavior may contribute to the delinquent behavior pattern. This pattern may be caused by mental retardation, epilepsy, brain damage, hyperkinesis, compulsion neurosis, childhood psychosis, and affect deprivation to name a few.

Past Studies

Specific social, psychological, and clinical psychiatric studies have broadened and extended ideas about causes and about the psychopathology of the entity. Although it is difficult to assess the relative contributions of the many individuals who have contributed to the growing understanding of the psychopathology of delinquency, Aichhorn clearly made the significant observations that made it possible for psychiatry to look beyond purely medical, biological, and inherited constitutional ideas for explanations. In his book *Wayward Youth*, he reported his observations about the wide variety of personality types that he encountered, and he described in vivid detail his clinical efforts to establish meaningful therapeutic relationships with such children. Eissler's *Searchlights on Delinquency* brought many of Aichhorn's ideas into sharp focus, including his observations of the connection between gross criminal behavior in the parent and delinquent behavior in the child.

The essential idea in the theories about delinquency in the early 1950's was that some defect or distortion in the conscience was present. Most experts thought that this abnormality was caused by a constitutional inability to develop an inner control system, by identification with a pathological parent or parent figure, by severe and cruel social and emotionally traumatic experiences in a particular social or cultural group, or by some combination of these factors. Healy and Bronner, pioneers in the field, thought that parental coldness was the major factor; however, Szurek and Johnson demonstrated in their clinical work the high probability of the existence of specific defects in the conscience.

The Johnson-Szurek thesis is that the antisocial behavior in the child is encouraged unconsciously by a parent or parents who participate in the process, vicariously gain pleasure in the child's deeds, and subtly carry out their own unconscious hostile and destructive feelings toward the child. As an illustration, a mother in a car pool laughingly admonished her son, who was biting another 5-year-old boy on his arm, by saying, "Johnny, don't bite him *so hard*." The mother remained quiet and detached when the other children came to the victim's rescue and began to pound Johnny quite actively. As knowledge about language (linguistics) and nonverbal behavior (kinesics) becomes more and more precise, it is evident that the child is learning constantly many of the beliefs, customs, and models of behavior he sees and experiences in his relationship with parents and peers.

Studies on pathological development have been paralleled by increasingly sophisticated studies on the child's moral development, as illustrated by the work of Woolf on moral development and the longitudinal personality development studies of Benjamin and others. We now recognize the importance of the nature and consistency of the mothering experience and later emotional experiences on the emerging character structure of the child.

Kaufman has made a number of important observations about the association between delinquency and loss of a significant love object by illness, abandonment, or death. The child develops grief and depression and continues a restless, angry search for the lost object, with resulting narcissistic and delinquent behavior.

Redl has made further contributions to the understanding of the psychopathology of antisocial behavior, especially in regard to his observation about the existence of unusual ego strengths in individuals with severe character defects. He suggested that, in the development of an adaptive pattern, certain personality functions become hypertrophic in order to compensate for the existing defect or deficiencies in character structure.

CURRENT IDEAS

Current ideas about the psychopathology in delinquent behavior usually contain these four elements: (1) The child feels significant emotional deprivation and strongly resents it. (2) The child cannot establish his own range of skills because his parents have not set the limits for him. (3) The parents, especially the mother, are very often overstimulating and inconsistent in their attitudes toward the child. (4) The child's behavior usually represents a vicarious source of pleasure and gratification for a parent and is often an expression of the parent's unconscious hostility toward the child, as the behavior is either overtly or covertly self-destructive to the child.

CLINICAL FEATURES

Antisocial and dyssocial types of behavior present a wide variety of clinical pictures to the psychiatrist. In the absence of confusion due to toxic or organic factors, the child is usually superficially tense when he is brought to a psychiatrist by a parent, court worker, or social worker. He is often sullen, defiant, and flippant; he answers questions briefly and in a matter-of-fact tone, uses denial extensively, and tends to minimize the reasons for the referral. Usually the child is reluctant to share inner emotional experiences, feelings, daydreams, jokes, favorite books, or television programs. He frequently projects personal difficulties onto a parent, sibling, or peer and almost always minimizes his involvement in any meaningful personal relationship. The usual and expected guilt feelings are frequently not present or are merely glossed over quickly without much evidence of personal discomfort.

DIFFERENTIAL DIAGNOSIS

Differential diagnosis requires a thorough and careful evaluation of the biological, psychological, and social factors that may contribute to the development of the maladaptive behavior. A detailed and accurate history, physical and neurological examinations, and psychological and various laboratory tests are required to evaluate brain damage, mental retardation, and similar causes of the behavior. Direct observation of the child in an interview and skilled evaluation of the parents and perhaps of the parents and child together may give valuable clues to the possibility of a conscience defect, affect deprivation, major and significant loss of a loved person, or a major connection between the parents' behavior and the child's symptoms of an antisocial nature.

An adequate differential diagnostic statement should make some attempt to define the interaction between the biological, psychological, and sociocultural forces and attempt to assess the possible precipitating causes and contributing factors to the behavior.

An 8-year-old girl was truant from school while her parents were away from home for two weeks. The girl was bright-normal intellectually, in good physical health, very closely attached to her father and her mother. The major past historical event was the death of her maternal grandmother, who was quite close to the child and to the mother, so that the child experienced a dual loss—of the grandmother and of the mother, who was depressed. The parents' trip was the first significant absence of the mother from the girl since the grandmother's death. The truancy seemed to be a cry to the mother, "Return home and take care of me." Probably, it also had oedipal fantasy meanings.

In the biological areas, the claims and statements about the significance and importance of abnormal electroencephalographic findings remain controversial and widely debated in professional circles—for example, the association between abnormal EEG clinical findings of the 14-per-second and 6-per-second cycle pattern and outbursts of uncontrolled aggression.

PROGNOSIS

The prognosis in treating antisocial and dyssocial reactions is poor to fair. Obviously, the prognosis is much better if the behavior pattern emerges for the first time after the child starts school, if it is recognized promptly, if proper and adequate intervention occurs, and if both the child and the parents are motivated to a genuine exploration of the underlying sources of the undesirable behavior.

The work of the Gluecks offers much hope, as they have pioneered the efforts to identify high-risk populations of predelinquents and to study the personality characteristics of children who seem to move on to a specific, repetitive type of delinquent behavior in later years. The sociological factors in delinquency have also been receiving increasing attention, and knowledge about them may well contribute to the understanding and management of the delinquent.

MANAGEMENT

The management of delinquency should be considered by general physicians and by psychiatrists in two areas—direct treatment and prevention.

Treatment involves a thorough diagnostic study and a definition of the extent and nature of the clinical problem. In most instances, it is necessary to work with the child and with the parents in a collaborative team approach, as advocated by Szurek, Kaufman, and many other writers. The individual therapy usually has some special features that vary considerably from most child psychotherapy.

1. The presence of early childhood defects or distortions makes it necessary for the therapist to present himself consistently as a warm, understanding person.

2. There should be a strong reality orientation in the collaborative process, with specific emphasis on requiring parents to set consistent and realistic limits on the child's behavior.

3. There should be recognition of the high probability that the parents may not want to give up their vicarious and usually unconscious pleasure in the child's behavior.

4. The specific therapeutic maneuvers called deceiving the deceiver, first advocated by Aichhorn and later elaborated on by Hoffer and others, may be useful if employed by a skilled therapist.

RESIDENTIAL TREATMENT

In many instances it is necessary to treat the delinquent in some type of residential institution to break the ties with the stimulative and destructive parent or to compensate in part for the absent or unavailable parental figure. Here, the multidimensional complexity of the dynamics of delinquency must be dealt with by an equally complex set of institutional factors. The personnel must somehow provide the food, clothing, shelter, health care, education, and opportunity for new learning through individual and group psychotherapy and thus try through the experiences in group living to give the child new and corrective emotional growth opportunities. Aichhorn's ideas about residential therapy have been reformulated by Redl and many others.

The treatment focus seems to be shifting away from punishment and retaliation to a greater focus on causes of problems of social isolation and social distance. The residential group attempts to focus on children with weak and inadequate personality resources and to provide them with some nurture to compensate for the individual child's feeling of being unloved earlier in his life.

PSYCHOTHERAPY

Whether in individual, group, or residential settings, it seems clear that most workers agree with Redl's idea that therapeutic work with delinquents, especially adolescents, requires much activity by the therapist. He suggests that it is important to keep the patient talking, to keep him active, to keep him reality-oriented as much as possible, to try to get enough of a relationship with the therapist so that the child can inhibit his tendency to act out impulses and to develop, instead, feelings of guilt, shame, remorse

—that is, more classical neurotic personal feelings.

Noshpitz has suggested several specific principles in psychotherapy with severe delinquents. First, the therapist should not encourage the emergence of instinctual behavior. ("You want to show me what you want to do; I want you to tell me instead.") Second, the therapist should recognize the child's fear of loss of control over his own impulses. Third, the therapist should recognize the child's inevitable wish for consistent limit-setting.

DRUGS

There is clinical evidence of better control of epilepsy and other behavioral disorders by new pharmacological anticonvulsants and tranquilizers. In the area of individual treatment, the possibility of using antidepressants in conjunction with specific brief abreactive psychotherapies, the use of phenothiazine drugs in the management of childhood psychoses, and the judicious use of milder tranquilizers and stimulants to aid in the management of hyperkinetic and impulse-ridden children seem promising. It is hoped that the current psychopharmacological revolution will have the same effect on psychiatric treatment as anesthesia did on surgery in that it may permit clinicians to use drugs more actively in children to interrupt maladaptive and faulty patterns of behavior, to facilitate the development of new and healthier patterns.

THE FUTURE

It seems reasonable to expect—with our rapidly urbanizing and industrializing country, the impact of the great increases in population in the world, the increasing facility of radio and television communication media, and the gradual liberalization of sexual and social morality—that the problems of dyssocial and antisocial behavioral patterns will remain important clinical matters for behavioral scientists in the future.

Physicians and psychiatrists—working in close collaboration with psychologists, sociologists, social workers, educators, judges, and many other personnel in the newly developing field of community mental health—must contribute their knowledge and skill in the evaluation, diagnosis, treatment, and management of delinquency in the years ahead. It is hoped that new therapeutic developments from psychologists and learning theorists will emerge, especially ideas about the use of operant conditioning. Group therapy approaches may be refined, which should prove to be useful with acute and less severe types of delinquency.

REFERENCES

Aichhorn, A. *Wayward Youth.* Viking Press, New York, 1935.

American Psychiatric Association. *Diagnostic and Statistical Manual of Mental Disorders,* ed. 2. American Psychiatric Association, Washington, 1968.

Cloward, R. A., and Ohlin, L. E. *Delinquency and Opportunity: A Theory of Delinquent Gangs.* Free Press of Glencoe (Macmillan), New York, 1960.

Cohen, A. K. *Delinquent Boys: The Culture of the Gang.* Free Press of Glencoe (Macmillan), New York, 1955.

Eisenberg, L., Gilbert, A., Cytryn, L., and Molling, P. A. The effectiveness of psychotherapy alone and in conjunction with perphenazine or placebo in the treatment of neurotic and hyperkinetic children. Amer. J. Psychiat., 117: 1088, 1961.

Eissler, K. R., editor. *Searchlights on Delinquency.* International Universities Press, New York, 1949.

Glueck, S., and Glueck, E. T. *Predicting Delinquency and Crime.* Harvard University Press, Cambridge, 1959.

Greenacre, P. Problems of acting out in the transference. J. Amer. Acad. Child Psychiat., 2: 144, 1963.

Healy, W., and Bronner, A. *New Light on Delinquency and Its Treatment.* Institute of Human Relations, Yale University, New Haven, 1936.

Johnson, A. M., and Szurek, S. A. The genesis of antisocial acting out in children and adults. Psychoanal. Quart., 21: 323, 1952.

Kaufman, I. Crimes of violence and delinquency in schizophrenic children. J. Amer. Acad. Child Psychiat., 1: 269, 1962.

Michaels, J. J. *Disorders of Character: Persistent Enuresis, Juvenile Delinquency, and Psychopathic Personality.* Charles C Thomas, Springfield, Ill., 1955.

Noshpitz, J. Notes on the theory of residential treatment. J. Amer. Acad. Child Psychiat., 1: 284, 1962.

Redl, F., and Wineman, D. *Controls from Within.* Free Press of Glencoe (Macmillan), New York, 1952.

Shaw, C. R., and McKay, H. D. Social factors in juvenile delinquency. In *National Commission on Law Observance and Enforcement, Report on the Causes of Crime,* vol. 2. United States Government Printing Office, Washington, 1931.

Woolf, M. The child's moral development. In *Searchlights on Delinquency,* K. R. Eissler, editor, p. 263. International Universities Press, New York, 1949.

CHAPTER NINE

Sociological Aspects of Juvenile Delinquency

MARCIA K. FREEDMAN, Ph.D.

INTRODUCTION

COHEN HAS FORMULATED the distinction between psychological and sociological approaches to crime by contrasting the psychological question "How do people become the kind of individuals who commit criminal acts?" with the sociological question "What is it about the structure of social systems that determines the kinds of criminal acts that occur in these systems and the way in which such acts are distributed within the systems?" Keeping this distinction in mind, one can see that the task of theory-building in sociology is enormous, in keeping with the size of the social system, which forms the basic unit of analysis. Sociological theories are, expectedly, far from parsimonious or elegant explanations; even so, clinicians may find them of use in patient management, since they help to illuminate the situations in which delinquent acts originate.

DEFINITION

The term "delinquency" suffers from looseness of definition. It may include all deviant behavior among the young—ranging from actions that are classed as criminal among adults, such as assault and robbery, to offenses that are strictly age-related, such as truancy, driving, drinking, and sexual activities. Furthermore, these deviant behaviors are punished differently in different communities and among different social classes. Explanations for given occurrences, therefore, tend to falter when applied to another set of circumstances.

EPIDEMIOLOGY

Delinquency has steadily increased in almost every country in the world. It appears to be a feature of modern industrial society, in which rapid technological change, high rates of mobility, and the conditions of urban life result in social instability, what sociologists refer to as *anomie* or normlessness. The concept of *anomie*, however, is insufficient to account for the various forms of deviance both between and within cultures.

CAUSES

Bordua, whose review of the subject is an excellent introduction, distinguishes two major approaches in theoretical attempts to explain delinquency on a sociological level—one that attributes delinquency and other manifestations of deviance to the lack of effective social controls, and the other that seeks to establish motivation for delinquent acts not in psychological terms but in cultural and subcultural terms.

LACK OF SOCIAL CONTROLS

Theories developed prior to World War II tended to reflect the first approach. Thus, Shaw and McKay's area approach was based in part on types of land use in big cities and the effects of immigration and urbanization on heterogeneous population groups. The resulting instability—that is, the lack of effective social control, particularly in the inner-city areas—was conducive to the formation of delinquent groups with their own codes of behavior, in which individual boys might find personal gratifications otherwise unavailable to them.

In such theories, the problem of motivation is not a serious consideration. It is assumed that motivation derives from participation in a specific social setting where the absence of controls and mutual support in the group are sufficient to perpetuate delinquent behavior. These early theories were subject to two major critical objections. First, if they accounted for the delinquent as an individual who came under the influence of a group, they failed to account for the origin of delinquent patterns. Second, they were limited in their application to disorganized urban areas.

SUBCULTURES

The second approach distinguished by Bordua arose in an effort to account both for motivation and for the origin of specific delinquent patterns. These patterns became theoretically formalized in the 1950's as subcultures. Cohen postulated the formation of delinquent subcultures as a response to status deprivation. Lower-class boys who cannot measure up to middle-class standards of success tend to seek a collective solution to their lack of social esteem and self-esteem through interaction with others similarly situated. The resulting delinquent subculture turns middle-class norms upside down and tends, therefore, to be malicious, hedonistic, and utilitarian. In effect, the subculture protects its members from their own recognition of the validity of middle-class judgment.

Cloward and Ohlin accounted for the formation of delinquent subcultures in a different way, which rests in part on Merton's theory of the origin of *anomie* itself. In this formulation, deviant behavior, of which delinquency is one form, results when some groups in the society do not have access to the means necessary to achieve cultural goals. Cloward and Ohlin's position is that the unjust distribution of opportunity, particularly with respect to income, drives lower-class adolescents either into the *illegitimate* opportunity structure (organized crime) or into alternate groups characterized by combat (gangs) or by retreatist behavior (drug-use subcultures).

Miller, whose work has focused specifically on gang delinquency, sees the origin of delinquent behavior in a distinctly lower-class culture rather than as any kind of reaction formation to middle-class culture or alienation from the dominant norms. Lower-class adolescents are simply reflecting the focal concerns of their milieu—trouble, toughness, smartness, excitement, fate, and autonomy.

Matza, taking quite a different tack, views delinquency from the perspective of classical criminology. In the legal context with which he is concerned, the most relevant factors are injustice and its consequences in indeterminate punishments, labeling, and resentment. In his view, delinquents are not necessarily committed to deviant *or* to conventional values. The beliefs that constitute the subculture of delinquency serve to permit rather than to compel delinquent acts. Their function is to neutralize the moral precepts of the law, and the result is drift between criminal and conventional action, with delinquent acts occurring only sporadically. Matza, in effect, reintroduced the lack of social controls as an important element in delinquency, albeit in more sophisticated form. The mere absence of controls does not necessarily result in delinquent behavior, but their absence provides the setting for activating the will to crime. "The conception of will," he said, "need not carry the whole burden of explanation, as it came close to doing in classical criminology. Instead, it may represent the missing element needed in social control theory by which the potential for delinquency implicit in drift can be realized."

VALUE OF SOCIOLOGICAL APPROACH

The theories mentioned here and other attempts to build total or partial explanations for delinquency are far more complex than this presentation may imply. At the risk of oversimplifying, however, it is worth pointing out certain of the shared strengths and weaknesses of sociological approaches to delinquency. By and large, as Bordua pointed out, they are incapable of empirical verification. Their theoretical constructs are highly abstract, and it is often difficult to specify the linkages between these abstractions and the particular acts that are said to flow from them.

EFFECTS OF INSTITUTIONS

The usefulness of sociological theories lies in their emphasis on the effects of institutions and in their stress on the collective nature of delinquency. It is well recognized, for example, that the occurrence of delinquency is often correlated with school failure. Failure in school is related not only to academic interest or ability but also to the successful negotiation of the school as a social system. There are critics like Friedenberg who deplore the school as a social system and who stress its purely custodial, antiexpressive controls. Nevertheless, those adolescents who succeed in school are generally those who are able to use the school as the locus of their peer group life as well as the setting for acquiring information and knowledge. To do this successfully generally requires acceptance of the norms and standards of the adults in the system.

Stinchcombe's study of expressive alienation among high school students led him to conclude that the open flouting of school authority (rebellion) occurs as a result of one or both of the following conditions: (1) when a student's future status does not depend on current performance— that is, among boys with limited academic ability or interest who see school as irrelevant to the low-status jobs they expect to hold; (2) when students, failing to accept the school's formal culture, in which they have inferior status, seek to usurp adult symbols. According to Stinchcombe, actual rebellion is most likely to occur among those school failures who are under the most pressure to succeed.

If an adolescent cannot or will not identify with the school, it does not necessarily follow that his only option is delinquent or deviant behavior. Nevertheless, the increase in years of schooling in the United States has had the effect of limiting alternatives for work. The consequent lengthening of the period of dependency is one aspect, but not the only one, of the social system that creates the conditions for delinquency.

ADOLESCENT GROUPS

In stressing collective behavior, sociological theories serve to focus on the adolescent group—what Matza calls the "situation of company"—which serves both as the locus of the action and as the source of mutual support. It has been commonplace, for example, to view the delinquent acts of middle-class suburban youths as individual aberrations of psychic origin. Recent reports, however, make it clear that, although the individual emotionally disturbed adolescent acts out in both the city and the suburb, a good deal of behavior that disturbs both kinds of communities takes place in groups.

The stress on situational factors also serves as a caution against assuming that all delinquent acts are the consequence of a deep commitment to delinquency, whether psychologically or sociologically induced. The fact that most delinquency and crime rates decline sharply with advancing age argues against such commitment. Furthermore, insofar as psychic disturbance is an element in delinquency, it may also be an element in other kinds of deviant, as well as in conforming, behaviors.

TYPOLOGIES

One promising new direction in the treatment of delinquency is the attempt to build typologies and classifications that combine demographic, cultural, and psychological factors. Types of delinquent behaviors and types of delinquents may then be more readily accounted for. In effect, some of the existing theories have set about this task from the opposite end—by first postulating the existence of one or more types and then attempting to explain them. It seems likely that these explanations may prove valuable—if not for the whole range of delinquent behaviors, at least for single types.

REFERENCES

Bordua, D. J. Sociological perspectives. In *Social Deviancy Among Youth*, p. 73. National Society for the Study of Education, Chicago, 1966.

Cloward, R. A., and Ohlin, L. E. *Delinquency and Opportunity*. Free Press of Glencoe (Macmillan), New York, 1960.

Cohen, A. K. *Delinquent Boys: The Culture of the Gang*. Free Press of Glencoe (Macmillan), New York, 1955.

Cohen, A. K. The study of social disorganization and deviant behavior. In *Sociology Today*, R. K. Merton, L. Broom, and L. S. Cottrell, Jr., editors, p. 461. Basic Books, New York, 1959.

Freedman, M. K. Background of deviancy. In *Social Deviancy Among Youth*, p. 28. National Society for the Study of Education, Chicago, 1966.

Friedenberg, E. Z. *Coming of Age in America*. Random House, New York, 1965.

Matza, D. *Delinquency and Drift*. Wiley, New York, 1964.

Miller, W. Lower class culture as a generating milieu of gang delinquency. J. Soc. Issues, 14: 5, 1958.

Shaw, C. R., and McKay, H. D. *Juvenile Delinquency and Urban Areas*. University of Chicago Press, Chicago, 1942.

Stinchcombe, A. I. *Rebellion in a High School*. Quadrangle Books, Chicago, 1964.

CHAPTER TEN

Sexual Deviations

HENRY W. WORK, M.D.

DEFINITION

DESPITE THE CENTRAL POSITION of sex in the developmental processes of the child, it is not common for younger children to be referred for psychiatric care because of a problem specifically related to sexuality. This becomes less true as the child increases in age. With adolescence, abnormal gratifications of sexual impulses increasingly cause parents to seek help. Even then, however, many of the symptoms that society feels are inappropriate in a sexual sense are more likely to receive attention through legal channels than through medical channels. This is particularly true of girls. The bulk of delinquent actions involving girls in most parts of this country consists of sexual activity of one sort or another.

Physicians may or may not regard such activity as abnormal. Normal sexual behavior is defined by society both as a general phenomenon and in relation to varying geographic customs. Since the cause of deviant sexual behavior is not fully known, it becomes a problem wherever it exceeds what is accepted as a norm for any particular community. In considering sexual problems, one must realize that sex is only one role in the gamut of human behavior. However, so crucial are the interpersonal activities connected with sex that deviant behavior in this role becomes of greater importance than many other activities of life.

Sexual deviation in children represents a greater degree of immaturity of emotional development than does similar pathology in adults. In another frame of reference, it can be considered an unusual continuation of the normal activity of one of the early periods of development. Since society decides whether sex shall be openly exhibited or carried on within the confines of the home, the outward aspects of sexuality must relate to the demands of society. When individual expressions of sex exceed community prohibitions, they may be considered sexual deviations.

EPIDEMIOLOGY

A number of sexual activities, such as masturbation, are extremely widespread in society. The fact that such expressions of sexual activity are universal does not mean that they are necessarily normal. In normal development the child goes through periods of genital sexual satisfaction, which include early masturbation, homosexual attachment to peers, and, finally, heterosexual strivings, leading toward intercourse with a mature partner of the opposite sex. Such normal development does not always proceed smoothly. If the child during his normal development subdues all his sexual impulses, the public is not particularly concerned. In this sense then, asceticism, with its complete inhibition of sexual drives, evokes only public apathy. However, when the child is overstimulated and develops an abnormal sexual appetite in any direction, heterosexual or homosexual, the promiscuity that evolves arouses public concern. The same is true of any of the deviations of sexual patterns occurring at any point during childhood.

Within this society there is a wide variety of sexual expectations and permissions. In general, the middle class sets the moral tone and has the most organized sexual codes. These consider the girl the more passive individual and are more likely to expect greater sexual activity on the part of the male. Some evidence suggests that these patterns are changing in the direction of earlier and more open expressions of heterosexual activity. Overt homosexuality has been fairly consistently frowned on in the American culture, especially by those parts of society that have only tolerated demonstrations of overt heterosexuality. Pathology, therefore, is brought to medical attention when it violates the mores of that segment of society in which it occurs.

The epidemiology of sexual abnormalities can also be understood as part of the relationship of the child to the parent as the child goes through the normal stages of development. Particularly important are those aspects of parent-child relations that seem to be stimulatory of sex activity. In certain classes of society, such stimulating activity may be quite common. Where parents and children live closely together, intercourse and other sexual activities are more commonly seen by the children, and in some instances there may be overt attempts on the part of the parents to stimulate sexual activity on the part of the children. Of increasing concern is the number of mothers who live alone with their sons and who in many unconscious aspects of living with them serve as stimulants to the child's developing sexuality. The practice of mothers sleeping with their sons may stir up an abnormal kind of sexual activity, without either being consciously aware of the distortion. This rouses up anxiety in the boy, which is often met by acting out and by increased amounts of sexual activity as he goes into his adolescence.

One etiological approach to homosexuality suggests that the condition is often noted in families with a dominating mother and a hostile or passive father who provides a poor masculine example. The boy, therefore, is stimulated by an excess of maternal or feminine contact during his early years and thus develops an abnormal concept of his own identity and his own sexual role.

Excessive inhibition of the childhood manifestations of sexuality also plays a role in the development of symptoms. The expressions of parental taboos often carry a message of intrigue and salacious delight, which serves to stir up the child. The value of the activity is increased by being forbidden. The development of specific deviations in these instances may relate to the emphasis used in suppressing the particular acts of the child. Coupled with more general anxieties, a mode of symptomatic expression is clearly demonstrated.

CLINICAL ASPECTS

The sexual deviations one sees in children are not grossly different from those seen in adults. Abnormal sexual patterns serve as an outlet for anxiety. Characteristically, the sexual pattern of deviate children includes a repetitive quality and a compulsive sort of activity to relieve the tension. The bulk of deviate sexual patterns in childhood appear to have a neurotic base. In many instances the child's sexual activity represents an unconscious wish of the parents.

The forms of sexual concern brought to the attention of the physician are similar to those described in adults. There is an important difference, however, since children are brought to a physician for help, with the complaints of a sexual nature being made by parents. When such children are brought in, the history is often very lurid and vivid. The parents complain of excess sexuality of an autoerotic nature, such as masturbation, or of a variety of homosexual and heterosexual contacts.

Especially when the history includes autoerotic complaints, one senses a gross exaggeration and fear on the part of the parents. The presenting parent, in most instances, is the mother. Characteristically, she presents the child with the statement that he masturbates frequently and that she is excessively concerned and feels that something drastic needs to be done. She often points out that she has herself made violent efforts to cut down on his masturbation by sewing up his pockets, threatening him, etc. It is often apparent in such cases that the child, although not innocent, is at least less involved in the symptomatic process than the mother making the complaints.

Similar stories continue to be true for children up through adolescence. At this time, stories of excessive heterosexuality are more common. It is important, therefore, to get an accurate history, one that reflects what is really going on in the child as opposed to the picture presented by the family. Similar stories are sometimes offered by teachers and others, who exaggerate minimal sexual activities and blow them up into major psychiatric disasters. Any child who begins to demonstrate sexual problems causes concern in those around him, and some of this concern reflects adult anxieties more than it does childhood practices.

In considering the sexual deviations of childhood, one must realize that overt sexual activity frequently accompanies psychotic conditions in childhood. In the regressive phenomena that are manifest in childhood schizophrenia, there may be sexual displays, obscene language, exhibitionism, etc. It is important to separate out these manifestations of an underlying psychotic condition from those neurotic situations wherein sexuality has become the primary symptom.

MASTURBATION

Masturbatory activities begin extremely early in life. Children during the second year are frequently observed playing with their genitalia and obtaining satisfaction from it. Parents are particularly prone to move in very quickly when any signs of genital autoerotic stimulation are seen. A certain number of children continue to masturbate more actively than others. Such masturbation is nearly always associated with some form of stimulating expression, conscious or unconscious, on the part of the parents. Masturbation occurs in small children as part of the psychotic process; however, during latency a certain number of children demonstrate more overt masturbation than others, and this causes considerable concern to teachers and other adults. At times, masturbation becomes part of an acting out behavior on the part of small gangs, particularly among boys. It is frequently associated with other evidences of sexual deviation, such as oral copulation. With the onset of adolescence, masturbation becomes a more overt sexual activity because of the end point of satisfaction that is then obtained. It is normal for younger boys to be taught about masturbation at this age.

Important in considering children who masturbate excessively is the guilt that is associated with it. This guilt is more or less implanted in our culture, although there is some evidence that it seems to be decreasing. Masturbation is a normal form of behavior and is regarded as pathological primarily because it may become excessive and because of the anxiety and concern that is related to it on the part of the child. Some younger children become excessively involved with masturbation and seem to have a compulsion to carry it on. These children usually demonstrate that they are masturbating because of anxiety. They freely talk about their inability to stop masturbating because of the pressure to carry it on. Such children are nearly always involved with other sexual activities at the same time.

HOMOSEXUALITY

Since nongenital, same-sex peer relations are a normal part of development, it is not always easy to determine when the child is deviating from the customary pattern. With the onset of adolescence, there is a stirring up of the relationships of children of both sexes, both to their own sex and to the opposite sex. The psychiatrist, then, sees homosexuality as a part of normal development and as a part of a confusion in the older child about his sexual identity. Whenever children are placed together in institutions, such as schools and residential homes, there is a stirring up of homosexual activity, manifested both by overt sexual relations and by the fears that children have about such relations.

Some children, however, demonstrate very early in life that they are uncomfortable with the opposite sex and have confused gender identifications. Evidence of such confusion is obvious in the boy who seems grossly attached to his mother and takes on a feminine type of habitus. He prefers to express his feminine relationship with individuals of his own sex and is concerned about relationships between sexes; however, he himself is more feminine than masculine in his identity. Although it is normal for the small boy to be dependent on his mother and cling to her, to continue this process beyond the normal oedipal resolution is obviously a sign of pathology.

TRANSVESTITISM

Although not necessarily related to homosexuality, transvestitism is a developmental phenomenon wherein the child is, in a sense, deprived of normal gender identity. Transvestitism in children is most commonly associated with a pathological relationship between the parent and the child of the opposite sex. A boy, for example, may be both consciously and unconsciously reared as a girl. He is placed in girls' clothing early and is offered only those satisfactions that are normal to the feminine sex. The boy, therefore, grows up with an exaggerated and deviant understanding of his own sexual role and appears to prefer, after a period of time, the habitus and activities of a girl. Such deviate developmental phenomena appear to be increasing, but they are also subject to prevention if one interferes early. The full meaning of transvestitism is currently under investigation, but it is not yet clarified.

ABNORMAL RELATIONS

Children are both the objects and the subjects of abnormal sexual relations. Unfortunately, many children are used by adults for their own sexual pleasure. Children are also encouraged, at times, to have relations with inanimate objects and lower animals. Such stimulation may in some instances be a form of abnormal activity on the part of the child that becomes deviant in terms of society's expectations of normality. Some children brought to psychiatric care because of excessive sexual activity give histories of early rape or other sexual exploitations on the part of adults. By virtue of the intense sexual stimulation offered to them, the children seek out all forms of sexual expression in order to carry out their compulsive needs to relieve their own tension. Consummated incest is most commonly observed between fathers and daughters, but a *forme frusté* occurs frequently between mothers and sons.

HYPERSEXUALITY

A certain number of children are brought in because of abnormal sexual desires. A 9-year-old child was not only masturbating frequently but attempting intercourse with animals and children of both sexes and a variety of ages. He clearly demonstrated the compulsive aspect of the whole process and was quite free in talking about his own needs to relieve tension. He had been brought up in a Mexican culture where there was a good deal of overt sexuality, but his concerns had not arisen until a second marriage by his father to a puritanically obsessive mother, who was concerned about his sexual activity and acted in many ways as a stress to drive him into more and more overt sexual action.

FETISHISM

In the process of separation of child from parent, it is frequently important—and normal—for the child to have an object related to the parent to which he can cling. This may be a blanket, a bottle, or a toy. Fetishism, however, and the use of objects to produce genital sexual satisfaction come much later, although it may, in many instances, be merely a translation from an earlier transitory object. The use of an inanimate object to enhance sexual satisfaction occurs normally in many adolescents. It is only when this becomes the primary choice of sexual satisfaction that the concept of sexual deviation is to be considered. It represents an immature solution of sexual identification and has to be handled as such.

PROSTITUTION

Some girls become involved in excessive sexual activity early in their adolescence. In almost all instances this comes about as a result of exploitation of the child by adults. Such exploitation is nearly always accompanied by some form of adult stimulation of the child. In many instances this is akin to the overactive sexuality described above. The actual course of such deviant behavior is an increase in the neurotic tension, which can only be relieved by excess sexual activity. Classically, these adolescents present a bland, hysterical personality pattern. The psychiatrist sees such deviant sexual behavior as a part of the total psychic activity of the individual. In this way, he is different from his legal colleague, who sees the symptom as a specific form of deviation from the practice of society and often as an insult against society. The medical problem is complicated, however, by the system that employs the girl and interferes with a clinical approach.

PROGNOSIS AND TREATMENT

Since the bulk of sexual deviations can be viewed as exaggerations of normal developmental processes, the physician must view them in the context of the overall personality. Although the prognosis for change of many of these sexual deviations is guarded, it is enhanced whenever the physician has the opportunity to see the child early, to try to understand the total family pattern in which he lives, and to put the symptom in perspective as part of the child's total life experience. The child is often obsessive and compulsive about these symptoms. Treatment, therefore, should include any form of psychiatric treatment that attacks such neurotic manifestations in their relationship to the total life experience of an individual. Management becomes a combination of psychiatric and legal approaches. The law often separates such individuals from society but, unfortunately, equally often places sexual deviates of all sorts together. The stimulatory aspect of sexual deviations becomes exaggerated by congregating individuals with similar problems.

The best opportunity to treat these individuals is when treating the neurotic process. Unfortunately, the older the child becomes, the less the desire for treatment in such sexual deviations is present. Younger children may be more responsive because the entire family can be brought into treatment, and the abnormal relationships of the family situation may be brought out into the open and possibly dissipated.

There is no clear agreement on the part of psychiatrists as to how sexual deviates should be handled. To some extent this reflects not only the intrinsic pathology but also the impact of this pathology on society. Since therapists themselves are a part of the community, they often reflect the moral values of the community, and sexual deviations are particularly susceptible to being viewed with moral implications. The treatment, however, continues to be that of understanding the meaning of the symptom to the individual, understanding the compulsion and its repetitious activity, and attempting to break up the satisfying aspect of the process in order to relieve the individual's tension.

REFERENCES

Bender, L., and Grugett, A. E. A follow-up report of children who had atypical sexual experience. Amer. J. Orthopsychiat., 22: 825, 1952.

Harrison, S. I. A girl reared as a boy. J. Amer. Acad. Child Psychiat., 4: 53, 1965.

Henry, G. W. *Sex Variants*. Hoeber Medical Division, Harper & Row, New York, 1948.

Himelhock, J., and Fova, S. F. *Sex Behavior in American Society*. W. W. Norton, New York, 1955.

Holemon, R. E., and Winokur, G. Effeminate homosexuality: a disease of childhood. Amer. J. Orthopsychiat., 35: 48, 1965.

Money, J. Hermaphroditism. Bull. Johns Hopkins Hosp., 97: 284, 1955.

Parsons, T. Age and sex in the social structure of the United States. In *Personality in Nature, Society and Culture*, C. Kluckhohn and H. A. Murray, editors, p. 269. Alfred A. Knopf, New York, 1953.

Reinhardt, J. M. *Sex Perversions and Sex Crimes*. Charles C Thomas, Springfield, Ill., 1957.

Sklansky, M. A. The management of puberty and sex in adolescence. In *Emotional Problems of Childhood*, S. Liebman, editor. J. B. Lippincott, Philadelphia, 1958.

Sperling, M. A study of deviate sexual behavior in children. In *Dynamic Psychopathology in Childhood*, L. Jessner and E. Pavenstedt, editors, p. 221. Grune & Stratton, New York, 1959.

Taylor, G. R. *Sex in History*. Thames and Hudson, London, 1962.

CHAPTER ELEVEN

Addiction and Alcoholism

ALFRED M. FREEDMAN, M.D., and
ETHEL A. WILSON

INTRODUCTION

ALTHOUGH PRECISE STATISTICS are unavailable, there is general agreement among medical, law enforcement, and other interested personnel that the number of children and adolescents using addictive substances has risen sharply in the two decades after the end of World War II.

Present-day addiction among young people is characterized by the use of a variety of substances—sometimes sequentially, sometimes simultaneously. It is not opiate addiction per se that is most characteristic at this time but the addictive behavior with which many children and adolescents respond to the stresses, both objective and subjective, to which they are subjected. Remarkable ingenuity has been displayed by children and adolescents in discovering unlikely substances that produce intoxication or other desired psychic effects and often lead to addiction.

ADDICTIVE SUBSTANCES

The simultaneous use of a wide variety of addictive substances has been observed among adolescents admitted to narcotic addiction treatment centers in metropolitan hospitals. Patients admitted for detoxification are commonly using heroin, amphetamines or barbiturates or a combination of the two, and codeine-containing cough medicines at the same time. Detoxification under these circumstances must be accomplished with particular care, since withdrawal from barbiturates, particularly, may be hazardous unless done very gradually and under careful medical observation.

Opioids

The vast majority of American addicts in recent years have used heroin primarily, with morphine, meperidine, and other opioids following in that order. It has been observed that among many adolescent addicts the withdrawal symptoms occurring on discontinuance of heroin use are so mild that they have obviously been using greatly diluted heroin. Such addicts are said to be addicted to the needle.

Marihuana

Although many young people who become narcotics addicts actually begin the use of heroin by the age of 16, a large proportion have used marihuana before becoming heroin addicts. The marihuana cigarettes commonly used today are prepared from the flowering tops of the hemp plant cannabis. It is known that marihuana differs from the opiates in that tolerance and physical dependence do not develop with its use and withdrawal symptoms do not appear on its discontinuance. The effects of the drug result from a relaxation of inhibitions, as is the case with alcohol.

Law enforcement officials have for many years considered the use of marihuana to be responsible for much criminal activity, but a number of studies of its use did not reveal a positive relation with violent crime. A group of marihuana users studied some years ago revealed that 13 per cent of the group began their use of the drug prior to adolescence, 64 per cent started between 12 and 17 years of age, and 13 per cent in their early twenties. The median age of original addiction was 15.3 years. The generally accepted knowledge of the use of marihuana by college and university students characterizes it as a significant adolescent activity at present, as it obviously has been for some time.

Amphetamines

Amphetamines have been used for therapeutic purposes, particularly in cases of narcolepsy, epilepsy, depression, behavior disturbances in brain-damaged children, obesity, and certain neurological disorders. Their addictive potential is now well-recognized. The use of amphetamines by students and certain groups of workmen, particularly truck drivers, to induce wakefulness is well known. However, their apparently widespread use, alone and in conjunction with other drugs, as part of the total addictive pattern, socially and psychiatrically, is more recent. Further, it is apparently world-wide, being prevalent in the Eastern as well as the Western hemisphere.

Barbiturates

The barbiturates, like the amphetamines, are known to be widely used by addicted adults, but there is now evidence of their substantial use by young heroin addicts. Many adolescents refer to their use of "goof balls," a term usually describing a combination of an amphetamine and a barbiturate.

Proprietary Drugs

Proprietary drugs, particularly cough medicines containing codeine and substantial amounts of alcohol, are a relatively easy path to addiction. Among hospitalized adolescent addicts it has been found that tremendous quantities of such drugs have been taken either prior to or simultaneously with heroin.

Hallucinogenic Drugs

Experimentation with hallucinogenic drugs, which alter sensory perception and produce hallucinations, has been conducted by adult intellectuals for some years. Quite recently, however, the use by university students of such substances as lysergic acid diethylamide (LSD-25), mescaline or peyote, and psilocybin has markedly increased. Such drugs have potential value in the exploration of altered states of consciousness if used under carefully controlled experimental conditions. There are, however, serious risks involved in their use, for they may precipitate psychosis, have serious side effects, or lead to addiction to other drugs.

Stramonium

Stramonium, a drug formerly used as a specific in treating asthma, has apparently been discovered by adolescents and used for intoxicative purposes.

Although the drugs enumerated above are most generally used by adolescents and young adults, a number of substances with intoxicating and addictive powers have been discovered by quite young children.

Glue

Glue-sniffing has become sufficiently common within a few years to warrant legal action against the sale of glue to minors in several cities. The glue used in making model airplanes is both a stimulant and an intoxicant, and its use can have serious toxic effects. Superficial inquiry indicates that there are hundreds of glue-sniffers, ranging in age from 8 to 14, in one small area of New York City. Records of arrests for glue-sniffing indicate sharp increases in other American cities as well.

Gasoline

Gasoline addiction in children has been reported but may be much more common than is generally known. It has recently been recognized as a matter for concern by the welfare and legal authorities in some of the developing nations of Africa. It is logical that so common and easily available an intoxicant should be used where there is not likely to be money for the purchase of drugs or similar substances. Automobiles can be found anywhere.

ALCOHOL

Alcoholism is generally considered an adult disorder that develops over a period of many years. However, a number of studies indicate that the use of alcohol by adolescents and young people is very common. Whether it is accurate to refer to children or adolescents as alcohol addicts is questionable, particularly since the classification of even adult users of alcohol is very complex. However, an increasing number of young people are arrested and convicted of drunkenness or related charges in many parts of the world today, and some young people have clearly reached a state of dependency on alcohol.

TOBACCO

Cigarette smoking, the near universal addiction of the mid-twentieth century, has been described as common among 9-, 10-, and 11-year-old children, and adolescents of 18 or 19 are already heavy smokers.

EPIDEMIOLOGY

A limited number of studies have been made of the incidence and prevalence of addiction and the distribution of narcotics addicts in the United States. Since most data are available from the records of law enforcement agencies and hospitals to which addicts have been admitted, the data, incomplete as they may be, provide information largely on adolescents and adults. A broad study of narcotics use among adolescent boys was done by a group at New York University between 1952 and 1956 (Chein et al.). Available for study were the records of all boys between the ages of 16 and 21 who had in the period 1949 to 1952 come to the attention of some official city agency in connection with narcotics. The list comprised 1,844 boys who had been involved in the use, possession, or sale of drugs.

Groups of boys interviewed during this research provided specific information on the steps that had led to addiction or, in the case of nonusers, had resulted in their rejection of drug use. Most of the users had heard about heroin before they actually had an opportunity to try it, usually at about 15 years of age. By that time, most of them had already seen someone inject or snort heroin. For most boys the first opportunity to use the drug came at about the age of 16 or 17, but a sizable group were 14 or less when this occurred. Sixteen seemed to be the age at which the boys were most likely to become users, with a greater proportion going on to regular use from this age group than from those who were either younger or older than 16 at first try.

Of the boys who served as a control group for the study—those who did not become users—40 per cent had also been given the opportunity to try heroin between the ages of 15 and 17, but none of them did so. The importance of learning what factors differentiated these boys from the previous group cannot be overemphasized. The authors of the study suggested that among the factors that did influence the nonusers were age; pertinent information about the result of drug use, which had a deterrent effect; and the boys' interpretation of the attitude of significant adults to drug use.

The urban neighborhoods in which drug use flourished, according to the above study, were the most underprivileged, crowded, and dilapidated areas of the city. They were further characterized by the lowest levels of income and education and the greatest breakdown of normal family structure.

Another study of drug use among juveniles and young adults conducted in Chicago at about the same time as the New York study revealed a similar situation. The areas in which the highest concentration of heroin addicts was found were also characterized by the highest rates of other social problems—low family income, low social status, deteriorated housing, a high proportion of recent migrants to the city, absence of effective community organization, high rates of adult crime, and lack of family and community control over the conduct of young persons. Because this group of heroin users seemed to have indulged in delinquent behavior before becoming addicted and did not commit crimes of a more serious nature after addiction, it was concluded that their delinquency was not a result of heroin addiction but a reflection of the same interests and problems that had led to drug use.

The data provided by the above studies is to a great extent equally valid today, but there is sufficient evidence to conclude that changes have occurred in the past 15 years, not only in the number or proportion of juveniles using drugs but also in the socioeconomic strata from which such users are drawn. There appears to be a steady increase in the number of arrests of young university students for possession, use, or sale of drugs of all varieties. Newspaper reports exposing such activities in wealthy suburbs of American cities are now quite frequent. Such information only emphasizes the complex causes of drug addiction and clearly destroys the validity of assigning complete responsibility to low socioeconomic class, lack of educational opportunity, abnormal family life, or a particular kind of addict personality. Although all these factors and, in all probability, physiological ones as well enter into the development of addiction, it must be recognized that addictive behavior has multifactorial origins, and disciplined scientific investigation is required for their elucidation.

TREATMENT

The difficulties in successful treatment of drug addicts have been demonstrated many times and over a prolonged period of time. Most pertinent in a discussion of young addicts is the study done by the Columbia University School of Public Health in 1957 (Alksne et al.). This was a follow-up of dischargees from Riverside Hospital, established in New York in 1952 for the treatment of addicts under 21 years of age. Of 147 dischargees interviewed, only 19 per cent were seen outside a prison or a hospital. Only 5 per cent of the 147 had abstained from the use of drugs after leaving the hospital. The 147 ex-patients were all who could be located of a total of 247 who had been admitted to the hospital in 1955. It was ascertained that 11 of the 247 were dead, an unusually high death rate for this age group. It seems that the majority of these deaths were due to overdoses of narcotics. It is also known that among addicts of all ages there is a high incidence of infectious diseases attributable to the use of shared unsterile needles for injecting heroin—such diseases as malaria, tetanus, syphilis, bacterial and mycotic endocarditis, and infective hepatitis.

Because of the demonstrated failure of most treatment programs for addicts, it becomes necessary to recognize that the emphasis on institutional programs, all of which have had as their goal complete abstinence from narcotics, may be misplaced. In the case of children and adolescents, certainly, it is difficult to accept maintenance on drugs of any type as a satisfactory aim, although that is now being seen as an experimental possibility for some adults. The aim of a treatment program designed for children should be not only withdrawal from the use of drugs but social and medical rehabilitation that leads to integration into the established institutions of society—school and employment.

Since the child's voluntary indulgence in glue-sniffing, gasoline inhalation, or marihuana smoking is apparently an attempt to withdraw from the real world in which he finds himself, one must accept the fact that basic changes in that world would contribute to a greater willingness by the child to experience and grow in it. However, basic social change occurs slowly, and the glue-sniffer cannot be put into a deep freeze while that is occurring.

There must be a careful examination of the society in which addiction develops and spreads. Attempts must be made to provide for children those social institutions, particularly schools and recreation, that engage them in experiences from which they do not seek to escape. At the same time, those children who, for whatever reason, have succumbed to drug use must be provided medical and psychiatric care that is realistically oriented to this disorder. The changes in patterns of drug use, the increasing involvement of young people from all socioeconomic classes, and the movement of drug dependence downward into ever-younger groups of children suggest the widening dimensions of the problem.

REFERENCES

Alksne, M. A., Trussell, R. E., Elinson, J., and Patrick, S., *A Follow-up Study of Treated Adolescent Narcotics Users.* Columbia University School of Public Health and Administrative Medicine, New York, 1959.

Allentuck, S., and Bowman, K. M. The psychiatric aspects of marihuana intoxication. Amer. J. Psychiat., 99: 248, 1942.

Bell, D. S., and Trethowan, W. H. Amphetamine addiction. J. Nerv. Ment. Dis., 133: 489, 1961.

Bromberg, W. Marihuana, a psychiatric study. JAMA, 113: 4, 1939.

Bromberg, W., and Rodgers, T. C. Marihuana and aggressive crime. Amer. J. Psychiat., 102: 825, 1946.

Bruun, K., and Hauge, B. *Drinking Habits among Northern Youth.* Pub. No. 12. Helsinki Finnish Foundation for Alcohol Studies, Helsinki, 1963.

Charen, S., and Perelman, L. Personality studies of marihuana addicts. Amer. J. Psychiat., 102: 674, 1946.

Chein, I., Gerard, D. L., Lee, R. S., and Rosenfeld, E. *The Road to H.* Basic Books, New York, 1964.

Clinger, O. W., and Johnson, N. A. Purposeful inhalation of gasoline vapors. Psychiat. Quart., 25: 557, 1951.

Cohen, A. K. The study of social disorganization and deviant behavior. In *Sociology Today*, R. K. Merton, L. Broom, and L. S. Cottrell, Jr., editors, p. 461. Basic Books, New York, 1959.

Cohen, S. *The Beyond Within: The LSD Story.* Atheneum, New York, 1964.

Dean, E. S. Self-induced stramonium intoxication. JAMA, 185: 882, 1963.

Drug Addiction Among Young Persons in Chicago. Illinois Institute for Juvenile Research and the Chicago Area Project, Chicago, 1953.

Easson, W. M. Gasoline addiction in children. Pediatrics, 29: 250, 1962.

Elkes, J. The dysleptics: note on a no-man's land. Compr. Psychiat., 4: 195, 1963.

Farnsworth, D. L. Hallucinogenic agents. JAMA, 183: 878, 1963.

Freedman, A. M., and Wilson, E. A. Childhood and adolescent addictive disorders. Pediatrics, 34: 283 and 425, 1964.

Glaser, H. H., and Massengale, O. N. Glue-sniffing in children. JAMA, 181: 300, 1962.

Hampton, W. H. Observed psychiatric reactions following use of amphetamine and amphetamine-like substances. Bull. N. Y. Acad. Med., 37: 167, 1961.

Harms, E. Drug addiction wave among adolescents. New York J. Med., 62: 3996, 1962.

Jacobziner, H., and Raybin, H. W. Glue-sniffing. New York J. Med., 62: 3294, 1962.

Jellinek, E. M. *The Disease Concept of Alcoholism.* Hillhouse Press, New Haven, 1960.

Kiloh, L. G., and Brandon, S. Habituation and addiction to amphetamines. Brit. Med. J., 2: 40, 1962.

McCarthy, R. G. *Teen-agers and Alcohol.* Rutgers Center of Alcohol Studies, New Brunswick, 1962.

Merry, J., and Zachariadis, N. Addiction to glue-sniffing. Brit. Med. J., 2: 1448, 1962.

Murphy, H. B. M. The cannabis habit. Bull. Narcotics, 15: 15, 1963.

Straus, R., and Bacon, S. D. *Drinking in College.* Yale University Press, New Haven, 1953.

United States House of Representatives. Subcommittee on Narcotics. *Report* to the House Committee on Ways and Means on the Illicit Traffic in Narcotics, Barbiturates and Amphetamines in the United States. United States Government Printing Office, Washington, 1956.

Wishik, S. M. Should our children pay for the cigarette commercials? Pediatrics, 31: 535, 1963.

CHAPTER TWELVE

Psychoses: I. Clinical Features

LEON EISENBERG, M.D.

HISTORY

A BRIEF HISTORICAL NOTE may serve to emphasize the recency of the renaissance of interest in childhood psychosis. Though the term "dementia praecox" was coined in 1860 by Morel to describe a psychosis in a 14-year-old boy, relatively little attention was given to the form of the earliest manifestations of dementia praecox by subsequent students of the disorder. Kraepelin is often cited as stating that onset occurred before the age of 10 in 3.5 per cent of 1,054 patients he reported. These were, however, retrospective diagnoses, and the differentiation between premorbid personality trends and the onset of psychosis per se was a matter of uncertain and arbitrary judgment from the history supplied to the physician. Bleuler, with a more specific concept of schizophrenic psychopathology, stated in 1911: "With a relatively accurate case history, one can trace back the illness to children, even to the first years of life, in at least 5 per cent of cases." The limitations of his experience with children are apparent in the further comment:

> At the present time we know of no differences between the infantile and other forms of the disease. . . . The prognosis of those cases in which the onset of the illness occurred before puberty does not appear to be too poor for the next few years . . . ; however, the case histories of adults admitted to the hospital show that at least part of these early cases relapse and then usually become markedly deteriorated.

The first specific consideration of childhood schizophrenia as a separate category dates from the earliest papers (1905–1908) of deSanctis, who proposed the term "dementia praecocissima" to designate this clinical subdivision. However, deSanctis included not only cases of childhood schizophrenia as the term is employed today but also others who had chronic brain syndromes and severe mental deficiency. Such wastebasket diagnoses, the loose usage of "childhood" to include onset as late as 16 or 17 years of age, and the preoccupation of psychiatrists with hospitalized adults—all contributed to a growing disbelief in the reality of schizophrenia in childhood. As recently as 1942, Bender wrote: "There are those who do not believe in childhood schizophrenia, not having seen a case. At the best, none of us have seen very many cases in which we could make a definite diagnosis, not knowing the acceptable criteria." Yet, not more than ten years later, Despert could write: "Although there are still people who believe that there is no such thing as schizophrenia in childhood, generally speaking we might say that the concept of childhood schizophrenia has passed from non-recognition to over-recognition."

Despert's warning against overrecognition or misdiagnosis has even greater cogency today, when terms like "autism" and "childhood schizophrenia" have entered the common parlance. The defective or brain-injured child who fails to be labeled psychotic at some way station in his parents' odyssey through outpatient and inpatient services is rare indeed. Thus, it seems appropriate to place emphasis on specificity in diagnosis—not as an obsessional exercise in pigeonholing but as a necessary precursor for systematic investigation of cause, course, and treatment.

CLASSIFICATION

Psychotic disorders are characterized by personality disintegration, faulty evaluation of external reality, impaired ability to relate to others, and ineffective work performance. Prominent manifestations include severe mood disturbance, incongruity between mood and thought, faulty stream of thought, delusions, hallucinations, and bizarre behavior. These descriptive terms devolve from the clinical study of adults; they serve as a general framework for the diagnosis in childhood but must be evaluated against age-appropriate behavioral norms for children. Failure to take developmental age into account can lead to false positives, based on spurious analogies between child and adult behavior, and to failure to recognize psychosis if the clinical picture in a child does not replicate the full syndrome seen in the adult.

Some child psychiatrists espouse the view that diagnostic differentiation within the group of severely disturbed children is neither useful nor possible. It is indeed true that there are cases in which no firm diagnosis can be made, but the great majority can be assigned to categories that have therapeutic as well as prognostic implications. The literature on childhood psychosis is replete with discrepancies in the research and clinical findings reported by different investigators; in large part, these differences stem from differences in diagnostic practices, which result in noncomparability of the populations under study. Since a diversity of disorders may present a clinical picture of psychosis, a tentative classification of psychotic disorders in childhood is set forth below.

I. Psychoses associated with impairment of brain tissue function
    A. Associated with intoxication (atropine, bromides, stramonium, cortisone, etc.)
    B. Associated with metabolic disorders (pellagra, amaurotic idiocy, etc.)
    C. Associated with degenerative disorders (Schilder's disease, dementia infantilis, etc.)
    D. Associated with infections (juvenile paresis, encephalitides, etc.)
    E. Associated with convulsive disorders (temporal lobe epilepsy, dysautonomia, etc.)
    F. Associated with trauma
    G. Associated with neoplasm
II. Psychoses without known brain tissue impairment
    A. Autistic psychoses
        1. Early infantile autism (Kanner)
        2. Symbiotic psychosis (Mahler)
    B. The schizophrenias
        1. Simple
        2. Acute undifferentiated
        3. Paranoid
    C. Psychoses associated with maturation failure
        1. Atypical child (Rank)
        2. Childhood psychosis (Szurek)
        3. Childhood schizophrenia (Bender)
        4. *Pfropfhebephrenia* (Weygandt and Kraepelin)
    D. *Folie à deux*
    E. Manic-depressive psychosis

Subclassifying the functional psychoses poses a difficult problem. No two authorities agree fully on the use of terms; some of the nonspecific diagnostic labels ("atypical child," "childhood psychosis") include conditions such as dementia infantilis, which this classification assigns elsewhere. The intent of this schema is to emphasize clinical specificity and to guide the student to an awareness of the differences in concept represented by the differences in labels. Subheadings A, B, D, and E in part II represent clinically definable and mutually exclusive categories. Subheading C is a residual category to cover terminology in disagreement with the principles of this classification but nonetheless meriting inclusion because of the frequency of their use.

PSYCHOSES ASSOCIATED WITH IMPAIRMENT OF BRAIN TISSUE FUNCTION

These disorders may mimic the clinical picture of the functional psychoses in all respects. They are usually differentiable by history, clinical features, and associated neurological and laboratory findings. Central nervous system pathology should be suspected in the presence of fulminating onset, marked disorientation, intellectual deterioration, memory impairment, and lability of affect. Only if the clinician is prepared to consider the presence of a central nervous system disease will he undertake specific diagnostic investigations. The identification of disorders subject to specific corrective measures can be life-saving for the patient. But even when the condition is one with a progressive and irreversible course, correct diagnosis is important in assisting the family and in sparing them futile and costly therapeutic endeavors. These disorders are covered in detail in the chapter by Laufer.

PSYCHOSES WITHOUT KNOWN BRAIN TISSUE IMPAIRMENT

These disorders differ clinically as well as neuropathologically from the syndromes associated with brain tissue impairment. *Consistent* structural or chemical abnormalities regularly associated with these clinical conditions have yet to be demonstrated; whether or not they can be ascribed to a psychogenic cause remains to be determined.

AUTISTIC PSYCHOSES

Early infantile autism. This was described by Kanner in 1943. The pathognomonic disorder was seen as "the children's inability to relate themselves in the ordinary way to people and situations from the beginning of life." The children did not withdraw from formerly existing participation with others, as is the case in schizophrenia, but rather from the start displayed an extreme autistic aloneness. Parents report that these children as infants failed to assume an anticipatory posture before being picked up and never displayed the molding that the normal child shows when cradled in his parents' arms. Parents, initially pleased by the child's goodness—that is, his ability to occupy himself for long periods without requiring attention—later become distressed by the persistence of this isolation when they observe that their arrival and departure are matters of indifference to the child.

The second distinctive feature noted by Kanner was failure to use language for the purpose of communication. In three of his original eleven cases, speech failed to develop altogether. The remaining children rapidly developed a precocity of articulation that, coupled with unusual facility in rote memory, resulted in the ability to repeat endless numbers of rhymes, catechisms, lists of names, or other semantically useless exercises. The parroting of words intellectually incomprehensible to the child brings into sharp relief the gross failure to use speech to convey meaning. The repetition of stored phrases and the presence of failure to recombine words into original and personal sentences give rise to delayed echolalia, pronominal reversal, literalness, and affirmation by repetition rather than by the use of "Yes."

A third characteristic is an anxiously obsessive desire for the maintenance of sameness, which results in marked limitation in the variety of spontaneous activity. These youngsters regularly display fear of new patterns and, once having adopted a pattern, incorporate it into the restricted set of rituals, which are endlessly iterated. Thus, a walk always has to follow the same course; bedtime to consist of a particular set of rituals; and repetitive activities like spinning, turning lights off and on, and flushing toilets occupy the child for long periods. Attempts to interfere with the pattern produce rage.

Fourth, the children display a fascination for objects, as distinct from their poor or absent relation to persons. So intense is this relationship that minor alterations in the arrangement of objects, not ordinarily perceived by the average observer, are at once apparent to autistic children, who exhibit panic until the change has been undone.

These children are separable from mentally retarded or brain-injured children by their good intellectual potential. In the children who speak, this can be discerned by the extraordinary, if perverted, use of language and the feats of unusual memory. In mute children, though the evidence is less persuasive, there is facility with performance tests, frequently at or above age level. Thus, Kanner has delineated a syndrome that is differentiated from childhood schizophrenia by virtue of detachment starting no later than the first year of life and from oligophrenia by evidence of good intellectual potential.

Infantile autism has become increasingly fashionable as a diagnosis but with concomitant dilution of its specificity. The mere presence of autistic phenomena, observable in many defective and brain-injured children, is regarded by some as establishing the diagnosis of infantile autism, even when associated findings point clearly to other primary disorders. In evaluating reports of etiological or therapeutic studies on autism, one must note the criteria by which the diagnosis has been established.

In a review of 100 cases of infantile autism seen on Kanner's service, few neurological or electroencephalographic (EEG) abnormalities and infrequent reports of complications of pregnancy or parturition were noted. Of the 200 parents, only 6 presented gross psychiatric abnormalities; of the 400 grandparents and 373 listed uncles and aunts, only 12 had come to psychiatric attention for major mental illness. Similarly, of the 131 known siblings, only 3 were autistic, and only 7 others displayed psychiatric disturbances.

The personality patterns of the parents revealed an unusually high percentage of obsessive, intelligent, and cold individuals; 87 per cent of the fathers and 70 per cent of the mothers had been to college, proportions greatly in excess of those characterizing a random sample of other private patients. A large number of the fathers were professional people who had attained distinction in their fields of endeavor. Although it is tempting to speculate that the emotional detachment, obsessiveness, and coldness of the parents may in some way be related to the syndrome in the children, it is noteworthy that at least 10 per cent of the parents did not fit the stereotype, and even those who did fit it have borne and reared other normal children. Moreover, similarly rigid parents have been seen who had not produced autistic offspring. If there is a relationship between child and parent characteristics, its significance is not immediately evident. Both may be manifesting the action of genetic factors, fully apparent in the child but only partially expressed in the parent; parental behavior may have induced the behavior in the child; or the experience of living with a severely disturbed child may have led his parents to withdraw from involvement with him.

Although the Hopkins studies have been negative with respect to organic abnormality, other investigators have drawn different conclusions. Knobloch and Grant stated that neurological disorders underlie the majority of cases of autism and schizophrenia in childhood. Schain and Yannet have described fifty cases of autism from the Southbury Training School; they reported a high incidence of seizures, EEG abnormalities, and associated neurological findings, but there is considerable question as to the appropriateness of the diagnostic allocation. White et al. have reported a high percentage of EEG abnormalities (53 per cent) under promazine sedation in childhood schizophrenics, an equally high percentage in nonpsychotic behavior disorders, but only 10 per cent among neurotic and none among control cases. These studies, together with a number of reports on small groups of autistic children with gross EEG or neuropathological disorders, are open to serious question as to diagnostic specificity.

Ferster has developed an interesting and provocative hypothesis on the genesis of autistic behavior by using an operant conditioning model. He provided a logical framework for therapeutic programs based on enlarging the autistic child's limited behavioral repertoire by positive reinforcement methods. Ferster's model has the striking virtue of being subject to experimental analysis. Research currently under way by Ferster and his associates is designed to evaluate the clinical efficacy of a therapeutic program based on his hypothesis.

A follow-up study of 63 autistic children demonstrated that the presence or absence of useful language by the age of 5 differentiated sharply between two groups of autistic children. Of the 30 children without effective speech, only 1 child subsequently attained a marginal social adjustment, and this child has since required psychiatric hospitalization. In contrast, about half of the 31 children with language have been able to maintain a social adjustment in the community and have progressed in school at about age level. Even the successful youngsters, however, continue to be characterized by an impoverishment of human relationships, a lack of social competence, and a schizoid personality. Many are painfully aware of their own maladroitness in interpersonal relations and tend to seek out solitary occupations. Outcome seemed to be more a function of the severity of the disorder than of the type or amount of treatment. However, it should be emphasized that efforts at psychiatric care—including residential placement, psychotherapy, and psychotropic drugs—are strongly indicated, pending the demonstration of specifically effective treatment modalities.

Symbiotic psychosis. Mahler has proposed that psychoses of early childhood should be divided into autistic and symbiotic varieties. The symbiotic disorders are characterized by later onset and by symptoms of anxiety, which may mount to panic when attempts are made to separate the child from his mother; that is, the psychopathology in such cases reflects failure at self-differentiation after the initial developmental stage of relating to the mother had been attained. If symbiotic psychosis is indeed a real clinical entity, it must be far less common than infantile autism, itself uncommon, in view of the infrequency of clinical reports.

The Schizophrenias

Among psychotic children there are a considerable number whose clinical manifestations meet the criteria set forth for the diagnosis of schizophrenia as it is seen in the adult. The term "schizophrenia" should be restricted to this group in view of the uncertainty about the relationship of the other psychotic syndromes in children to the adult schizophrenias. The term has been used in the plural, the schizophrenias, to emphasize the heterogeneity of the syndromes classified under this rubric. These schizophrenic reactions in childhood probably do not occur before the age of 8 years and are seen with increasing frequency as children approach adolescence.

The proposed subdivision into three types—simple, acute undifferentiated, and paranoid—reflects clinical experience in which the other types described in adults are either nonexistent or so rare as not to warrant listing here.

Psychoses Associated With Maturation Failure

This residual category is intended to accommodate a heterogeneous set of clinical syndromes embodied in terminologies at variance with this classification but so widely used as to require identification. With greater specificity of diagnostic practice, many cases currently labeled under this heading would be reallocated to the organic psychoses, to autism, or to schizophrenia.

The heterogeneity of the cases associated with maturation failure make impossible a meaningful comparison of etiological and therapeutic findings. Thus, whereas Bender reported a 40 per cent rate of schizophrenia among parents, Creak and Ini noted a low incidence of psychiatric abnormality in the parents of the psychotic children they have examined, a finding comparable to our observation among parents of autistic children. The one systematic search for chromosomal abnormalities in schizophrenic children thus far reported was completely negative.

Attempts to evaluate therapeutic results are confounded both by diagnostic uncertainties and by differences in criteria for outcome. Whereas Bender is persuaded of the value of electroshock, Clardy and Rumpf reported the contrary, based on observations of children earlier seen at Bellevue. Szurek reported, after intensive psychotherapy, a 14 per cent improvement rate among cases of childhood psychosis, whereas Brown found a 37 per cent improvement rate after intensive psychotherapy and therapeutic nursery care for atypical children. The overall figures from Hopkins and from Bellevue indicate that about one-quarter of the children were able to attain an adequate social adjustment in the community.

Atypical child and childhood psychosis. Rank and Szurek have indicated in their definitions for these terms that they do not consider it fruitful to differentiate among schizophrenia, chronic brain syndromes, mental defect, and severe neurosis in assigning cases to these categories, which appear to be coterminous; any child who displays severe developmental deviations with marked impairment of social adjustment appears to qualify for inclusion.

Childhood schizophrenia. According to Bender, childhood schizophrenia is "a clinical entity occurring in childhood before the age of 11 years which reveals pathology at every level and in every area of integration and patterning within the central nervous system, be it vegetative, motor, perceptual, intellectual, emotional, or social." The fundamental pathological process is taken to be a diffuse encephalopathy, an inference from clinical considerations, since there are no neuropathological reports. Bender suggested subclassification into three clinical types: the pseudo-defective or autistic regressive type; the pseudoneurotic or phobic, obsessive-compulsive, hypochondriac type; and the pseudopsychopathic or paranoid, acting out, aggressive antisocial type. Follow-up studies from Bellevue are reported to reveal that some two-thirds of the cases were diagnosed in later adolescence or adulthood as schizophrenic. There is, of course, the question about the independence of the second diagnosis insofar as knowledge of the earlier diagnosis may have influenced the clinician who saw the patient as an adult. However, it seems from these follow-up studies that a significant proportion of the cases classified as childhood schizophrenia by Bender display adult schizophrenic syndromes.

Pfropfhebephrenia. Kraepelin coined the term "hebephrenia engrafted upon defect" to characterize the psychotic states observed in a colony of mental defectives. Such disorders may represent: (1) psychosis and mental defect, both secondary to central nervous system disease; (2) deteriorated, functionally defective end states of originally psychotic children; and (3) psychotic episodes in primarily defective children. Bizarre mannerisms are frequent among the inmates of the traditional colonies for defectives; some represent the behavioral consequences of the neglect and deprivation so frequently accorded these unfortunate children; others may be part of the basic central nervous system disease. But even these latter symptoms may be correctable by appropriate environmental manipulations, since every living organism can learn. Modification of the aberrant behavior may free the child for the adoption of more constructive traits, or it may serve the purpose of making him more acceptable in the social group by removing characteristics that stigmatize him.

FOLIE À DEUX

Folie à deux is an induced or imposed psychosis in which a relatively healthy person shares the symptoms of a psychotic person with whom he has a close relationship. The disorder appears in the context of an intense relationship between two persons, the great majority of which are family relationships. By definition, the relatively healthy partner is able to abandon the symptoms when separated from the psychotic partner.

MANIC-DEPRESSIVE PSYCHOSIS

True instances of this disorder in childhood are exceedingly rare. Anthony and Scott, in a scholarly review of the literature, were unable to uncover any instances in children younger than 11 who met the following criteria: a psychiatric state conforming to the classical clinical description, a positive family history, cyclothymic premorbid personality, periodicity, evidence of an endogenous illness in that cycles alternate with minimal reference to external events, psychotic severity, and current rather than retrospective assessment. Much of the controversy in the literature about the existence of depressive illness in childhood stems from a confusion of a psychodynamic interpretation of the meaning of symptoms with a clinical diagnosis based on overt behavior and longitudinal course. By the latter criteria, manic-depressive psychosis appears never to occur in early childhood and to be exceedingly rare prior to adolescence.

PROGNOSIS

The foregoing review will have made it evident that no overall statement about outcome is justified. For those disorders ascribable to defects in central nervous system function, the prognosis is that of the underlying organic disorder. For the functional psychoses, prognostic statements are just as difficult to offer, since it seems certain that in this category are entities of a wide variety of types. The field may in many respects be comparable to the state of mental deficiency fifty years ago, before the success of efforts to separate out the many different syndromes that share only the final common manifestation of defective intelligence.

TABLE I

Outcome of Childhood Schizophrenia

Author and Year	Number Recovered	Case Total
Before 1940		
Sukhareva (1932)	0	25
Grebelskaya-Albatz (1934)	1	22
Lurie et al. (1936)	1	13
Lutz (1937)	0	20
Potter and Klein (1937)	1	14
Creak (1937)	3	9
Despert (1938)	3	29
Total	9 (7%)	132
Since 1940		
Lurie et al. (1943)	4	17
Bender (1951)		
Shock-treated	36	143
Refused shock treatment	2	50
Eisenberg (1956) (autism)	17	63
Szurek (1956) (psychosis)	14	100
Brown (1963) (atypical child)	47	129
Total	120 (24%)	502

Rutter has drawn attention to the I.Q. score of the psychotic child as an important prognostic indicator. Despite the clinical impression of the unreliability of I.Q. testing in such children, he found a correlation of 0.80 between initial scores and those on follow-up. Moreover, the likelihood of clinical recovery seemed more related to I.Q. than to speech function, with recovery rare in children testing at less than 50. He suggests, and I believe correctly, that my earlier observations on the presence or absence of useful speech by age 5 as a predictor of outcome may have been "largely due to the high correlation between absence of speech and low intelligence."

A tabular comparison of the outcome of cases of childhood psychosis reported in literature before and after the year 1940 indicates the change in the concept with time. The much better results reported in the recent era suggest, in the absence of any evidence of specific treatment methods, that contemporary clinicians include cases previously given other diagnoses (see Table I).

CURRENT STATUS

The so-called functional disorders remain the subject of considerable dispute among competent and experienced clinicians. Resolution of the conflicting views awaits careful investigation based on new methods of study as well as greater conceptual clarity.

The argument for careful clinical specification of subtypes rests on therapeutic, etiological, and prognostic grounds. To evaluate the comparative effectiveness of current or future treatment methods, one must begin by delineating comparable populations and assigning them to control and experimental groups. The uses and the limitations of penicillin, for example, could hardly have been ascertained if clinicians had not been able to differentiate colds, pneumonias, and neoplasms. This thesis holds with even greater forcefulness for attempts to isolate causes. Abnormal metabolic findings that may characterize one clinical syndrome may be lacking in a second; if both are indiscriminately presented to the biochemist, his findings will be puzzling and inconsistent. If the clinician is to be able to offer meaningful prognoses to assist parents in planning for the care of their children, he must be able to differentiate disorders that have different likelihoods of favorable outcome. Differential diagnosis is no academic exercise; it is the very stuff of medicine.

REFERENCES

Anthony, J., and Scott, P. Manic depressive psychosis in childhood. J. Child Psychol. Psychiat., 1: 53, 1960.

Bender, L. Childhood schizophrenia. Nerv. Child., 1: 138, 1942.

Bender, L. Childhood schizophrenia. Psychiat. Quart., 27: 663, 1953.

Bleuler, E. *Dementia Praecox or the Schizophrenias*, J. Zubin, translator. International Universities Press, New York, 1950.

Book, J. A., Nichtern, S., and Gruenberg, E. Cytogenetical investigations in childhood schizophrenia. Acta Psychiat. Scand., 39: 309, 1963.

Brown, J. Follow-up of children with atypical development. Amer. J. Orthopsychiat., 33: 855, 1963.

Clardy, E. R., and Rumpf, E. M. Effect of electric shock treatment on children having schizophrenic manifestations. Psychiat. Quart., 28: 616, 1954.

Creak, M., and Ini, S. Families of psychotic children. J. Child Psychol. Psychiat., 1: 156, 1960.

Eisenberg, L. The autistic child in adolescence. Amer. J. Psychiat., 112: 607, 1956.

Eisenberg, L. The course of childhood schizophrenia. Arch. Neurol. Psychiat., 78: 69, 1957.

Eisenberg, L. The fathers of autistic children. Amer. J. Orthopsychiat., 27: 715, 1957.

Eisenberg, L., and Kanner, L. Early infantile autism 1943–1955. Amer. J. Orthopsychiat., 26: 556, 1956.

Ferster, C. B. Positive reinforcement and behavioral deficits of autistic children. Child Developm., 32: 437, 1961.

Kanner, L. Autistic disturbances of affective contact. Nerv. Child., 2: 217, 1943.

Kanner, L. Irrelevant and metaphorical language in early infantile autism. Amer. J. Psychiat., 103: 242, 1946.

Kanner, L. Problems of nosology and psychodynamics of early infantile autism. Amer. J. Orthopsychiat., 19: 416, 1949.

Knobloch, H., and Grant, D. K. Etiologic factors in "early infantile autism" and "childhood schizophrenia." Amer. J. Dis. Child., *102*: 535, 1961.

Mahler, M. S. On child psychosis and schizophrenia: autistic and symbiotic infantile psychoses. Psychoanal. Stud. Child, *7*: 286, 1952.

Rank, B. Intensive study and treatment of pre-school children who show marked personality deviations, or "atypical development" and their parents. In *Emotional Problems of Early Childhood*, G. Caplan, editor, p. 491. Basic Books, New York, 1955.

Rutter, M. The influence of organic and emotional factors on the origins, nature and outcome of childhood psychosis. Develop. Med. Child Neurol., *7*: 518, 1965.

Schain, R. J., and Yannet, H. Infantile autism: an analysis of 50 cases and a consideration of certain neurophysiologic concepts. J. Pediat., *57*: 560, 1960.

Szurek, S. A. Psychotic episodes and psychotic maldevelopment. Amer. J. Orthopsychiat., *26*: 519, 1956.

White, P. T., DeMyer, W., and DeMyer, M. EEG abnormalities in early childhood schizophrenia. Amer. J. Psychiat., *120*: 950, 1964.

CHAPTER THIRTEEN

Psychoses: II. Treatment

RUTH L. LAVIETES, M.D.

INTRODUCTION

THE THERAPY of childhood psychosis is complicated by three factors. One is the variety of behavioral syndromes subsumed under this diagnosis. If this is indeed one disease, it encompasses behaviors that range from virtual unawareness of the human environment to a disposition toward disorganized thinking under environmental stress. A second factor is the considerable difference of opinion as to the cause, since therapeutic choice depends on the causal theory held by the therapist. The third factor is the poor prognosis, especially with the severely psychotic child; this causes therapists to engage in therapeutic experimentation, with each new approach appearing to have initial success. Although various therapeutic interventions are discussed separately here, they are usually combined. It would not be unusual for a schizophrenic child to receive elements of all of the therapeutic modalities discussed below, although usually one or another receives greater emphasis.

In the discussion that follows, the designation "childhood psychosis" is used to mean psychosis without known brain tissue impairment. This includes the form appearing in early infancy (early infantile autism), later infancy (symbiotic psychosis), later childhood (childhood schizophrenia), and adolescence (schizophrenia).

PSYCHOTHERAPY

The first efforts at the psychotherapy of childhood schizophrenia were made in the late 1940's. Initially, psychotherapeutic techniques were derived from the treatment of neurotic children. When these proved fruitless, particularly in the more severely disturbed children, therapists experimented with innovative methods, which were initially based on trial and error and subsequently brought into existing theoretical frameworks. Since psychotic children tended to collect in special centers set up for their study and care, therapeutic techniques of varying types became established in these separate centers, which have, by and large, continued to refine their methods. As a result of this and the generally poor prognosis, there is no systematized psychotherapy of childhood schizophrenia, and varying methods are found from one center to another.

The type of therapeutic intervention employed in childhood psychosis depends on the therapist's etiological theory of the disease. For those who espouse vigorous psychotherapy, etiological emphasis lies in deficient life experience of the child, due either to constitutional inability to elicit or benefit from normal experience or from a pathological environment. Among the theories underlying psychotherapy are the following: (1) The child retreats as a result of gross emotional deprivation or painful contact with people. (2) The child is unable to erect an inner maternal image and thus cannot develop ego or superego, cannot use identification or introjection, and cannot establish a sense of reality. He therefore withdraws to an omnipotent world, which constitutes an attempt at restitution of the lost or never achieved maternal object. (3) Autism is a psychotic defense in which the ego restores oneness with the object as a delusional defense against separation from the mother. (4) The absence of crucial experience at some critical period causes an inability to endow human beings with appropriate significance.

There is considerable conflict of opinion as to the ultimate effectiveness of psychotherapy for psychotic children, although there is little doubt that it frequently results in symptomatic improvement. Autistic children may achieve socialization, enabling them to function outside of a special institution, while retaining considerable personality limitation and ego vulnerability. The resolution of intrapsychic conflict produces relief of anxiety or reduction of psychotic defenses, but in childhood psychosis, unlike neurosis, the intrapsychic conflict does not appear to be the cause per se of the disease; therefore, one could not expect to achieve resolution of the illness. It is possible that, no matter how early the illness is detected, certain crucial experiences have been missed that make the course irreversible. Prognosis depends on the degree of severity of the illness, ability to alter contributing factors in the parents, the age at which treatment is instituted, the quality of treatment, and the vigorousness with which it is pursued. The personality characteristics necessary to do psychotherapy with psychotic children are optimism, persistence in the face of little reward, firmness and strength, and the ability to withstand countertransference temptations, particularly that of overidentification with the child.

Generally, psychotherapeutic techniques with psychotic children fall into three phases, based on the functional level of the child, regardless of cause or previous treatment. Markedly disturbed autistic children may be able to undergo only the first or possibly the second phase. Less disturbed or borderline children may begin with the third phase.

FIRST PHASE: OVERCOMING THE AUTISTIC BARRIER

Methods for penetrating the shell of the withdrawn, regressed child have been extensively studied. In order to develop the initial awareness of human beings, the therapist establishes himself as an all-important factor in the child's life, often caring for him physically, offering unconditional acceptance, using the child's receptive channels by mirroring them, removing obstacles to gratification, and helping him express his impulses while gratifying them safely. Music, rhythmic activities, food, extensive physical contact, and understanding and participation in the child's primitive magical language, gestures, and fantasies may be used by the therapist to insinuate himself into the behavior pattern of the child. The child may be encouraged to relive primitive stages of development that have been previously missed or have been unsatisfactory—for example, sucking on a bottle or messing with clay as a substitute for feces. Certain necessary frustrations, such as the control of destructive behavior, come from the same therapist who gratifies so freely, thus providing the basis for object relationship.

SECOND PHASE: DEVELOPMENT OF EGO FUNCTIONS

With the therapist acting as an auxiliary ego and providing such necessary ego functions as translating primitive impulses into language, acting as a stimulus barrier, interpreting events, etc., therapy concentrates on the development of the ego functions of relationship to persons, perception of reality (awareness of self and external reality), postponement of gratification, and clarification of impulses and feelings. The therapist acts as a boundary while helping the child establish his own boundaries. Thus, the child is helped to cope more successfully with internal and external pressures, developing more appropriate behavior.

THIRD PHASE: RESOLUTION OF INTRAPSYCHIC AND INTERPERSONAL PROBLEMS

This phase, the goal of which is the understanding of the conflict that caused the withdrawal, is applicable to those psychotic children who can utilize it. It is somewhat similar to the treatment of severe neurosis but with considerable modification of technique, such as the therapist's active participation in and limitation of fantasies so that they do not become too frightening, the emphasis on intellectual controls, regulation of life outside of therapy, working with the part of the ego that is intact, and utilization of the corrective relationship to the therapist to provide understanding of previous frustrating experiences. The resolution of internalized conflicts and relief of anxiety attached to primitive fantasies result in a freeing of additional sources of ego strength and in the development of more adaptive gratifications than the previous pathological interaction.

GROUP THERAPY

In the past few years, group psychotherapy with psychotic children has been used in a few centers. Small groups of children with regressive behavior and disturbances in self-identity, perception of reality, and use of communicative language meet several times weekly with one or more therapists. Isolation, panic, and further regression may occur initially, but in time group formation occurs, as the children become aware of each other and the therapist. This permits the introduction of group activities and structure, which are tolerated for longer and longer periods of time. Finally, interpretations are given regarding the difference between reality and nonreality, self and object, and the relationship between feeling and behavior. Children perceive their own and others' behavior as dystonic, which helps to develop control. Therapy of the children is usually combined with group or individual therapy of the parents and, where possible, with school attendance.

It is felt that the therapeutic group develops a group ego, which provides support for the defective egos of the individual patients. For symbiotic psychotic children, the therapeutic symbiosis they require is provided by the group ego. Results include the achievement of communicative speech, some measure of self-identity, and movement upward in the development scale, such as achievement of toilet-training. The avoidance and self-protective aspects of their behavior, such as ritual and mannerisms, may decrease.

MILIEU THERAPY

With the rise of residential and day treatment programs for children, the importance of milieu in the treatment of psychotic children received increasing attention. The protean nature of the impairments in this illness sometimes calls for intervention in all life experiences. Programs that provide care for a major period of the child's life are able to provide a controlled, consistent milieu that is in itself therapeutic.

Such programs consciously attempt not only to integrate all the child's experiences—physical care, education, recreation, psychotherapy, etc.— but also to develop an attitude on the part of all personnel, professional and nonprofessional, that meets the child's dynamic needs. Various centers define these needs differently. The emphasis may be on giving the child permission to regress to previous stages of psychic development and to relive them with therapeutic personnel; on providing the child with sensitively timed doses of human contact, according to his tolerance; or on providing a clear-cut structure of expectation to which the child is expected to adapt. The therapeutic prescription carried out by the staff strives to be internally consistent, in accordance with the theoretical understanding of childhood schizophrenia held by the center.

Milieu therapy provides multiple activities; a peer group that allows identification, necessary regression, or acting out; flexibility in individually designed programs; multiple adults from whom the child can choose; clinically controlled and manipulated experiences; an atmosphere of being accepted and wanted rather than of being deviant; and opportunities for diluted relationships. One of the important requirements in establishing a totally therapeutic atmosphere is to provide the entire staff with organized controlled opportunities to work out their own feelings of rivalry with each other; of resentment, guilt, and helplessness with the children; and of any other factors that interfere with optimum consistency of efforts.

Consciously designed milieu therapy necessarily takes place in selected residential or day treatment centers where a major segment of the child's time is spent and where sufficient time and personnel are available for this time-consuming effort. Psychotic children are referred for such programs on the basis of the degree of psychopathology in the child and parents and the ability of the home and community to tolerate their behavior and provide necessary services. Some psychopathological features for which milieu therapy is particularly recommended are inability to maintain contact with parents, lack of experience of gratification in interpersonal relationships, and the combination of uncontrollable impulses with very weak ego structures.

Results of intensive programs are generally good, considering that the most severely disturbed psychotic children are selected for them. Since these programs combine the best of all available therapies while adding the special dimension of milieu therapy, they should and do produce the best results, although they are the most costly.

EDUCATIONAL THERAPY

Although educational principles are commonly used in combination with other treatment modes and enter into all psychotherapy of psychotic children, in some centers the educational experience is the definitive intervention with the child. This form of treatment has been receiving greater emphasis with psychotic children in the last decade as other therapeutic methods have yielded disappointing results.

Educational therapy is generally in the hands of teachers, usually with psychiatric supervision or consultation. Emphasis is placed on the external reality demands, structure of the classroom situation, and ego modes of functioning. Anxiety is reduced by clarity of expectation and predictability. Children are taught perceptual discrimination, relationships in time and space, functioning of the body, and the realities of various social relationships. They are trained to put thoughts and feelings into words, to coordinate motor activity, and to master the operational tools for learning. The capacities to play, to learn, and to participate actively are encouraged. The strengthening of skills through emphasis on intellectual functioning serves to promote self-esteem and identification with peers. The teacher addresses himself to the healthier aspects of the child's functioning by imposing a graded series of reachable challenges. The defenses of intellectualization and obsessiveness, often very useful to psychotic children, are promoted indirectly. The focus is on learning to live in the world.

The rationale for educational therapy is that the psychotic child, having irreversible personality defects, must develop those areas of function that are least damaged—namely, the capacity to imitate, to respond to cues, to learn adaptive skills, and to live as if he were a total person. The goals are, in the main, similar to those of psychotherapy. Although psychotherapy attempts to resolve the basis for psychotic withdrawal, educational therapy attempts to bypass it. The latter is generally emphasized for the more severely ill children or by those who feel that resolution of the psychosis is not possible. The results of all types of therapy with psychotic children are most often given in terms of the numbers who are able to attend schools subsequently. Using this criterion, educational therapy yields results comparable to or better than other forms of treatment. Whether this is done at the sacrifice of more total self-realization of the child has not been clarified.

BEHAVIOR THERAPY

Behavior therapy, which is the application of principles derived from learning theory research to the modification of abnormal behavior, has its origins in two sources. One is the classical conditioning experiments of Pavlov, and the other is in various learning theories. Although clinical application to adults began a couple of decades ago, its systematic application to psychotic children is of relatively recent origin, the first reports of its use appearing around 1960.

The most commonly used clinical technique with psychotic children is free operant conditioning. The child has an alternative between courses of action that he controls by means of an operation or action. For example, if it is desired to teach a mute child to say a word, a desired reward is withheld from him until he says it. Each time he performs correctly, he is rewarded, which reinforces the learning. Much less commonly employed is the technique of aversive conditioning, whereby undesirable behavior, such as bizarre gestures, is followed by an unpleasant consequence, such as darkening of the room or even an electric shock.

Since the severely psychotic child has very few sources of gratification already in his experience that motivate him to utilize free operant conditioning, the use of this technique must be preceded by a careful study of the child to discover ways of providing gratification and establishing controls. Food is by far the most commonly used reward. Other social rewards are physical contact, verbal praise and reassurance, reading, singing, playing music, and dancing.

This therapy rests on the theory that behavioral principles, reliably demonstrated in learning laboratories, are also applicable to managing, modifying, building, and maintaining the behavior of severely disturbed psychotic children. The basic concept on which this rests is that behavior, both normal and abnormal, is learned. Psychotic behavior is a learned reaction that was originally established as a barrier either against a hostile world or as a defense for an organism unable to cope with ordinary life experiences. The persistence of the behavior is maladaptive and prevents the individual from moving beyond his infantile survival needs. The psychotic symptoms are no longer necessary and, if eliminated, will enhance the child's use of environmental supports and thus bring him greater rewards in the form of social adaptation.

Behavior therapy has been used primarily with autistic children who have responded very poorly to all other methods of therapy. Since it is nonverbal and requires little or no conceptualization on the part of the child, it is particularly suitable for these children. Because autistic psychosis begins very early in life, giving the child a pathological behavioral repertoire by the time he emerges from infancy, he is deprived of the ordinary social reinforcements that normal children constantly receive as a feedback from their behavior. The autistic child's behavior may be self-reinforcing, as he may establish contact with the environment only by means of undesirable behavior. For example, because of his resistance to initiating contact, he may be ignored unless he screams.

Behavior therapy is seldom used as the sole therapeutic tool. It is usually combined with some form of psychotherapy, milieu therapy, or educational therapy. Its specific goal is the elimination of highly maladaptive target symptoms that prevent the child from deriving benefit from other forms of therapy or from life experiences. These target symptoms are the social behavior of psychotic children that serve to reinforce their isolation and regression, such as muteness, lack of eye contact, bizarre gestures or vocalizations, avoidance of human interaction, stereotyped behavior, temper tantrums, and insistence on repetition.

The use of behavior therapy with psychotic children is too new to evaluate results systematically. In addition, since behavior therapy is imbedded within other therapeutic modalities, it is difficult to separate results, except in terms of specific symptoms for short periods of time. Since behavior therapy has been tried with those children who have proved most resistant to any therapeutic intervention, goals must necessarily be limited. Some workers have reported successful long-lasting symptomatic results. Others have reported variable responses and a high rate of relapse. The question of whether the learned response can be transferred to another person without loss remains unanswered. It is also apparent that operant conditioning is best in strengthening existing behavior and less useful in initiating new behavior.

TREATMENT OF PARENTS

The degree to which parents of psychotic children receive treatment and the type of treatment they receive depends on the theoretical orientation of the therapist treating their child.

Those psychiatrists who believe that pathological attitudes on the part of parents, especially mothers, play a large part in the genesis of the child's illness recommend direct psychotherapy or even psychoanalysis of the parents. Some of the pathological parental factors held responsible are the parent's distortion of reality and teaching of unreality, primitive destructive fears and wishes, unconscious need for a psychotic child, and inability to sense the child's needs or to exercise basic authority with him. Therapists with an organic theory of the origin of childhood psychosis recommend guidance of the parents in adjusting to their child's illness. Group therapy is often used to give parents the opportunity to cope with their reaction of confusion, anxiety, guilt, isolation, hostility, and helplessness. Parents can also be helped to mobilize community resources for their child's special needs.

Parents are also seen as an adjunct to the child's psychotherapy, providing information for the therapist or creating a home environment designed in accordance with specific therapeutic guidelines.

Family therapy, which has been increasingly used recently with psychotic children, provides the therapist with details and clarity of family interaction, the degree to which family members recognize mutual needs, the methods with which they communicate with one another, and their distortions of reality. For young autistic children, the family therapist can demonstrate to the parents how to relate and handle the child. He may interfere with the destructive and self-injuring behavior of the child; show expectation of response, conformity, and growth; or break the parental habit of treating the child as if he doesn't comprehend his surroundings.

REFERENCES

Cohen, R. S. Some childhood identity disturbances: educational implementation of a psychiatric treatment plan. J. Amer. Acad. Child Psychiat., 3: 488, 1964.

DeMyer, M. K., and Feister, C. B. Teaching new social behaviors to schizophrenic children. J. Amer. Acad. Child Psychiat., 1: 443, 1962.

Ekstein, R., Bryant, K., and Friedman, S. Childhood schizophrenia and allied conditions. In Schizophrenia: A Review of the Syndrome, L. Bellok, editor, p. 555. Logos Press, New York, 1958.

Hewitt, F. M. Teaching speech to an autistic child through operant conditioning. Amer. J. Orthopsychiat., 35: 927, 1965.

Kaufman, I., Frank, T., Friend, J., Heims, L., and Weiss, R. Adaptation of treatment techniques to a new classification of schizophrenic children. J. Amer. Acad. Child Psychiat., 2: 460, 1963.

Kemph, J., Harrison, S., and Finch, S. Promoting the development of ego functions in the middle phase of treatment of psychotic children. J. Amer. Acad. Child Psychiat., 4: 40, 1965.

Speers, R. W., and Lansing, C. *Group Therapy in Childhood Psychosis.* University of North Carolina Press, Chapel Hill, 1965.

Weiland, H., and Reidrick, R. Consideration of the development and treatment of autistic childhood psychosis. Psychoanal. Stud. Child, 16: 549, 1961.

CHAPTER FOURTEEN

Brain Disorders

MAURICE W. LAUFER, M.D.

INTRODUCTION

THE AMERICAN PSYCHIATRIC ASSOCIATION classifications under the heading "disorders caused by or associated with impairment of brain tissue function" cover a number of categories of clinical importance. But there is need for more general consideration of what may contribute to the particular pattern of dysfunction displayed by a particular child.

One consideration is the nature of the cause. Another is the particular time in the child's development in which the causative factor begins to operate and the duration of time in which it does so. Another aspect is the severity or degree of insult from the etiological factor involved. Another contributing variable is the general status of the child. This itself is a composite of genetic factors, the extent of the central nervous system involvement, and the efficiency of parental management and interaction. For example, a highly intelligent child who has benefited from good child-parent interactions may more readily find or respond to ways of coping with a specific learning disability than another child who is not so fortunate.

The degree and kind of disability presented by a child with some form of cerebral dysfunction is highly dependent on parental reactions and expectations, the meaning of the child and his behavior for this set of parents, and the expectations of his sociocultural milieu. One pair of parents may derive gratification from a hyperactive, aggressive youngster, as indicating they have produced "a real boy"; another pair of parents may be overwhelmed by the same picture. A child with a specific learning disability may be reacted to more negatively in an upper-middle-class family than in a lower socioeconomic milieu.

CAUSES

Consideration of this area may be distorted by the popular concept of brain damage as implying the prime and invariable role of traumatic insult to the brain. Both theoretically and practically it seems more appropriate to consider three general categories, all of which may lead to the same syndromes. The first of these is *maldevelopment*, in which there is a structural deviation from the normal due to a variety of possible causes other than trauma. The second does indeed reflect actual *damage* to central nervous system structure being formed or already formed due to such factors as trauma, infection, hemorrhage, and hypoxia. The third is *malfunction* without known structural change—for instance, the results of insufficient stimulation or of excessive stimulation at significant points in development or the results of distortion in the child-parent interaction.

When components of any of these categories impinge on a developing brain and psyche, there may be a greater effect than in an adult. There seem to be critical periods for the development of various functions. If there is interference at one of these times, it may be very difficult for the function ever to be developed adequately. In addition, a child's development follows both a segmental and sequential plan; therefore, early interference may have a profound and ever-increasing effect, since subsequent phases of development are distorted by what has previously gone awry.

However, in a developing organism an early insult may be overcome in several ways. One is by compensatory overdevelopment of other functions. Or, in accordance with the concepts of equipotentiality, an uninjured area may to some extent take over the role of the injured one. Or, in later phases of development, that which was deficient earlier may no longer be critical in terms of total functioning.

Prenatal causes of central nervous system dysfunction are metabolic, genetic, infectious, toxic, and psychogenic factors. Perinatal causes are prematurity, postmaturity, prolonged labor, rapid labor, abnormalities of presentation, induction of labor, accidents of labor, effects of medication, immunological incompatibility, and normal mechanics of labor. The item "normal mechanics of labor" is in recognition of the fact that there are significant stresses and strains on the fetal passenger, even in a normal delivery, and that first-born males seem particularly susceptible to developing sequelae.

Postnatal (to 5 years of age) causes are infections, injuries, medications, poisons, toxins, metabolic or vascular disturbances, psychogenic-environmental factors, neoplasms, and convulsive disorders. The item "psychogenic-environmental factors" suggests that disturbances of human relationship and inadequate, excessive, or distorted stimulation and human interaction may have an effect on the developing central nervous system and lead to the development of one of the syndromes of cerebral dysfunction.

SYNDROMES OF CEREBRAL DYSFUNCTION

In order to develop a conceptual overview of the possible distortions of cerebral function that may result from the causes just outlined, Denhoff et al. have advanced the concept of syndromes of cerebral dysfunction. These are possible but neither invariable nor inevitable results of aberrations of central nervous system function and are partly stylized constructs for the purposes of description and classification. There are many possible variations. The symptom picture in a given child is the final result of the organically based tendency toward a deviation of function and the way the child adapts to and compensates for this. The latter, in turn, is a composite of the child's ego strength, coping mechanisms, and state of child-parent equilibrium (see Table I).

TABLE I
Syndromes of Cerebral Dysfunction

Area	Clinical Manifestations
Neuromotor	Cerebral palsy
Neurosensory	Central blindness, deafness, anesthesia
Consciousness	Epilepsy
Communication	Dysphasias, aphasias
Intellectual	Mental retardation
Perception, association, conceptualization, expression	Specific learning disabilities
Object relations	Some forms or components of psychoses of childhood
Impulse control, motility	Hyperkinetic impulse disorder

These syndromes often occur in varying combinations. One syndrome may represent the major presenting area or complaint, and another may contribute a major disability. For instance, in both epilepsy and mental retardation, hyperkinetic impulse disorder may be a component of the patient's disability.

Several of these syndromes—such as mental retardation, disorders of communication, and psychoses of childhood—are treated elsewhere in this book and will not be dealt with in detail here.

HYPERKINETIC IMPULSE DISORDER

Hyperkinetic impulse disorder and specific learning disabilities are often grouped together under the headings of "minimal brain injury" or "minimal neurological impairment." The two syndromes often occur together, but they may be found separately.

The possible causative factors or combination of factors are categorized above. The most recent and possibly most authoritative estimate of incidence has been given by Masland as occurring in from 5 to 10 per cent of the school population. Since various causative factors may occur in all categories of the population, the symptom pictures may be found in all classes. They are more common among the socioculturally deprived, but their impact may be greater in more intellectually oriented groups in the population.

Clinical description. Hyperkinetic impulse disorder may have its onset in the earliest days of life. It is particularly common in first-born males. Since the new mother is apt to be tense, fearful of inadequacy as a female, and convinced that the newborn, in some mysterious and primitive way, can divine and affirm or deny her essential worth as woman and mother, their initial encounter is fraught with significance.

A newborn who is already afflicted with hyperkinetic impulse disorder may be unduly sensitive to stimuli and may respond in an undifferentiated, massive, aversive manner. This may call to mind Freud's concept that there is a boundary to the developing ego or *Reitzschutz* that protects a human organism against being overwhelmed by stimuli and that this is in some way deficient in these infants. When a mother picks up the infant preparatory to feeding and he stiffens, arches his back, spits, squalls, and thrashes in wild protest, to the frantic mother this may represent the awful confirmation of her secret dread—that she has been rejected by the baby as inadequate. Her subsequent attempts to force the baby to conform only stimulate further negative reactions in the baby and may lay the groundwork for an ambivalent but predominantly negative relationship.

Frequently, the converse of this sequence occurs, and the child is unusually placid, limp, and floppy, sleeping much and developing slowly in the initial months.

It is more common, though, for the infant to be active in the crib, have a rapid developmental schedule, sleep little, and cry much past the traditional first three months of colic. The infant often gets out of the crib on his own very early, undissuaded by the parents' attempts to bar his exit. Once out of the crib and able to get about, the infant is apt to do so relentlessly, getting into everything and generally fingering, breaking, or disintegrating objects. As time goes on, his sphere of activity widens and rapidly encompasses yard, neighboring territory, and street.

The toddler phase scarcely exists but is replaced by a gallop. As he gets older, the mother often complains that his constant activity keeps him from sitting through a meal, other children complain that he can't play ball because he can't stay at his assigned base, fathers complain that they can't teach him to fish or to work with them, teachers complain that he can't stay still in line or sit still in his seat, and so it goes.

Although hyperactivity is one of the hallmarks of this state, it does not always mean that quantitatively the degree of activity is greater than that of other children, though this may be so. Rather, it may be that the activity is relatively continuous and not turned off in inappropriate situations, such as school or church. Hutt and Hutt showed that hyperkinetic children were far less likely than normal children to reduce their locomotor activity when their environment was structured by social limits.

Often coupled with hyperactivity is short attention span or ready distractibility, which may be better viewed as involuntary. The child is unable, without great and conscious effort, to inhibit his response to any stimulus that comes along, regardless of appropriate meaning or significance. In addition, the child seems incapable of attending to more than one stimulus at a time.

As Hutt and Hutt suggested, the hyperkinetic child is a short sampler, incapable of attending to any stimulus for more than ten seconds because of his rapid decay of memory traces. As soon as each stimulus has been explored, its central effects are lost, and the child comes back to it as if it were a fresh stimulus. Serial, repetitive sampling and monotonous, repetitive activity may be important learning and adaptive mechanisms for such children and may contribute to the apparently contradictory behavioral phenomenon of perseveration so often found.

Another set of phenomena, probably related, is impulsiveness and inability to delay gratification. The children are often accident-prone. In school, they may rapidly attack an exam and only do the first two questions, or they may rush quickly but inaccurately through all the questions. They may be unable to wait to be called on in school and may answer for everyone else, and at home they cannot be put off for even a minute.

They seem to have a need to handle and finger things, which often seem to disintegrate in the process. Hutt and Hutt pointed out that in these children, as in very young ones, the primary mode of contact between child and environment is by manipulation; they are seldom able to maintain visual fixations independently of manipulation; and they find it very hard to solve a problem visually before tackling it manually.

The children are often explosively irritable. This may be set off by relatively minor stimuli, and they themselves may seem puzzled and dismayed over this phenomenon. They are frequently emotionally labile, easily set off to laughter and to tears, and their mood and performance are apt to be variable and unpredictable.

Not all the phenomena described are always seen together; there may be just one or two of these characteristics. Further, each item of behavior is often induced by difficulties in the emotional sphere, as in the child who is hyperactive and irritable as a result of inner tension and anxiety. But these behavioral phenomena may have their origin in altered central nervous system function as well as in emotional disturbance.

There are often other manifestations. Among these are a preoccupation with water play and a fascination with spinning objects. There may also be disturbances in left-right discrimination (internal and projected on the environment); in spatial orientation; in temporal orientation (internal time-telling or clock time-telling); in visual or auditory perception; in visuomotor performance and hand-eye coordination; in fine motor coordination; in figure-background discrimination; in the abilities to abstract, conceptualize, and generalize; and in the abilities to assimilate, retain, and recall.

Concomitant emotional difficulties are frequent. The fact that other children grow out of this kind of behavior and that the hyperkinetic does not grow out of it at the same time and rate, the variability of performance, the temporary response to pressures, the fact that in most cases the child is not retarded and therefore "has no excuse for his behavior," the general nuisance value and inexplicability of the behavior—all may lead to adult dissatisfaction and pressures. The resulting negative self-concept and reactive hostility are worsened by the child's frequent recognition that he isn't right inside.

The impaired functions are ego functions, and their poor performance may both create and worsen difficulties in a circular manner. Because of them, the child performs poorly and unacceptably, resulting in criticism and other pressures. The impaired ego may also make it harder for the child to tolerate and adapt to the feelings evoked in him by these pressures. Such children are prone to develop almost any kind of psychiatric disability in response to those special problems, the normal needs for adjustment required in the process of psychological-sexual-social maturation, and those that may be imposed by psychological difficulties within the parents. These children are definitely not immune to the development of true neurotic pictures, but Kurlander and Colodny have stressed that these children may present a superficially identical picture, which they class as "pseudoneurosis."

Mechanism. The basic underlying mechanism for the development of this hyperkinetic picture is not known. In the course of their development, hyperkinetic children outgrow this mode of behavior. This may be connected with the interrelationship between the diencephalon, which·probably is fully formed and in full functional integrity at birth, and the cortex, which is by no means fully formed at birth but continues to grow at least beyond the fifth year of life and possibly to adolescence. One set of theories has suggested a reverberating feedback type of circuit between cortex and diencephalon. This postulates that, as the cortex grows in mass, it is eventually able to exert greater influence and allow for the more organized, localized, and discriminating responses characteristic of growth and for the ability to inhibit, which is one characteristic of maturation. Other theories have stressed the role of the diencephalon as the rostral component of the reticular activating system and its possible role as a first-stage sorting, routing, and patterning mechanism for impulses coming in from sensory receptors to the various higher levels of the central neuraxis.

It has been suggested that in the first few months after birth the newborn infant operates under a homeostatic principle that induces great discomfort when any tension accumulates, with a great need to discharge this tension and return to the previously undisturbed state. Dysfunction of the diencephalon could make the individual unusually sensitive to stimuli flooding in from both peripheral receptors and viscera. This could well make a young infant respond with greater than usual urgency to what might otherwise be regarded as a normal amount of tension coming from the usual organic sources, such as hunger or a full bladder, and be hypertonic, querulous, and irritable.

Others have proposed that the rostral portions of the reticular activating system are concerned with ability to respond differentially to stimuli, to inhibit, to establish, and to alter set—all of which seem important in the production of this syndrome.

Diagnosis. Diagnosis has many facets. Most important is the history, which may reveal factors thought to be of etiological significance and also the kind of behavioral characteristics that have been described.

A neurological exam may be negative or show a variety of soft signs. Strabismus, mild central facial weakness, and mixed dominance are common.

Archimedes spiral after-effect testing may be part of the diagnostic evaluation. In this, the patient stares at a rotating disk on which a black and white spiral has been mounted. With abrupt cessation of the rotation, an afterimage is normally seen, with the illusion of either expansion or contraction of what is being looked at, depending on the direction in which the spiral had been rotating. This is the normal response and tends not to occur in children with cerebral dysfunction with cortical involvement.

Standard scalp electroencephalography (EEG), though often showing no abnormalities, may be useful. Almost any kind of EEG abnormality may be seen, focal or generalized. Bioccipital slow waves or spike-wave complexes are fairly frequent.

A special form of electroencephalography has proved useful and also tends to support the concept of diencephalic involvement. It is an adaption of the photo-Metrazol threshold technique first described by Gastaut as "a clinical neurophysiological test which provides a method for the exploration of certain subcortical structures, among which the most important are those of diencephalon and most especially of the thalamus." The results of this test were given in quantitative form (the photo-Metrazol threshold) as the number of milligrams of pentylenetetrazol (Metrazol) per kilogram of body weight required to obtain a specified type of response clinically and in the EEG when the patient was exposed to the flickering of a stroboscope light within a certain range of frequencies. Gastaut presented evidence to show through both human and animal studies that a photo-Metrazol threshold that was lower than normal indicated damage to or dysfunction of the diencephalon.

Modifying this procedure by using only the appearance of a spike-wave burst in the EEG as the end point and also standardizing on a stroboscope frequency of 15 flashes a second, in children from 7 to 12 years, the normal threshold was established as 6.5 mg. or above, borderline abnormal was 5.1 to 6.4 mg., and less than 5.1 mg. was clearly abnormal.

A group of 50 children who were sufficiently disturbed behaviorally to require residential treatment were selected and divided into two subgroups. One group of 32 children presented the symptom picture of hyperkinetic impulse disorder; the other group of 18 children did not. In the group with hyperkinetic impulse disorder, the mean photo-Metrazol threshold was 4.54 mg. per kilogram. In the group without hyperkinetic impulse disorder, the mean photo-Metrazol threshold was 6.35 mg. per kilogram. Statistically, the difference between the means for the two groups was highly significant.

A further highly instructive finding was the effect of administration of amphetamines, found clinically efficacious in the hyperkinetic picture, on the photo-Metrazol threshold. In a group of hyperkinetics, the mean photo-Metrazol threshold when not receiving amphetamines was 4.8 mg. per kilogram; the same subjects, when receiving amphetamines, showed a mean threshold of 6.7 mg. per kilogram. Thus, the use of amphetamines resulted in a rise of the mean threshold from an abnormally low to a normal figure. The difference between these two means is statistically significant.

Psychological testing may also be of value. Children showing only the behavioral aspects of hyperactivity, distractibility, impulsiveness, and variability tended not to show classical organic signs but on projective testing manifested their characteristic behavior in having a flow of associations, contaminations, and inability to delay. In those who showed visual-perceptual difficulties, problems with spatial organization, and other phenomena suggesting cortical and diencephalic involvement, the classical test signs became common. These included performance scores markedly lower than verbal scores on the Wechsler test, impairments of various subtests, distortions shown in the Bender-Gestalt, and organic signs in the projective tests. These, incidentally, often improved, as did the photo-Metrazol threshold, when amphetamines were used.

Psychiatric examination, in addition to clarifying the particular defense mechanisms and conflicts, may suggest the presence of a basic, pervading, organically based anxiety alluded to by Kurlander and Colodny as "primary anxiety" and called "body anxiety" by others.

Treatment. The first requisite is that the physician communicate to both parent and child his concept of the underlying central nervous system aspect and the rationale for treatment. There are wide variations in the possible responses of all concerned—from relief, to indignation, to feelings that this must be something irreparable, to agonizing confirmation of the suspicion that something is different, to a conviction that this must mean being crazy. Opportunities must be provided for ventilation of such feelings. The physician must also give an indication of prognosis. It can be stated with confidence that the hyperkinetic syndrome of behavior will be outgrown—treated or untreated—when the child is between 12 and 18 years of age. As yet, there is no way of predicting for a given individual when this favorable outcome will occur. And this prediction applies with such certainty *only* to the hyperkinetic aspect and not necessarily to learning or emotional complications or sequelae.

Nonetheless, it is important that the hyperkinetic picture be treated without waiting for its eventual disappearance. The mode of treatment is pharmacological, but there is some disagreement as to which medications are most efficacious. In children, there tends to be a paradoxical effect of medications affecting the central nervous system in that sedatives tend to stimulate and stimulants, on the other hand, tend to diminish rather than increase hyperactivity and other components of the syndrome.

There has been extensive experience with the amphetamines, both dextrorotatory and racemic. Which of these forms will work best is quite unpredictable. In children under 6 years, the general range has been 1.25 mg. to 7.5 mg. of the dextrorotatory form, once daily after breakfast, and 2.5 to 15 mg. of the racemic form. For children over 6 years, these figures are doubled. In most cases, a single dose after breakfast is efficacious, but it may be necessary to add another dose during the course of the day or to substitute or combine with longer-acting forms. The dose thus determined needs to be reviewed at six-month intervals. With maturation, the need may diminish, but with bodily growth it may increase.

With time, the need for the medication will vanish, and this point may be recognized in two different ways. One is that the discontinuance of the medication does not allow the return of hyperkinetic symptoms. The other is that, instead of reducing overactivity, the usual effects of amphetamine —that is, overstimulation—begin to appear.

Some possible distortions are to be noted in evaluating the efficacy of the medication. One is that both child and parents may expect, by some kind of magic, that *all* behavioral problems will be erased and that, if they do not, the medication is not worthwhile. Professionals, parents, and children alike need to keep in mind that emotionally determined problems will not be erased by these medications.

Another important side reaction is that, even if the hyperactivity was due to aberrant central nervous system function, in the course of time it may have become incorporated in the psychic and defensive structure of the child, so that chemical interference with this hyperactivity may evoke great anxiety within the child. Dealing with this requires careful and thoughtful exploration with the child.

Another medication that has been used with apparent success is methylphenidate hydrochloride (Ritalin) in high dosages. Various phenothiazines have been suggested as helpful. Most of these have seemed helpful predominantly where there is anxiety that may have been present before or that may have been stimulated by the abrupt cessation of hyperactivity, which had come to serve a defensive purpose. Particularly useful is thioridazine (Mellaril), 20 to 60 mg. daily.

Another occasionally helpful medication, one without the side effects of the amphetamines, is 2-dimethylaminoethanol, in doses of 100 to 300 mg. daily.

Although these medications may, in a most amazing and beneficial way, control the organically based hyperkinetic aspects, they do nothing directly for emotional ones. When the latter are minimal and purely secondary to the difficulties in accomplishment related to the hyperkinetic picture, they may rapidly vanish without specific treatment. However, as was indicated earlier, these children may be more susceptible than others to the development of significant emotional disturbance.

Stone suggested that there is a link between and a common reservoir for the energy systems of the psychic apparatus and the neural apparatus. If the latter is damaged, then compensatory mechanisms that are called into play require greater than usual energy. This, in turn, makes the psychic apparatus more vulnerable to emotional stress. Conversely, in an emotionally threatening situation, energy being mobilized for psychic defense results in a worsening of the neurologically based dysfunction, as there is less energy available for the previously used compensatory mechanism. This accords with the frequent observation that the neurologically based dysfunctions worsen under conditions of psychic stress. Conversely, when psychological status is improved, as by psychotherapy, more energy is made available to the central nervous system, with concomitant improvement in the symptoms associated with cerebral dysfunction. The child with cerebral dysfunction not only often needs but can profit from psychotherapy and should not be barred from consideration for it, as has been the case in so many child guidance clinics.

Since anxiety is often tremendously high and the damaged ego impaired in its attempts to adapt to stimuli, the child attempts to control and structure his environment to ensure that sensory experiences are, as far as possible, minimal and predictable. This may result in what look like obsessional and ritualistic maneuvers. These, however, differ from the true neurotic obsession in that there is neither fixation at the anal-sadistic level nor ambivalence in object relationships. These children are capable of intense attachments and open expressions of love and hate. Sarvis suggested that they may defend themselves against an evil self-image and paranoid attitudes by identification with the aggressor, the mother, or extension of the mother in general. This may lead to a danger of characterological effeminacy and may be a hazard to boys with unresolved oedipal attachments to their mothers.

When the children are not only allowed but helped to structure their environment, their anxiety diminishes. Thus, their parents and teachers need to set up a structure that is predictable with experiences of manageable intensity. This applies to the physical, temporal, and interpersonal environment alike and should be one of the major areas of work with the parents. It may range from informational aspects to an intensive casework approach in dealing with their feelings of guilt, bewilderment, and hostility. An almost universal requirement is to help the parents recognize that the fashionable permissiveness is not beneficial for these children. They also need to be helped to recognize that, despite their deficiencies in some areas, these children face the normal tasks of maturation and attendant problems, including the need to introject standards and to form a normal, flexible superego. Therefore, they do not benefit from exemption from the requirements and expectations applicable to other children.

Stone cautioned the therapist to be careful in his interpretations, to focus on the reduction of irrational anxiety and guilt, to counteract feelings of omnipotence, to neutralize projections, and to improve reality-testing. The therapist may need to be more than usually active, serve as an auxiliary ego, help the patient recognize the areas of realistic deficiency, and work with him on means to overcome this problem.

SPECIFIC LEARNING DISABILITY

Specific learning disability is frequently associated with hyperkinetic impulse disorder, though each may occur alone. Specific learning disability refers to an impairment of the ability to learn scholastically up to a level appropriate to the individual's intellectual endowment. It is due to some disorder of cerebral function, rather than being emotionally, intellectually, or socially determined. There are many possible reasons for impairment of learning ability, dealt with in detail in other chapters of this book. It is only desired here to emphasize that abnormal cerebral function may in itself be a significant cause, possibly in 5 to 10 per cent of school children.

ACUTE AND CHRONIC BRAIN DISORDERS

As cited in the APA classification, acute and chronic brain disorders tend to be characterized by impairments of orientation, memory, intellectual functions, judgment, and affect.

SYNDROMES ASSOCIATED WITH INTRACRANIAL INFECTIONS

In the acute phase of epidemic encephalitis, encephalitis lethargica, or Economo's disease, the children may be hyperactive, excited, anxious and apprehensive, or confused, with delirium and hallucinations. In the chronic phase, they may be completely uninhibited, aggressive and destructive in uncontrollable rages, sexually preoccupied, emotionally labile, selfish, and suspicious. They may be moody; have spells of crying, laughing, or screaming; and have hallucinations. Sometimes, but by no means always, there may be accompanying intellectual deterioration.

In St. Louis, encephalitis, headaches, lethargy, and seizures are often noted in the acute phase, and irritability and changes in behavior such as described above are relatively uncommon in later phases.

Measles encephalitis seems to induce personality changes a number of years later in a relatively high proportion of children. Phenomena seen include hyperactivity, difficulties in concentration, tics, tantrums, emotional lability, pointless fabrications, and impairment of school performance, which may be associated with impairment of verbal abilities, confusion of figure-ground relationships, and perceptuomotor distortions.

Pertussis encephalopathy is a much less common complication, but in those who incur it, the late sequelae are apt to be severe. In addition to the usual hyperactive, unpredictable, impulsive, and destructive behavior, there may be disturbances of relationships and reality-testing severe enough to be classed as prepsychotic or psychotic.

Case reports of infectious mononucleosis encephalitis, of influenzal encephalitis, and of mumps meningoencephalitis in children are alike in suggesting a relative and remarkable freedom from significant psychiatric sequelae.

The meningitides are more likely to result in neurological and intellectual defects than in significant psychiatric residuals.

SYNDROMES ASSOCIATED WITH POISONS OR DRUGS

These are prominently represented by lead poisoning. In the acute phase, the symptoms may be predominantly neurological, with irritability, convulsions, and coma. Some studies have suggested that there may be a sociocultural aspect to the ingestion of lead-containing substances, reflecting lack of care and supervision and proper maternal training or a culturally derived habit of clay-eating. Many authors stress that this behavior is purposeful, occurring in a setting of emotional disturbance and family tension. This may contribute to the emotional instability so common in the late sequelae of lead poisoning. Many children become markedly retarded. Others have lesser degrees of intellectual deficit but tend to be hyperactive and distractible and have visual-perceptual and visuomotor problems and specific learning disabilities. In one study, out of twenty children who had suffered lead poisoning in early life, only one was performing adequately in school.

Barbiturates may result in clouded sensorium, impaired judgment, and mental deterioration.

Amphetamines—along with barbiturates, alcohol, and agents such as lysergic acid diethylamide (LSD)—are being used increasingly by adolescents for alterations of mood, alertness, energy, and states of consciousness, which are their acute effects. In adults, depression and psychotic states have been described with continued use, and reports of similar results may be expected for adolescents.

Gasoline addiction, in the form of inhalation, deserves some attention. This, along with sniffing of tar, is something seen commonly but tran-

siently in many young children. A few, however, become really addicted to
it. In the acute phase, while sniffing, they may have hallucinations, auditory and visual, then become drowsy and lose consciousness. In the
chronic phase, there are predominantly signs of neurological disability. It
is interesting that one child who practiced this habit for eleven years
showed no evidence of a chronic brain syndrome.

Glue sniffing—sniffing of tubes of plastic cement and airplane glue—
was quite common in the early years of the 1960's but seems somewhat
less prevalent now. The acute phase is characterized by euphoria, excitement, exhilaration, and altered body sensations. There may be neurological phenomena, such as ataxia, diplopia, tinnitus, drowsiness, stupor, and
unconsciousness. In the subacute phase, there may be irritability, inattentiveness, and episodes of drowsiness and unconsciousness. There have not,
as yet, been reports of chronic brain syndrome.

Medications given for therapeutic purposes may induce hallucinations.

CONGENTIAL SYPHILIS

Formerly a frequent problem, congenital syphilis is much less so now. The
now rarely seen juvenile general paresis may result in progressive mental
deterioration. There may be apathy, forgetfulness, irritability, restlessness,
night terrors, temper tantrums, and impulsive behavior, often antisocial.
Less often than in adults, there may be euphoria, expansiveness, delusions,
and hallucinations.

DISORDERS OF GROWTH, METABOLISM, AND NUTRITION

Among the inborn errors of metabolism, phenylketonuria has been prominently mentioned as contributing to mental retardation. There has been
an increasing number of observations of altered behavior, not only in
those who are retarded but also in children who present the same metabolic defect but without significant retardation. They may have a dull,
expressionless facies, be negativistic and apprehensive, and have speech
disturbances. Others are reported to display striking psychotic behavior,
manifested by withdrawal from reality, failure to relate to people, echolalia, and stereotyped, catatoniclike posturing. There may be loosening of
associations, rambling, bizarre and disconnected primary process type of
thinking.

Another inborn error of metabolism said to evoke a psychotic picture is
that of cystathioninuria.

Acute porphyria may be accompanied by confusion, irritability, restlessness, insomnia, delirium, and hallucinations.

Dietary deficiency—as of niacin in pellagra, of thiamine in beriberi, and
of the very prevalent kwashiorkor in deprived areas of the world—may
lead to apathy, increased irritability, and some degree of intellectual impairment.

Endocrine disturbances may have psychiatric complications. In diabetes mellitus, hypoglycemia associated with difficulties in establishment of insulin dosage is common and may result in confusion and irritability. Hyperthyroidism may cause tension, anxiety, irritability, and emotional instability.

Intracranial Neoplasms

These are not so often associated with personality and behavior disorders in children as in adults. One form in which they are relatively common is that of craniopharyngioma, where there are apt to be mood swings, lassitude, inertia, sadness, hallucinations, and excitement.

It has been suggested that there is a characteristic difference in reaction between children suffering from cerebral and from cerebellar tumors. The latter are said to be generally sweet, cooperative, and alert, and the former are said to be irritable and uncooperative.

Other than these statements, most reviews suggest that there is nothing really specific about a child's reaction to an intracranial tumor. Regressive tendencies, emotional instability, irritability, anxiety, withdrawal, and learning difficulties seem to reflect the fact fundamentally that cerebral functioning is impaired. This interferes with the child's ability to deal with emotional stresses already present and now intensified.

Familial Dysautonomia

A central nervous condition, not a tumor, that evokes similar effects is that of familial dysautonomia. The behavioral picture resembles that of hyperkinetic impulse disorder, with marked body anxiety and many secondary emotional reactions in child and parents.

Syndromes Associated with Trauma

In the acute phase, the patient may be delirious, confused, and stuporous to comatose. But the sequelae are of more concern. In many respects, children may show a postconcussion syndrome that is very similar to that noted in adults and about which there is continuing argument as to how much is neurologically based and how much is psychologically based.

The children may display marked irritability, restlessness, difficulty in concentration, ready fatigability, emotional instability, headaches, vertigo, sensitivity to change in position and to lights, noise, and confusion. Some degree of amnesia is characteristically present, and there may be some degree of impairment of intellectual functioning. Withdrawal, aggressiveness, and enuresis are common. So are sleep disturbance and the persistent recurrence of anxiety dreams in which the real or fantasied circumstances of the accident are recapitulated.

Undoubtedly, there are important psychological aspects to this. Symbolically as well as factually, the head contains the organ of control, and injury to it raises the specter of loss of control, including fantasies of insanity. Children, like adults, who have had a head injury in circumstances beyond their control may feel and fear that nothing is safe and predictable and may generate tremendous anxiety on this account, especially since the parents were unable to protect against this trauma.

Children, however, have a special vulnerability. As they go through the various phases of psychosexual development, acculturation, and superego formation, almost every phase has components or potentials for ambivalent or straightforward hostile and aggressive feelings within the child. Because of the characteristics of childish and primary process thinking, it is common and almost inevitable that the child will react to the traumatic accident as punishment and retaliation for his unacceptable wishes and thoughts. He may not only fear repetition of this or similar incidents, because the underlying drives or wishes continue unabated, but fear this even more because of the reactive hostility generated by the trauma he has suffered.

The situation is often worsened by implicit parental prohibition against some catharsis and working through of the traumatic event and the child's feelings. So often, the parents, meeting their own needs but justifying their actions on the ground that the child shouldn't be reminded, forbid discussion of the event and develop elaborate schemes for avoidance of it. This not only prevents abreaction but makes it an even more frightening and menacing event as far as the child is concerned. Thus, regardless of the as yet uncertain proportion or contribution of a neurological component, psychotherapy for the child and counseling for the parents are often indicated.

A complication of head injury, subdural hematoma, is more apt to result in neurological and intellectual deficit than any significant psychiatric picture.

Epilepsy

Common to all the diverse manifestations of epilepsy is some alteration in the state of consciousness and some impairment of complete control of actions. Both aspects may have psychological implications for both the patient and significant others—parents, teachers, siblings, other children, and their parents.

Regardless of the type of seizure, there is often a distortion of the body image and self-concept. Sometimes this appears as a vague generalized unease or feeling that something is wrong. Sometimes there is an amazing specificity and, even in cases where there has not been a clinical diagnosis of epilepsy as yet, the child may have a conviction of something being wrong in the head. Since the head is so heavily cathected as the organ of control and is often sexualized and endowed with phallic significance, this may lead to a child's view of himself as crazy, impotent, or out of control. This, in turn, may be responded to by aggressiveness, withdrawal, inability to learn, counterphobic mechanisms, and a vast variety of behaviors that either act out or deny these distorted views of himself.

Grand mal seizures. In the most common form of epilepsy, grand mal, the patient is generally thought to have no awareness or recollection of the seizure itself, though he may have some recollection of the aura, when one is present, and may react to it as a warning of impending death. Unless he has his seizures only in sleep, this is likely to mean that he may suddenly awaken to find himself bruised, soiled and wet, with bitten tongue, surrounded by a ring of curious and horrified onlookers. This is enough in itself to make him think there must be something horribly wrong with him. This feeling would certainly be intensified by the negative reactions, on up to actual ostracism, of teachers, playmates, and their parents. Although this type of reaction is fortunately diminishing with the spread of public information and understanding, it is by no means entirely absent today. This, too, creates or accentuates a poor self-image with the kinds of psychological reactions previously indicated.

Special note must be made of the reactions of the parents. Very often, despite the spread of intellectual understanding, they react—consciously or unconsciously—to the presence of grand mal seizures as a curse and affliction, a punishment for them, retribution for some misdeed in act or thought. They anxiously search their past and that of their marital partner for what it was that might have brought this upon them—masturbation, sexual activity, disobedience or hostility to parents, hostility to siblings, tainted stock, and a whole host of malignant fantasies. With this come ambivalent feelings toward the afflicted child—pity and anger.

One of the most common reactions is overprotection, sometimes, unfortunately, fostered by medical and other advisers. The parents may limit the child's range of activities in all sorts of ways "so that he won't hurt himself in a spell." A variant of this is to fail either to set limits for the child or to require performances from the child unlike those the same parents would set or require for their other children. Both these modes of overprotection are exceedingly damaging to the child. They confirm his view of himself as someone different and interfere with the process of socialization and internalization of controls, with obvious distortion of psychological development.

Petit mal seizures. The situation is not so drastic for the child with petit mal or its variants, but there are similarities. The child with petit mal, who has sudden lapses of consciousness, may find it inexplicable and distressing that he seems to have missed something the teacher was saying or that he is suddenly behind the others in what they are reading. A child with akinetic or myoclonic seizures may be tremendously disturbed over the fact that, while drying the dishes, he suddenly drops or hurls a dish— not just once but many times. The frequent anguished cry is: "What's the matter with me? I must be crazy!"

Seizures with behavioral alterations. There are seizure types in which alterations of behavior may be the outstanding symptomatic manifestation. First in prominence is the grouping of temporal lobe or psychomotor seizures. Here, the seizure may be characterized by automatisms and aggressive outbursts ranging from verbal expressions of rage to actual destruction or assault. Some patients with bilateral temporal lobe EEG abnormalities have been described as psychotic.

Scott and Kellaway gave a more precise account of the types of psychic phenomena that may be encountered in temporal lobe epilepsy. These include (1) hallucinations, generally reliving an emotionally charged experience; (2) perceptual illusions, temporary distortions of subjective relationships with surroundings; (3) change of emotional tone, most often fear, terror, or dread; (4) disorders of thought or language, arrest of thinking processes, aphasia, forced thoughts or words; and (5) automatisms, actions, simple to complex.

There have also been accounts of behavioral disorders in children who showed a temporal or occipital spike focus without any overt evidence of seizures. These children could show a hyperkinetic picture or oscillations in behavior, difficulty in relating to others, withdrawal or hostile aggressive attacks, enuresis or nightmares, or poor school work and paroxysmal headaches.

Contrasted with this is the description by Goldensohn and Gold of prolonged episodes of behavioral disturbance, which seemed similar to temporal lobe epilepsy but which, in the EEG, showed only generalized and not temporal lobe abnormalities. These episodes lasted as long as seventy-two hours, with confusion, hostility, negativism, withdrawal, with or without automatisms, but with apparent retention of consciousness.

Another type of seizure is that described by Gibbs and Gibbs as "hypothalamic and thalamic epilepsy," with which they associate the 14-per-second and 6-per-second positive spike pattern in the EEG in the sleep state, with attacks of rage and antisocial and vicious behavior, including murder, as possible concomitants of such seizures.

Epileptic personality.   Conflicting accounts as to the interseizure behavior of epileptics raise the often-debated question of the epileptic personality, described variously as egocentric, sensitive, irritable, rigid, resistive, suspicious, and hostile. This is complicated by the problem of subclinical seizure activity. Many studies with depth intracerebral electrodes have shown that there may be abnormal subcortical electrical activity, even when the scalp or direct cortical electroencephalogram shows no abnormality whatsoever. Conceivably the behavior of an epileptic between overt seizures may reflect the effects of subclinical seizure activity. Then there is the contribution to the epileptic's behavior of his own adversely altered self-image and his reactions to the real or fantasied depreciation of him by others.

Some small part of what has been considered the epileptic personality may derive from the frequent concomitant presence of hyperkinetic impulse disorder. Many of the medications used to treat epilepsy tend to accentuate and make worse or even to precipitate the appearance of hyperkinetic impulse disorder. They may also unfavorably alter other behavioral characteristics, obtund the individual, or make him more irritable, depressed, or suspicious and thus contribute to the stereotype of the epileptic personality.

The seizures themselves—particularly those that are severe, prolonged, and repeated—can cause or accentuate a process of cerebral deterioration and the development of a chronic brain syndrome. They can have a particularly potent effect in this direction when the epilepsy is of the organic or symptomatic type. There is, therefore, a predisposition toward a chronic brain syndrome to begin with.

Taking all these aspects together, the epileptic personality does not seem to be a necessary and typical accompaniment of convulsive disorder.

Intellectual effects. The problem of intellectual capacity and function is significant emotionally because of the stereotype of inevitable intellectual deterioration being associated with epilepsy and the reverberating impact this may have on significant adults and then the child. There may, indeed, be some interference with learning because of the frequent association of hyperkinetic impulse disorder and of specific learning disability. Clinical and subclinical seizures may hamper learning capacity. So may medications used to control the seizures. So may the child's emotional turmoil.

But with present-day medications and methods, epileptics, excluding those whose epilepsy is originally due to a profound cerebral insult, have the same range of distribution of intellect as the general population. The efforts of public health educators and lay organizations to communicate this will help to reduce not only the misinformation but also some of the emotional hazards connected with epilepsy.

Emotional factors. The role of emotional factors in epilepsy—in precipitation and in treatment—is an area in which some rather sweeping statements have been made. Perhaps to counteract the thesis that an epileptic grand mal was a recapitulation of man's ancestral piscine struggle to get out of the water onto dry land, the hypothesis was offered that an epileptic seizure was an attempt on the part of the patient to dive back into the uterine existence from which he had been dispossessed. These both seem as fallacious as most sweeping generalizations. Bona fide epilepsy seems to require some biological, physicochemical abnormality or predisposition. Given this, stress—generalized or specific—may precipitate a particular seizure, which is not the same thing as causing the epilepsy. In a person who does not have the epileptic predisposition, a similar constellation of emotional stresses and psychological structure will be reacted to in ways other than the production of a seizure.

Nonetheless, emotional aspects are very important. The very existence of seizures may create highly important psychological difficulties. In turn, emotional conflicts may precipitate seizures. Next, in a setting of emotional disturbance, seizures may, symptomatically at least, diminish this. There are two possible mechanisms for this. One may be relatively physiological in that the seizure may literally discharge tension. Another may be symbolic because of the particular psychological meaning of the seizure to the child or significant adults—punishment, expiation, orgasm, death, resurrection, etc.

The important thing to note is that there is no single, classical, pathognomic constellation of psychodynamics, interrelationships, and family involvements that inevitably and invariably causes or results from epileptic seizures; there are, rather, a whole host of special and different situations. Gottschalk has tried to find a common denominator. He has speculated that there is a blocking of any nonspecific drive or strong emotion from gratification or expression by either an internal autonomous inhibiting factor or an external agent or situation. When this occurs in children who have a lower seizure threshold and less mature and more primitive impulses and emotions than other children, they are apt to respond with seizures. In these mixed pictures, psychotherapy is of the utmost value, reduces the tendency toward seizures, speeds a favorable outcome, and diminishes the need for medication.

As a final grace note, one may refer to the phenomenon, shared by the idiots of whom Dostoievsky wrote and by the great Russian author himself, of deriving gratification from a seizure, so that some have found means to induce it. More common in retardates than in geniuses, it may be for some the equivalent of an orgasm; for others, it may be relief from a drab existence; for still others, it may be at least an end to the tormenting feelings building up as a prodrome to a seizure.

REFERENCES

Birch, H. G., editor. *Brain Damage in Children.* Williams & Wilkins, Baltimore, 1964.

Denhoff, E., Laufer, M. W., and Holden, R. The syndromes of cerebral dysfunction. J. Okla. Med. Ass., 52: 360, 1959.

Denhoff, E., and Robinault, I. *Cerebral Palsy and Related Disorders.* McGraw-Hill, New York, 1960.

Gastaut, H. Combined photic and Metrazol activation of the brain. Electroenceph. Clin. Neurophysiol., 2: 249, 1950.

Gibbs, E., and Gibbs, F. Electroencephalographic evidences of thalamic and hypothalamic epilepsy. Neurology, 1: 136, 1951.

Goldensohn, E. S., and Gold, A. P. Prolonged behavioral disturbance as ictal phenomenon. Neurology, 10: 1, 1960.

Gottschalk, L. A. Effects of intensive psychotherapy on epileptic children. Arch. Neurol. Psychiat., 70: 361, 1953.

Hutt, S. J., and Hutt, C. Hyperactivity in a group of epileptic (and some non-epileptic) brain-damaged children. Epilepsia, 5: 334, 1964.

Kurlander, L. F., and Colodny, D. Pseudoneurosis in the neurologically handicapped child. Amer. J. Orthopsychiat., 35: 733, 1965.

Laufer, M. W., Denhoff, E., and Solomons, G. Hyperkinetic impulse disorder in children's behavior problems. Psychosom. Med., 19: 38, 1957.

Masland, R. *Testimony before a Subcommittee of the Committee on Appropriations, House of Representatives, 89th Congress, First Session,* part 3. United States Government Printing Office, Washington, 1965.

Sarvis, M. A. Psychiatric implications of temporal lobe damage. Psychoanal. Stud. Child., 15: 454, 1960.

Sarvis, M. A. Evil self-image: a common denominator in learning problems. Ment. Hyg., 49: 308, 1965.

Scott, J. S., and Kellaway, P. Epilepsy of focal origin in childhood. Med. Clin. N. Amer., p. 415, March 1958.

Stone, F. H. Psychodynamics of brain-damaged children. Child Psychol. Psychiat., 1: 203, 1960.

CHAPTER FIFTEEN

Mental Retardation

LEON CYTRYN, M.D., and
REGINALD S. LOURIE, M.D.

INTRODUCTION

Recent Interest in Mental Retardation

Mental retardation may be viewed as a medical, psychological, or educational problem, but in its final analysis it is primarily a social problem. This explains the fact that throughout history the attitude toward the mentally retarded often reflected the general social attitudes of a given people or a given culture.

In more modern history there were three distinct junctures characterized by great public interest and professional creative thinking in the field of mental retardation. Characteristically, they all followed crucial periods of great social upheaval, resulting in a popular adoption of gradually more liberal, more truly democratic attitudes toward society's less fortunate members, including the mentally retarded.

The first germinal period in the field of mental retardation coincided with the time of the French and American revolutions and the ideas of equality and rights for all men, which upset the feudal, vertical social structure. The times of Itard and his pioneering labors were also the times of Pinel, who unchained the insane, and the beginning of a popular vote and social legislation.

The second period followed the revolutions that swept Europe in 1848, in the wake of which a further liberalization of public opinion and gradually increasing legislative justice took place. In such a favorable climate, the ideas of Guggenbühl, Séguin, and Howe about special educational opportunities for the mentally retarded spread rapidly throughout Europe and North America.

The third, our present period, in turn followed the cataclysm of World War II. The great resurgence of professional and public interest in mental retardation and its sudden respectability are the result of several, not necessarily related, factors. Again, probably the most important was the radical change in the social climate felt everywhere on the local, national, and international level. As if to atone for letting the ravages of World War II happen, the postwar trend has been toward securing equal rights and opportunities for all human beings, including the traditionally downtrodden. These include the colonial nations of Asia and Africa, racial and religious minorities everywhere, the old, the very young, the poor, and the sick. Government involvement in an increasing range of social issues has become universally accepted, despite some opposition of advocates of laissez-faire policies of the past.

Thus, the social climate has been favorable for overcoming the traditional public inertia regarding mental illness and mental retardation. Suddenly, the retarded were viewed as individuals with inherent needs and rights. Various civic groups became champions of those rights in the forum of the federal, state, and local governments. In the United States, in the best American tradition of self-help, the National Association for Retarded Children, founded in the 1950's by groups of parents of retarded children, has been the *spiritus movens* of the radical change in public opinion in favor of the retarded.

HISTORICAL SURVEY

Early attitudes. There is very little information about the problems of mental retardation in antiquity, in medieval times, and even in modern history up to the beginning of the nineteenth century. We find only scanty references scattered among ancient religious and medical writings, indicating some awareness of the problem. Hippocrates mentioned anencephaly and other cranial malformations associated with severe retardation. The laws of Sparta and ancient Rome included provisions for extermination of severely retarded children in infancy, a practice revived recently during the infamous Nazi regime.

In medieval Europe the mentally retarded were at best tolerated as jesters and freaks of nature and at worst considered to be evil creatures, in alliance with the devil. This latter belief was particularly popular during the Reformation. In contrast, Asian religious leaders such as Confucius in China and Zoroaster in Persia advocated humane treatment of the mentally retarded in their teachings. Jewish Talmudic scholars exempted the mentally retarded from criminal responsibility.

The era of humanism saw more interest on the part of the church authorities and the beginning of a more protective attitude. This interest was not shared, however, by the scientific and medical community, as attested by the conspicuous absence of any writings on mental retardation up to the beginning of the nineteenth century. Mental retardation was often considered a variant of insanity, and it was not until 1689 that Locke made a clear distinction between the two.

Nineteenth-century attitudes. The spirit of the French Revolution heralded the beginning of efforts to rectify all kinds of social injustices and to put an end to the subhuman treatment of the mentally retarded. Significantly, the medical profession became caught up in the spirit of the times, and this led to pioneering work of several of its members. In the early part of the nineteenth century, Itard in France laid the groundwork for the future development of the education and training of the mentally retarded through his patient efforts with the wild boy of Aveyron.

In the middle of the nineteenth century, Guggenbühl in Switzerland introduced the idea of institutional treatment of the mentally retarded. His meteoric rise to fame gave impetus to the establishment of special educational institutions for the retarded, first throughout Europe and then in the United States and Japan. Guggenbühl's naive notions that the diverse forms of mental retardation were only expressions of cretinism and his promise of total cure, which prompted his downfall, should not detract from his contribution to the field. He made mental retardation a respectable field of medicine and educational endeavor and established special institutions for the mentally retarded throughout the civilized world.

Séguin published the first textbook in this field, *The Physiological and Moral Instructions of Idiots.* After his emigration to the United States in 1848, he contributed greatly to the fruitful, pioneering activity in this country in the field of mental retardation.

Howe, through his efforts to legislate state support for the care and instruction of the feebleminded, helped the development of institutional care throughout the United States and Canada. By taking a realistic approach to the limitations of special education, Howe wisely avoided the pitfalls experienced by Guggenbühl.

Unfortunately, the enthusiasm of the early and middle parts of the nineteenth century, which led to the establishment of institutions for retarded children as places of learning and instruction, gave way to a pessimistic attitude in the latter part of the nineteenth century. This was probably a result of the great disappointment felt when the promises of the early pioneers for total reversibility or cure of mental retardation failed to materialize. The emphasis was then put on vocational rather than scholastic aspects of training and on concentration of effort on the mildly retarded, to the exclusion of the more severely afflicted group. The change in attitude also affected the character and goals of the institutions for the mentally retarded. They were viewed no more as means of rehabilitation and education but rather as means of isolating the mentally retarded from the mainstream of community life. This trend was reinforced by several pseudoscientific speculations, which cloaked in modern terms the medieval concept of the inherent badness of the mentally retarded.

The efforts of the medical profession during this period were largely diverted from fruitful research and were directed toward finding ways of checking the menace of mental retardation by various means of eugenic control, ranging from sterilization to euthanasia and, more recently, birth control. The physicians remaining in the field, like their counterparts in mental hospitals, became isolated from academic centers of learning and research, since their subject was not deemed worthy of scientific investigation.

Twentieth-century attitudes. The beginning of the twentieth century witnessed the perpetuation of professional lethargy, but there were forces astir that, in time, brought about a radical change, a renewed aura of scientific respectability, and indeed an unprecedented appeal, with everybody clamoring to get on the bandwagon. Several crucial discoveries may be credited for this unusual phenomenon. Garrod's concept of the inborn errors of metabolism was probably the first in the chain of significant events that attracted the curiosity of the medical academic community. Fölling's discovery of phenylketonuria in 1934 helped to popularize Garrod's concepts and in time pointed to possibilities of preventing mental retardation by circumvention or avoidance of the defective metabolic pathways. The same was true of the unraveling of the metabolic defect in galactosemia, which was followed by the detection of a host of other metabolic disorders. The genetic principles elaborated by Mendel and improvement in laboratory techniques gave impetus to the development of the rapidly expanding science of genetics. Improvements in obstetrical techniques, control of syphilis, and the discovery of Rh incompatibility, soon followed by the introduction of exchange transfusions, were among other important factors that suddenly opened new, exciting vistas in the field of mental retardation for the medical researcher and clinician alike.

A favorable public opinion coupled with the enthusiastic endorsement by the scientific community could not fail to bring about a radical, positive approach to the problem of mental retardation. One civilized country after another adopted new laws and introduced means to further research and ensure the welfare of the mentally retarded. The United States actually lagged behind many countries on both sides of the Iron Curtain, especially when it came to the provision of decent facilities for care and education. Even today, many state institutions for the mentally retarded are a festering sore, an ugly medieval relic in this most affluent country.

However, in the early 1960's, under the direction and initiative of the late President Kennedy, a thorough program was prepared by a panel of experts. It addressed itself to the complexities of the problem and made sweeping recommendations that were, in part, adopted through ordinary legislative channels. Governmental support, favorable public opinion, and research opportunities keep attracting an increasing number of physicians to the field of mental retardation. To use a metaphor, mental retardation was the ugly maiden who was kept in the attic for a long time. Suddenly, suitors have begun to arrive in numbers, since they discovered that the prospective bride is not so homely after all, and, in addition, she now has a handsome dowry.

PROBLEMS OF DEFINITION, NOMENCLATURE, AND CLASSIFICATION

The problem of adopting a universally acceptable system of defining and labeling mental retardation has long vexed many individual workers in this field and lately has attracted the attention of national and even international scientific and governmental bodies. The still-existing confusion may be attributed primarily to the complexity of the problem of mental retardation, which defies simple conceptualization.

Definition. The biomedical and sociocultural adaptational models represent the two major approaches to the conceptual definition of mental retardation. The adherents of the former in our country and in the U.S.S.R. insist on the presence of basic changes in the brain as a *sine qua non* in the diagnosis of mental retardation. The proponents of the latter, on the other hand, emphasize the social functioning and general adaptation to accepted norms. Each of these approaches has many ramifications that complicate the issue even further.

Brain damage may be viewed as a demonstrable anatomical lesion, an alteration of the basic constituents of the brain tissue, a metabolic disturbance of the nerve cell, diminished capacity for interneuronal impulse transmission, or a combination of all these factors.

The sociopsychological approach focuses on the developmental impairment in infancy and preschool years, on learning difficulties in school age, and on poor social-vocational adjustment in adulthood. The prevailing cultural norms against which an individual's performance will be judged, rather than his neuropathology, may be decisive in defining the degree of social inadequacy—that is, the inability to learn and adapt to the demands of a society and to be self-sufficient. Thus, individuals classified as mentally retarded in our technological, complex society might have been competent and successful in a more primitive and intellectually less demanding environment.

There is no known technique for *direct* assessment of intelligence or intellectual potential, nor is there a correlation of the latter with anatomical and functional impairment of the central nervous system. It is futile, therefore, with our present knowledge, to view mental retardation in a unidimensional frame of reference. Rather, it has to be considered as a multidimensional phenomenon that involves overlapping physiological, psychological, medical, educational, and social aspects of human functioning and behavior. This broader view is reflected in the definition of mental retardation adopted by the American Association on Mental Deficiency in 1961: "Mental retardation refers to sub-average general intellectual functioning which originates in the developmental period and is associated with impairment in adaptive behavior." This description circumvents the question of cause, the problem of nature versus nurture, and the clinical course of mental retardation—that is, its treatability or even curability. Because of the avoidance of these highly controversial areas, it provides a useful, practical, operational definition acceptable to all disciplines.

Nomenclature. Mental deficiency, which was the term used in the first edition of the American Psychiatric Association's manual on terminology and classification to designate subaverage intellectual functioning, is often used interchangeably with mental retardation. However, the World Health Organization has recommended the use of the term mental subnormality, which in turn is divided into two separate and distinct categories: mental retardation and mental deficiency. According to this nosology, mental retardation is reserved for subnormal functioning due to environmental causes in the absence of central nervous system pathology, and mental deficiency describes subnormal functioning due to pathological causes. Mental deficiency is also used often as a legal term, applied to people with an I.Q. below 70.

The term feeblemindedness was often used in American literature in the past and is still in use in Great Britain, where it generally denotes the milder forms of mental retardation. The term oligophrenia is in common use in the U.S.S.R., Scandinavia, and some other Western European countries. Amentia appears only infrequently in modern psychiatric literature.

Our choice of the term mental retardation only reflects the widest preference of all professional groups.

Classification. The pluridimensional character of mental retardation is also reflected in the various approaches to classification of this condition. Essentially, they all deal with the developmental characteristics, potential for education and training, and social and vocational adequacy. The degrees or levels of retardation are expressed in various terms. The American Psychiatric Association uses the terms borderline mental retardation (I.Q. 68 to 85), mild mental retardation (I.Q. 52 to 67), moderate mental retardation (I.Q. 36 to 51), severe mental retardation (I.Q. 20 to 35), and profound mental retardation (I.Q. under 20). The following terms are recommended by the World Health Organization: mild subnormality (I.Q. 50 to 69), moderate subnormality (I.Q. 20 to 49), and severe subnormality (I.Q. 0 to 19). The American Association on Mental Deficiency adopted the terms borderline (I.Q. 70 to 84), mild (I.Q. 55 to 69), moderate (I.Q. 40 to 54), severe (I.Q. 25 to 39) and profound (I.Q. 0 to 24) (see Table I). The terms idiot, imbecile, and moron still enjoy some popularity in Europe but are seldom used in the United States (see Table I).

EPIDEMIOLOGY

It is estimated that 3 per cent (5,400,000) of the U.S. population are mentally retarded. This often quoted estimate is only approximate, since there are no precise data available except in a few areas of the country.

TABLE I

Developmental Characteristics of the Mentally Retarded [a]

This table integrates chronological age, degree of retardation, and level of intellectual, vocational, and social functioning.

Degree of Mental Retardation	Preschool Age 0–5 Maturation and Development	School Age 6–20 Training and Education	Adult 21 and over Social and Vocational Adequacy
Profound	Gross retardation; minimal capacity for functioning in sensorimotor areas; needs nursing care	Some motor development present; may respond to minimal or limited training in self-help	Some motor and speech development; may achieve very limited self-care; needs nursing care
Severe	Poor motor development; speech minimal; generally unable to profit from training in self-help; little or no communication skills	Can talk or learn to communicate; can be trained in elemental health habits; profits from systematic habit training	May contribute partially to self-maintenance under complete supervision; can develop self-protection skills to a minimal useful level in controlled environment
Moderate	Can talk or learn to communicate; poor social awareness; fair motor development; profits from training in self-help; can be managed with moderate supervision	Can profit from training in social and occupational skills; unlikely to progress beyond 2nd grade level in academic subjects; may learn to travel alone in familiar places	May achieve self-maintenance in unskilled or semiskilled work under sheltered conditions; needs supervision and guidance when under mild social or economic stress
Mild	Can develop social and communication skills; minimal retardation in sensorimotor areas; often not distinguished from normal until later age	Can learn academic skills up to approximately 6th grade level by late teens; can be guided toward social conformity	Can usually achieve social and vocational skills adequate to minimum self-support but may need guidance and assistance when under unusual social or economic stress

[a] Adapted from *Mental Retardation Activities of the U. S. Department of Health, Education, and Welfare*, p. 2. United States Government Printing Office, Washington, 1963.

The distribution of mental retardation is uneven in different age groups. In the preschool years, only about 1 percent of the population are diagnosed as mentally retarded, since only the severe forms of this disorder are recognized on routine examination. The highest incidence is found in school-age children, with the peak at ages 10 to 14. This reflects the close supervision and continuous evaluation of the children's intellectual and social performance in a school setting, with availability of standards of academic performance and the use of standardized intelligence tests. The inadequacy of these yardsticks for future life performance is attested to by the abrupt drop in the frequency of mental retardation after school age, when most of those who were identified as mentally retarded blend into the general population.

The overwhelming majority (87 per cent) of the mentally retarded fall into the mild category, and the remainder (13 per cent) belong to the moderate, severe, and profound groups.

Roughly 126,000 children born each year in this country are expected to be mentally retarded. It is estimated that of the total number of mentally retarded only about 60,000 to 90,000 belong to the severely and profoundly retarded categories; they require custodial care in a sheltered environment. The moderately retarded group number about 300,000 to 350,000; they can be trained in self-care, rudiments of social adjustment and judgment, and sometimes performance of simple productive tasks in a sheltered environment. These groups provide the bulk of mentally retarded individuals in institutions. The mildly retarded group includes roughly 5,000,000 people; they can be educated to a limited extent and are potentially able to adjust, at least marginally, to the demands of society and to employment. This group comes predominantly from the lower socioeconomic strata of our society, and it is believed that many of its members are retarded due to environmental deprivation. The lower socioeconomic groups also supply a disproportionately large number of the moderately and severely retarded, but the discrepancy in these groups is not so great as in the mildly retarded group. There seems little doubt that more stringent developmental evaluation of preschool children and more uniform school standards would result in a far greater number of children identified as moderately retarded in the preschool and school age population.

CAUSES AND SYNDROMES

PRENATAL FACTORS

Since Garrod's original description of alkaptonuria in 1908, the inborn errors of metabolism have commanded the attention of researchers and clinicians, exceeding by far their relative frequency. The total of all the hereditary metabolic defects probably accounts for about 4 to 5 per cent of mental defectives, but the lessons already learned from the study of these disorders point to exciting diagnostic, therapeutic, and preventive possibilities. The introduction of paper chromatography played a major role in the rapid growth of the list of known amino acidurias, and several ingenious but rather simple methods allow for routine mass screening of large populations for biochemical abnormalities. Tolerance tests with suspect substances or related compounds permit the detection of heterozygous carriers and individuals with a milder form of a disease. Further biochemical research may bring the number of metabolic disorders to 10 per cent of the mentally retarded group.

The success of dietary measures in phenylketonuria (PKU), maple syrup disease, and galactosemia represent a major triumph in the medical treatment of mental retardation, which hitherto operated on a hit-or-miss basis. Although the mechanism of injury to the central nervous system in these disorders is not known, it is believed to be a result of abnormal accumulation of metabolites. The therapy is based on the principle of dietary omission or reduction of a specific dietary ingredient that cannot be properly metabolized because of a specific enzymatic block. This in turn helps to eliminate the abnormal accumulation of the metabolites, thus avoiding the potential injury to the central nervous system. Another therapeutic approach consists of dietary *addition* of essential metabolites, such as the addition of cystine in homocystinuria.

The intensive research in the area of the inborn errors of metabolism promises an increased understanding of normal and abnormal cerebral functioning. The exact role of various enzyme systems in the brain during various stages of embryogenesis and in the first few years of life is still unknown, but many exciting clues still await further clarification. The apparent simplicity of a single metabolic block is deceptive, since the accumulation of a metabolite leads to a sequence of secondary and tertiary events. Each of these events, singly or in combination, may be responsible for the ultimate damage to the developing brain. Too much or too little of a normal compound or the presence of an abnormal one may be involved. This exciting search, potentially of great significance to the entire field of mental illness, is facilitated by the fact that several inborn errors of metabolism, such as PKU and galactosemia, can be approximated in animals by feeding them large amounts of phenylalanine or galactose, without, of course, reproducing the basic enzymatic defect.

The recent advances in tissue and organ transplant hold out an exciting possibility of direct treatment of congenital enzymatic defects by transplanting enzyme-producing tissue, such as liver, from a normal donor to the affected individual, thus meeting the challenge head on instead of circumventing it.

Disorders of amino acid metabolism

PHENYLKETONURIA (PKU). First discovered by Fölling in 1934, phenylketonuria has become known as the inborn error of metabolism associated with mental retardation par excellence. The intensive study of its many aspects with the attendant publicity was greatly responsible for the recent interest of the medical community in mental retardation. The information gained from the study of PKU serves as a model of investigation of other hereditary biochemical disorders, which has already led to the discovery of a host of inborn enzymatic defects.

PKU is transmitted as a simple recessive autosomal Mendelian trait. Its frequency in the United States and various parts of Europe ranges between 1 in 10,000 to 1 in 20,000. Although the disease is reported predominantly in people of North European origin, sporadic cases have been described in Negroes, Yemenite Jews, and members of Mongolian races. The frequency among institutionalized defectives is about 1 per cent.

The basic metabolic defect in PKU is an inability to convert phenylalanine, an essential amino acid, to tyrosine because of the absence or inactivity of the liver enzyme phenylalanine hydroxylase, which catalyzes this conversion. This in turn gives rise to several abnormal biochemical findings, such as: (1) elevated phenylalanine in the blood (10 to 25 times normal) and cerebrospinal fluid, excretion of an abnormal metabolite, phenylpyruvic acid, in the urine as well as phenylalanine (30 to 50 times normal) and several derivatives; (2) a related disturbance of tryptophan and tyrosine metabolism, leading to a marked decrease in serum serotonin and lower than normal blood levels of epinephrine and norepinephrine.

The majority of patients with PKU are severely retarded, but some patients are reported to have borderline or normal intelligence. Eczema and convulsions are present in about a third of all cases. Electroencephalogram (EEG) is abnormal in about 80 per cent, even in patients without convulsions, showing irregular spike-and-wave discharges. The majority of patients are undersized, and the head tends to be small. Although the clinical picture varies, typical PKU children are hyperactive and exhibit erratic, unpredictable behavior, which makes them difficult to manage. They have frequent temper tantrums and often display bizarre movements of their bodies and upper extremities and twisting hand mannerisms that sometimes resemble the behavior of autistic or schizophrenic children. Verbal and nonverbal communication is usually severely impaired or nonexistent. Coordination is poor, and perceptual difficulties are many. The original description of PKU patients as blond and blue-eyed (due to a relative deficiency of melanin, a by-product of tyrosine) applies to some, especially in the younger age group.

The best known screening test depends on the reaction of phenylpyruvic acid in the urine with ferric chloride solution to give a vivid green color. This test has its limitations, since it may not become positive until the baby is 5 or 6 weeks old and it may be positive in other amino acidurias. Another screening method, commonly used, is the Guthrie test, which measures the phenylalanine level in the blood, using a bacteriological procedure. In addition to these simple screening methods, there are several chromatographic and biochemical tests available for the purposes of individual management and research.

Early diagnosis is of extreme importance, since a low phenylalanine diet, in use since 1955, results in significant improvement in both behavior and developmental progress. The best results seemed to be obtained with early diagnosis and the start of the dietary treatment prior to 6 months of age. The attainment of even normal or near-normal intelligence is possible if the dietary treatment is begun before 3 months of age. In addition, children on this diet become more responsive, less hyperactive, and much easier to manage. There is also an improvement in the EEG pattern and a diminution or cessation of seizures.

Dietary treatment is not without dangers. Phenylalanine is an essential amino acid, and its complete omission from the diet may lead to such severe complications as anemia, hypoglycemia, edema, and even death. The problem has become more complicated with the recent knowledge of patients with elevated phenylalanine levels in the blood, as picked up on screening tests, who do not seem mentally retarded and do not excrete phenylpyruvic acid in their urine but do have a relatively low tolerance for phenylalanine. When these infants are not monitored well while on dietary treatment, resulting in low blood levels, they are likely to develop serious complications from phenylalanine depletion. It remains to be clarified whether this condition represents an independent entity, phenylalaninemia, or a partial or arrested form of PKU, due perhaps to the influence of a modifying gene. At any rate, it points out the importance of caution and careful follow-up in the diagnosis and treatment of PKU and other metabolic disorders.

Dietary treatment of PKU can often be discontinued at the age of 5 or 6 years, although no alternate metabolic pathways capable of keeping the blood phenylalanine levels in normal range have been discovered as yet. Sometimes, however, withdrawal of the diet results in deterioration of behavior and recurrence of seizures. Evaluation of the dietary benefits is further complicated by the fact that some PKU children have normal or near-normal intelligence and behavior on a normal diet.

The parents of PKU children and some of these children's normal siblings are heterozygous carriers and can be detected by a phenylalanine tolerance test, which may be of great importance in genetic counseling of these people.

The exact mechanism of the brain damage in PKU is still unknown. Some researchers think that the high phenylalanine concentration interferes with the usual respiration of brain tissue or normal functioning of essential enzyme systems. Of particular psychiatric interest are the hypotheses that link both the mental deficiency and the behavioral abnormalities in PKU to the related disturbance in tryptophan metabolism, notably serotonin deficiency. However, the role of serotonin both in PKU and in psychotic disorders is still controversial and must await further clarification through careful biochemical and behavioral studies.

MAPLE SYRUP DISEASE (MENKES DISEASE). First discovered by Menkes in 1954, maple syrup disease is an inborn error of metabolism transmitted by a rare single autosomal recessive gene. The biochemical defect interferes with the decarboxylation of the branched chain amino acids: leucine, isoleucine, and valine. As a result, these amino acids and their respective keto acids accumulate in the blood and cause overflow amino aciduria. The urine has a characteristic odor, which gave the condition its name and which is due to the derivatives of the keto acids.

The diagnosis can be suspected by the use of ferric chloride or dinitrophenylhydrazine, each of which interacts with the urine to give, respectively, a navy blue color or a yellow precipitate. The pathological changes are relatively minimal and consist mainly of poor formation of myelin in the brain.

The clinical symptoms appear during the first week of life. The infant deteriorates rapidly and develops decerebrate rigidity, seizures, respiratory irregularity, and hypoglycemia. If untreated, most patients die in the first months of life, and the survivors are severely retarded. Some variants have been reported with transient ataxia and only mild mental retardation.

Treatment follows the general principles established in PKU and consists of a diet very low in the three involved amino acids. The reports to date are very encouraging, indicating the possibility of fairly normal physical and intellectual growth of patients on the dietary regimen.

As in PKU, the exact nature of brain damage is still not clear.

HARTNUP DISEASE. This rare disorder took its name from the family in which it was detected. Like the preceding diseases described, it is transmitted by a single recessive autosomal gene. The symptoms are intermittent and variable and tend to improve with age. They include a photosensitive pellagralike rash on extension surfaces, episodic cerebellar ataxia, and mental deficiency. Of particular importance to psychiatrists is the fact that transient personality changes and psychoses may be the only manifestation of the disease, and these milder cases do not come to medical attention until late childhood or adolescence.

The metabolic defect involves defective tryptophan transport, and biochemical findings consist of a marked amino aciduria and increased excretion of indican and indole derivatives. The diagnosis can be made by paper chromatography of the urine.

Treatment with nicotinic acid and antibiotics such as neomycin may relieve the skin rash and possibly the ataxia, but it does not affect the mental retardation.

CITRULLINURIA. This is one of three recently described rare disorders involving the urea cycle. It probably involves an enzymatic defect in the conversion of citrulline into argininosuccinic acid. As a result, the level of citrulline in the blood, cerebrospinal fluid, and urine is elevated. The disorder is accompanied by mental retardation.

HYPERAMMONEMIA. This is another rare defect involving urea synthesis, probably resulting from a metabolic block in the conversion of ornithine to citrulline. The serum ammonia is elevated, and mental retardation has been reported.

ARGININOSUCCINIC ACIDURIA. This third disorder of the urea cycle is as rare as the two preceding ones. The biochemical defect involves a block in the conversion of argininosuccinic acid to arginine in the brain. As a result, the argininosuccinic acid is elevated in the cerebrospinal fluid and to a lesser extent in the blood and urine.

The clinical manifestations include mental retardation, grand mal seizures, brittle white hair, and intermittent coma.

All three disorders of the urea cycle are being experimentally treated with a low protein diet.

IDIOPATHIC HYPERGLYCINEMIA. The biochemical findings in this rare condition consist of a marked elevation of the blood and urine glycine levels. Ingestion of leucine by the patient precipitates ketosis. The nature of the metabolic defect is unknown as yet.

The clinical picture is characterized by intermittent vomiting and ketosis, severe mental deficiency, and choreoathetosis. In contrast, the commoner condition, glycinuria, is not usually accompanied by mental disability. Dietary therapy is now in the experimental stage.

HISTIDINEMIA. This defect in histidine metabolism is transmitted by a single autosomal recessive gene and involves a block in the conversion of histidine to urocanic acid resulting from histidase deficiency. This in turn leads to an elevated histidine level in serum and urine. The urine also contains imidazole pyruvic, imidazole lactic, and imidazole acetic acids in increased amount, which give a positive ferric chloride test (green).

Mild mental retardation and sometimes speech defect are a part of the clinical picture.

HOMOCYSTINURIA. The metabolic defect in this rare disorder consists of a reduction or absence of cystathionine synthetase activity. Homocystine is excreted in the urine. The patients have an odd appearance and are mentally retarded. Subluxation of the lens of the eye is a characteristic clinical feature. Therapy is still in the experimental stage and involves the addition of cystine to the diet.

LOWE'S OCULORENAL DYSTROPHY. This disorder, transmitted by an autosomal recessive gene, presents a varied clinical picture that includes some of the following eye defects: buphthalmos, microphthalmos, cataracts, and corneal opacities. The renal ammonia production is decreased, and a generalized amino aciduria is found.

CYSTATHIONURIA. The metabolic defect in this disease consists of a block at the site of cleavage of cystathionine to cysteine and homoserine. Cystathionine is found in the urine, and the patients are mentally retarded.

HYPERPROLINEMIA AND OAST-HOUSE DISEASE. These are two further examples of rare amino acidurias associated with mental retardation. The number of known amino acidurias will no doubt continue to increase as more retarded and brain-damaged individuals have their blood and urine studied by chromatographic methods.

Disorders of fat metabolism. It is generally assumed that disturbances in lipid metabolism related to the central nervous tissue are genetically determined, resulting from an enzymatic defect. The exact nature of the enzymatic blocks and their localizations in the chemical chain of reactions are still unknown. However, the nature of the various metabolic products causing injury to the various components of the central nervous system (CNS) has been determined by biochemical analysis in most of the disorders discussed below. These can be roughly divided into two groups: The first includes diseases characterized by an increase and storage of lipids in the CNS, and the second involves diseases characterized by a decrease in lipids in the CNS, resulting in demyelination.

There are several hypotheses as to the nature of the metabolic disorder in the diseases involving accumulation of lipids in the tissue. (1) Normal lipid is produced at an excessive rate. (2) The normal lipid is produced at a regular rate, but an abnormality in the end organ tissues results in accumulation. (3) An abnormal lipid is produced. Specific enzymatic defects have been recently demonstrated in some of these disorders.

CEREBROMACULAR DEGENERATIONS. The cerebromacular degenerations represent a group of disturbances in which there is progressive mental deterioration and loss of visual function. They are all transmitted by an autosomal recessive gene. The four types of cerebromacular degeneration differ as to the age of onset. The earliest one, Tay-Sachs disease, occurs chiefly among Jewish infants, particularly those from Eastern Europe; the others are found in members of all races.

The accumulation of lipid substances, gangliosides, in neurons (the nerve cells) throughout the CNS is a characteristic shared by all forms of this disorder. In the Tay-Sachs variant, there is also an accumulation of gangliosides in the ganglion cells of the retina; in others the ganglioside deposits are found in the outer retinal layers.

The gangliosides can be chemically identified after brain or rectal tissue is obtained by biopsy. Neuraminic acid, a characteristic component of gangliosides, is elevated in the brain tissue but not in the spinal fluid.

Tay-Sachs disease begins in infants 4 to 8 months of age. The infants become hypotonic, slow down in their developmental progress, and become weak and apathetic. In addition, there are spasticity, accompanied by persistent primitive postural reflexes, cherry red spots in the macula lutea of each retina, convulsions, and progressive physical and mental deterioration leading to death in 2 to 4 years.

The Jansky-Bielschowsky type, also called the early juvenile or late infantile form of cerebromacular degeneration, has its onset at 2 to 4 years of age. There is a pigmentary degeneration of the macula and progressive dementia.

The juvenile form, Spielmeyer-Stock-Vogt-Koyanagi, occurs in early school-age children. This variant is characterized by a much slower degenerative process and usually starts at the age of 5 or 6 years, when impairment of vision appears as the first symptom. The impairment is progressive and leads to blindness due to the atrophy of the optic nerve and pigmentary degeneration of the macula. Ataxia, convulsions, and mental deterioration complete the picture. The course is protracted over a period of 10 to 15 years.

The late juvenile form, Kuf's disease, is rare and occurs after 15 years of age.

All these variants of cerebromacular degeneration are progressive, and there is no treatment available to date.

NIEMANN-PICK DISEASE.   This disease is transmitted by an autosomal recessive gene and occurs predominantly in Jewish infants.

The biochemical defect involves storage of sphingomyelins in the neurons, liver, and spleen, which can be identified by biopsy of the rectum or the brain. The blood and the bone marrow contain foam cells and vacuolated leukocytes. Brady demonstrated recently the reduction of activity of a specific enzyme that catalyzes the hydrolysis of sphingomyelin in tissues of patients with Niemann-Pick disease.

The clinical picture consists of a developmental arrest and mental regression accompanied by abdominal enlargement due to hepatosplenomegaly, anemia, general emaciation, and occasionally a cherry red spot in the retina, similar to that found in Tay-Sachs disease. The onset is usually in infancy, following an initially normal development. Occasional cases have a later onset and a relatively slow chronic course, characterized by ataxia and a lesser degree of mental deficiency. No treatment is known at present, and death occurs in most cases in early childhood, before the age of 4.

GAUCHER'S DISEASE. This lipidosis also occurs mostly in Jewish children and has an autosomal recessive mode of genetic transmission.

The metabolic abnormality, as shown by Brady et al., consists of a diminution of enzyme activity—namely of the enzyme that catalyzes the breakdown of glucocerebroside. This leads to an accumulation of the cerebroside kerasin in the neurons and in the cells of the reticuloendothelial system. Characteristically, there is an accumulation of Gaucher cells—that is, large, pale, round cells filled with kerasin—first in the reticuloendothelial system and then in other tissues. The demonstration of these Gaucher cells in the bone marrow or in biopsy material from the brain or rectum serves as a diagnostic proof of this disease. Clinically, the illness occurs in two forms.

The acute infantile form has its onset in infancy, after several months of normal development, and is characterized by progressive mental deterioration and developmental arrest. Hepatosplenomegaly, abdominal and cranial enlargement, hypotonia, and opisthotonus complete the clinical course, which is usually fatal before the end of the first year of life.

The chronic form has an insidious onset, usually any time before the tenth year of life, but occurs occasionally in adolescents and young adults. There is less or no involvement of the CNS, and the main clinical symptoms are physical, including hepatosplenomegaly, anemia, thrombocytopenia, and bone changes leading to pathological fractures and severe deformities. The course is chronic, characterized mainly by chronic physical handicaps.

BIGLER AND HSIA SYNDROME. This rare disorder is transmitted by an autosomal recessive gene. Its biochemical abnormality consists of an elevation of triglycerides in the blood.

The clinical features include hepatosplenomegaly and mental retardation. No treatment is available.

PROGRESSIVE LEUKOENCEPHALOPATHIES. This group consists of several clinical syndromes characterized by a degeneration of the cortical white matter, with the onset varying from infancy to adulthood and even senility. The central pathological feature in all of them is the demyelination of the cerebral white matter, followed by a degeneration of the axon cylinders. In some cases there is an extension of the degenerative process to the cerebellum and the basal ganglia. The histopathological findings may be demonstrable in the biopsy material of the brain.

The genetic mode of transmission is autosomal recessive, except for Merzbacher-Pelizaeus disease, which is transmitted by a sex-linked recessive gene. Schilder's disease may often occur sporadically.

The clinical course is characterized by progressive dementia, developmental regression, hypotonia, spasticity, ataxia, cortical blindness and deafness, convulsions, and paroxysmal attacks of laughing. The nature of the clinical symptoms depends on the localization of the degenerative process. The prognosis is usually hopeless, and no treatment is available.

The four variations of this disorder are not always distinguishable from each other, and their classification is based primarily on the time of onset and the duration of the illness. Sometimes the clinical course is so acute as to suggest an encephalomyelitis. Some cases, however, manifest remissions lasting for years, during which progress of the disease is arrested.

Schilder's disease may begin at any age but is more common in older children and adults. There is demyelination of cerebral white matter to sudanophilic neutral fat. Long tract signs, such as spastic paraparesis or tetraparesis, are usually the first symptoms, followed by cortical blindness and deafness, convulsions, and dementia. Some cases are reported as responding to steroids, but caution is indicated in evaluation of these reports. The disease is chemically identical to but clinically different from multiple sclerosis.

In Krabbe's disease the developmental regression begins in the first year of life. The biopsy material of the brain contains peculiar multinucleated giant cells, globoid cells containing glycolipids.

Metachromatic leukodystrophy, histochemically, is characterized by demyelination and accumulation of metachromatic sulfatide in the brain and peripheral nerves. The metachromatic material may be demonstrable in the urinary sediment or by Austin's fluff test. The onset is usually in the first two years of life, but the disease may begin later, even in adulthood. The clinical course leads progressively to dementia and neurological deterioration.

In Merzbacher-Pelizaeus disease, the onset is usually in the first years of life, beginning with ataxia and nystagmus, followed by a progressive dementia, spasticity, and rigidity.

Disorders of carbohydrate metabolism

GALACTOSEMIA. Galactosemia is transmitted by an autosomal recessive gene. Its metabolic defect, detected in 1956 by Kalckar et al., consists of the inability to convert galactose to glucose because of the enzymatic defect of galactose 1-phosphate uridyltransferase. This is absent in the liver and in red blood cells, the latter fact being very helpful in substantiating the diagnosis in early infancy.

The urinary findings include the presence of galactose and general amino aciduria. The reducing substances in the urine may be detected by the use of Benedict's solution and Clinitest tablets but not by the use of Tes-Tape, which is specific only for glucose. The heterozygous carriers can be detected by a galactose tolerance test, but the tolerance test may also be abnormal in infants recovering from severe diarrhea and in patients with liver disease or hyperthyroidism.

Galactosemia, like PKU, is a fine example of rewarded combined effort in basic and applied research. The pinpointing of the exact location of the enzymatic defect, circumvention by dietary adjustment, and early detection, which allows for a prevention of serious brain damage, are held out as an example and a promise to researchers in other metabolic disorders.

The clinical manifestations begin after a few days of milk feeding and include jaundice, vomiting, diarrhea, failure to thrive, and hepatomegaly. If untreated, the disease may be fatal within a short time, or it may lead to progressive mental deterioration, associated with cataracts, hepatic insufficiency, and occasional hypoglycemic convulsions.

A galactose-free diet, instituted early, prevents all clinical manifestations and allows normal physical and mental development. Moderate amounts of milk may be reinstituted under careful monitoring at the beginning of school age, since the patients usually develop alternate metabolic pathways of galactose metabolism.

GLYCOGEN STORAGE DISEASE (VAN GIERKE'S DISEASE). There are several forms of this autosomal recessive metabolic disorder of glycogen metabolism, involving several essential enyzmes. The variant most frequently associated with mental retardation is the neuromuscular form of glycogenosis characterized by glycogen storage in the nerve cells, muscles, and other tissues, such as of the liver, heart, kidneys, adrenals, and the reticuloendothelial system.

The clinical manifestations usually begin in the neonatal period and include hepatomegaly, failure to thrive, acidosis, frequent hypoglycemic convulsions, and mental retardation. Hypotonia and heart involvement leading to cardiac failure are often encountered. Only symptomatic treatment for this disorder is available.

MCQUARRIE TYPE OF HYPOGLYCEMIA. The mode of transmission in this metabolic abnormality is autosomal recessive. The major feature is a recurrent hypoglycemia associated with convulsions and coma, caused by a deficiency of alpha cells in the pancreas. The symptoms appear early in life, often shortly after birth, and lead to progressive mental retardation. Therapy with adrenocorticotropic hormone (ACTH) or glucagon is effective and prevents mental retardation.

LEUCINE-SENSITIVE HYPOGLYCEMIA. This rare autosomal recessive condition is characterized by episodic hypoglycemia, associated with coma and convulsions, after ingestion of leucine, an amino acid commonly found in the diet. Mental retardation develops if the condition is not recognized and treated. Hypoglycemia following a leucine tolerance test is diagnostic for this disease. Treatment is dietary and consists of a low protein diet or a leucine-deficient diet.

FRUCTOSE INTOLERANCE. The genetic pattern is auto-somal recessive in this disorder, which is characterized by episodes of hypoglycemia after the intake of fructose or sucrose. The nature of the biochemical defect is still uncertain but may involve a deficiency in liver aldolase. Mental retardation results in unrecognized and un-treated cases but may be prevented by dietary measures, which con-sist of a replacement of sucrose and fructose by other sugars.

SUCROSURIA AND HIATUS HERNIA. It is yet uncertain whether this represents a genetic disorder. The characteristic findings include sucrosuria after a normal diet, esophageal hernia, and mental retardation. Omission of sucrose in the diet is *not* effective in pre-venting mental deterioration.

Miscellaneous metabolic disorders

IDIOPATHIC HYPERCALCEMIA. The pattern of inherit-ance in this disorder is that of an autosomal recessive trait, and hy-persensitivity to vitamin D probably represents the metabolic aberra-tion. The serum calcium is elevated but may be occasionally normal, and suspicion may be ruled out only after three or four determina-tions.

The clinical features include irritability, mental retardation, a pe-culiar elfin facial appearance, short stature, hypotonia, hypertension, strabismus, and nephrocalcinosis.

Several therapeutic approaches are in use, of which the mainte-nance of patients on cortisone is the most commonly used in this country. The more severe form of the illness does not respond to therapy and often leads to early death or progressive mental deterio-ration.

HYPOPARATHYROIDISM. The cause of hypoparathyroid-ism is obscure, but a familial tendency has been reported. The onset in most cases is during childhood. Early diagnosis and early institu-tion of treatment may prevent physical and mental deterioration.

The metabolic error consists of a deficient production of parathy-roid hormone by the parathyroid gland. Laboratory findings include elevated phosphorus and diminished calcium levels in the blood. Ad-ministration of Parathormone restores blood calcium and phosphorus to normal levels, which is of diagnostic value.

The clinical picture is dominated by episodic tetany and tonic con-vulsions. X-rays may reveal calcifications in the brain with a predilec-tion for the basal ganglia. Symptoms of hypocalcemia and mental deterioration often develop in protracted cases.

Treatment in early-recognized cases consists of administration of calcium and vitamin D or A T 10. In untreated cases of long stand-ing, the mental deterioration is irreversible.

PSEUDOHYPOPARATHYROIDISM. The metabolic defect

in this autosomal recessive disorder resides in the renal tubules. They fail to inhibit reabsorption of phosphorus in response to Parathormone, which is produced in normal quantity. The laboratory findings are similar to those in hypoparathyroidism.

The illness is characterized by tetany, convulsions, intracranial calcifications, a peculiar round face, and many skeletal abnormalities, particularly of the hands. Mental retardation follows the repeated seizures. Treatment includes vitamin D and calcium.

PSEUDOPSEUDOHYPOPARATHYROIDISM. The autosomal recessive metabolic abnormality still bearing this cumbersome name produces signs similar to pseudohypoparathyroidism, including mental retardation, despite a normal blood level of both calcium and phosphorus. No treatment is available.

GOITROUS CRETINISM. Cretinism as a condition associated with mental retardation has been known since antiquity. Throughout modern history up to the middle of the nineteenth century, all forms of mental retardation were considered as variants of this condition.

The classical endemic variety occurs in certain regions as a result of iodine deficiency in the diet. Sporadic athyreosis, congenital absence of the thyroid gland, is the common variety in this country and may be caused by transplacental transmission of immune bodies against thyroid from the mother.

Other varieties of sporadic cretinism occurring in individuals with adequate iodine intake have attracted a lot of attention lately. Several variants are described, all resulting in faulty synthesis of thyroid hormone but associated with varying metabolic defects determined by autosomal recessive genes. Listed among the biochemical abnormalities in asymptomatic heterozygous carriers are the absence of dehalogenase, a defect in production of thyroxin in the thyroid gland, and a defect in the deiodinating monoiodotyrosine. In some cases associated with deafness, a disposition to various thyroid disorders in the patient's relatives was reported.

The clinical signs in all varieties include hypothyroidism, goiter (except in athyreosis), dwarfism, coarse skin, disturbances in ossification, hypertelorism, and a large tongue (see Figure 1). Mental retardation becomes a part of the clinical picture if the disease is unrecognized and untreated in infancy. This is explained by the essential role that thyroxin plays in the formulation of structural proteins and lipids in the central nervous system during early infancy. The children are sluggish, their voices hoarse, and speech does not develop. Among the laboratory findings are a low basal metabolism rate, depressed protein-bound iodine, and a high cholesterol level. The radioactive iodine uptake is low, except in the variety reported by Stanbury, which is recessively inherited.

FIGURE 1. Inadequately treated cretinism in a 5-year-old boy. (Courtesy of Dr. Richmond S. Paine, Children's Hospital, Washington, D.C.)

Treatment with thyroid extract may avert most of the symptoms if instituted early in life. It is not effective in adult cretins. Endemic goitrous cretinism is treated and prevented by the ingestion of small amounts of iodine.

CRIGLER-NAJJAR DISEASE (FAMILIAL NONHEMOLYTIC JAUNDICE). This defect in the bilirubin metabolism in the liver produces a nonhemolytic jaundice and represents an autosomal recessive trait. The indirect bilirubin in the serum is elevated, which leads to a gradual development of brain damage (kernicterus) and mental deterioration.

PYRIDOXINE DEPENDENCY. The exact mechanism in this autosomal recessive disorder is unknown, but it probably involves some enzyme system in which pyridoxine (vitamin B_6) acts as a coenzyme. The affected infants have abnormally high pyridoxine requirements.

The clinical symptoms consist of seizures accompanied by EEG changes beginning toward the end of the first week of life. If the condition remains untreated, it results in spasticity and mental deficiency.

The diagnosis may be established by intravenous administration of 100 mg. of pyridoxine, which results in a dramatic cessation of seizures and improvement in the EEG. Therapeutically, the addition of 10 mg. of pyridoxine to the daily diet is required to keep the patient symptom-free.

WILSON'S DISEASE (HEPATOLENTICULAR DEGENERATION). This disorder of copper metabolism has a recessive mode of inheritance. The two variants of this disease, the juvenile and the adult forms, are inherited independently as separate entities.

The biochemical changes are similar in both forms and consist of a diminished blood level of copper-containing ceruloplasmin. This is accompanied by excessive copper deposits in various tissues, chiefly in the liver and the brain. The resulting liver cirrhosis and degeneration of the lenticular nucleus gave the disease its name. Other laboratory findings include an elevated copper excretion in the urine and amino aciduria involving primarily the aromatic amino acids (phenylalanine, tyrosine, and threonine). The latter is being explained on a basis of kidney damage due to copper deposits or blamed on a defect in a copper-containing enzyme, tyrosinase.

The heterozygous carriers are asymptomatic but often manifest abnormal levels of ceruloplasmin in the blood and a tendency to various hepatic difficulties. A copper-loading test is available for detection of heterozygous carriers.

The clinical signs in both forms of the disease include cirrhosis of the liver, progressive emotional and mental deterioration, pseudobulbar palsy, fatuous facial expression, spasticity, and a greenish brown ring in the iris (Kayser-Fleischer ring).

The juvenile form begins between the ages of 7 and 15. Inattentiveness in school and dystonia are usually the first signs. This form is usually unresponsive to treatment, since the dystonia is related not to copper deposits but to hepatic dysfunction, which causes brain damage to the basal ganglia. The nature of the relationship between the hepatic disorder and the brain damage, found also in other liver diseases, is unknown.

The adult form usually begins with tremors and dysarthria but may begin with psychiatric symptoms. It has a good prognosis. There are several treatment methods available, all aiming at lowering the serum copper level and increasing the urinary copper excretion. Penicillamine, a copper-chelating amino acid derived from penicillin, is presently the most effective therapeutic agent. Penicillin-sensitive patients may require the concomitant administration of steroids. Dimercaprol (British anti-lewisite; BAL) is also used with fair results.

GARGOYLISM (HURLER'S DISEASE). Most cases of this

disorder are transmitted by an autosomal recessive gene, but sex-linked recessive transmission involving only males has also been observed. The basic metabolic disturbance, the nature of which is still unknown, results in the accumulation of a mucopolysaccharide, chondroitin sulfate B, and glycolipids in the brain, liver, spleen, and connective tissue.

The biochemical findings include chrondroitin sulfate in the urine and characteristic foam cells in the blood and bone marrow; the lymphocytes contain metachromatic inclusions, and X-rays show several characteristic abnormalities, such as elongation of the sella turcica, beaking of the thoracic spine on the lateral view (kyphosis), club-shaped lower ribs, thickening of the long bones, misshapen metacarpal bones and phalanges, and skull malformations (see Figure 2).

The clinical course is slow and progressive and starts usually at a very early age, leading to death before adolescence. The hepatosplenomegaly causes abdominal enlargement. The stature is dwarfed, and

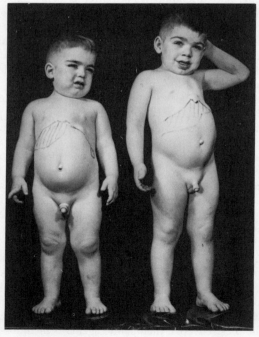

FIGURE 2. Two brothers with Hurler's disease (gargoylism). Note the characteristic facies and the hepatosplenomegaly. (Courtesy of Dr. Richmond S. Paine, Children's Hospital, Washington, D.C.)

the face acquires a peculiar appearance that gave rise to the name of the disease. The facial characteristics include bushy confluent eyebrows, thick lips, large tongue, and coarse features. The spadelike hands and sometimes hypertelorism and hydrocephalus complete the picture. There is nearly always a progressive mental deterioration, which often precedes the characteristic facial appearance. No treatment is available.

The differential diagnosis may present some problems. The superficial resemblance to cretins is easily ruled out by X-ray findings and by the hepatosplenomegaly as well as biochemical findings. Gargoylism may also resemble Morquio's disease, a hereditary condition characterized by skeletal deformities and dwarfism without impairment of mental development.

Chromosomal aberrations. Lejeune's discovery in 1959 of the existence of 47, instead of 46, chromosomes in patients with Down's syndrome (mongolism) ushered in a new, exciting era of cytogenetic research. The introduction of new, simplified techniques permitted the study of chromosomal patterns in large populations, which led to the discovery of many abnormalities often associated with mental retardation. The degree of mental retardation is usually more severe in autosomal aberrations and milder in sex chromosome aberrations. With the exception of Down's syndrome, the reported number of patients with chromosomal disorders is rather small, but the great scientific interest in their study is due to the hope of finding a key to the mapping of genetic loci for various enzymes, an important step for the better understanding of inborn errors of metabolism and other genetic disorders. There have been some exciting recent findings by Paine and others of deviations in various enzymatic levels in Down's syndrome that may help identify the genetic loci on chromosome 21. Such findings represent another step toward the better understanding of genetic activity and its correlation with clinical findings. Many similar clinical features are found in several seemingly unrelated chromosomal syndromes.

AUTOSOMAL DISORDERS. a. Down's syndrome (mongolism): Since the classical description of mongolism by the English physician Langdon Down in 1866, this syndrome has remained the most discussed, most investigated, and most controversial in the field of mental retardation. Its cause still remains obscure, despite a plethora of theories and hypotheses advanced with variable acclaim in the last hundred years. There is agreement on very few predisposing factors in chromosomal disorders, among them increased age of the mother and possibly increased age of the father and X-ray radiation. The problem of cause is complicated even further by the recent recognition of three distinct types of chromosomal aberrations in Down's syndrome:

1. Patients with trisomy 21 (3 of chromosome 21 instead of the usual 2), who represent the overwhelming majority of mongoloid patients, have 47 chromosomes, with an extra chromosome 21. The karyotypes of the mothers are normal. A nondisjunction during miosis, occurring for yet unknown reasons, is held responsible for this disorder.

2. Nondisjunction occurring after fertilization in any cell division will result in mosaicism, a condition in which both normal and trisomic cells are found in various tissues.

3. In translocation, there is a fusion of two chromosomes, mostly 21 and 15, resulting in a total of 46 chromosomes in affected patients, despite the extra chromosome material. This disorder, unlike trisomy 21, is usually inherited, and the translocation chromosome may be found in unaffected parents and siblings. These asymptomatic carriers have only 45 chromosomes.

Recent biochemical studies in Down's syndrome revealed increased levels of galactose 1-phosphate uridyltransferase and of acid and alkaline phosphatases, elevated activity of glucose 6-phosphate dehydrogenase and 5-nucleotidase, and diminished blood serotonin levels. These abnormalities were found only in the trisomic type. The enzyme levels were in the high normal range in the translocation type of the disease, a fact that may differentiate these two varieties without the cumbersome chromosomal studies. These biochemical findings suggest that the surplus genetic material in mongolism results in a derangement of genetic homeostasis, involving many genes or gene complexes. The question of the prime cause of this metabolic derangement awaits further clarification.

The incidence of Down's syndrome in the United States is approximately 1 in every 700 births. Down, in his original description, mentioned the frequency of 10 per cent among all mentally retarded patients. Interestingly enough, the frequency of patients with Down's syndrome in institutions for the mentally retarded today also approximates 10 per cent. In a middle-aged mother (over 32 years), the risk of having a mongoloid child with trisomy 21 is about 1 in 100, but when translocation is present, the risk is about 1 in 3. These facts assume special importance in genetic counseling. Occasionally Down's syndrome is associated with acute lymphatic leukemia.

The neuropathological findings are limited to a tendency toward embryonic convolutional patterns of the brain, a small cerebellum and brain stem, abnormalities of the pituitary gland and irregular disposition of ganglion cells in the third cortical layer. Cardiac anomalies, particularly septal defects, are often found, as is hypogonadism.

Mental retardation is the overriding feature of Down's syndrome. The majority of patients belong to the moderately and severely retarded groups, with only a minority having an I.Q. above 50. According to many sources, patients with Down's syndrome are placid, cheerful, and cooperative, which facilitates their adjustment at home. The picture, however, seems to change in adolescence, especially in institutions, where a variety of emotional difficulties, behavior disorders, and (rarely) psychotic illnesses may be seen.

The diagnosis is made with relative ease in an older child but is often difficult in newborn infants. The most important signs in newborns include general hypotonia, oblique palpebral fissures, abundant neck skin, small flattened skull, high cheekbones, and a protruding tongue. The hands are broad and thick with a single palmar transversal crease, and the little fingers are short and curve inward (see Figure 3). Moro's reflex is weak or absent.

There are more than one hundred signs or stigmata described in Down's syndrome, but they are rarely found all in one individual. In addition to the signs enumerated above, among the most frequently encountered are a high cephalic index, epicanthal folds, fissured tongue, dwarfed stature, small rounded ears, strabismus, white speckling of the iris (Brushfield spots), and lax ligaments. The dermal ridges on the palms and soles have a characteristic configuration, which is often diagnostic. Occasionally, one sees a patient with only a few of these stigmata, looking relatively normal. Many of these have normal or even superior intelligence.

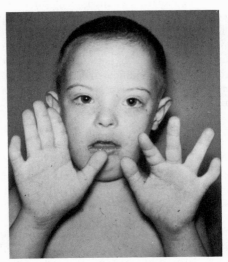

FIGURE 3. Child with Down's syndrome (mongolism). Note the facial features, the single palmar crease, and the short and incurvated little fingers. (Courtesy of Dr. Beale H. Ong, Children's Hospital, Washington, D.C.)

Life expectancy used to be about twelve years. But with the advent of antibiotics, few young patients succumb to infections, and one may contemplate a normal or near-normal life expectancy for most patients. Despite numerous therapeutic recommendations, no treatment has proved to be effective.

b. Cat-cry syndrome (*cri du chat*): This aberration consists of a missing part of the fifth chromosome. The affected children are severely retarded and show many stigmata often associated with chromosomal aberrations, such as microcephaly, low-set ears, oblique palpebral fissures, hypertelorism, and micrognathia. The characteristic catlike cry—due to laryngeal abnormalities—which gave this syndrome its name, gradually changes and disappears with increasing age.

c. Trisomy 13: This abnormality is also known as holoprosencephaly and is characterized by rudimentary olfactory lobes. The term arhinocephaly was used in the past. Among the clinical signs are low-set ears, cleft palate, cleft lip, sloping forehead, single transversal palmar crease, polydactyly, and abnormal dermal patterns. Many associated congenital defects have been described. The patients are mentally retarded and often have minor motor seizures and apneic spells.

d. Trisomy 18: This abnormality occurs with a frequency of 1 in 500 live births. X-ray radiation of the gonads prior to conception has been suggested as the causative factor. The cases reported to date show a preponderance of females (80 per cent). The clinical picture includes mental retardation, low-set ears, micrognathia, cardiac anomalies, prominent occiput, hypotonicity at birth followed by hypertonicity, short stature, equinovarus, and overriding fingers and toes. As in other chromosomal aberrations, there is a characteristic dermatoglyphic pattern.

ANOMALIES OF THE SEX CHROMOSOMES. As a group, these disorders are associated with milder forms of mental retardation and sometimes with normal and even superior intelligence.

a. Klinefelter's syndrome: The male patients with this disorder have testicular atrophy evident at puberty and signs of feminization, such as gynecomastia. Their karyotypes usually show an XXY pattern. There is a darkly stained Barr chromatin body in the nuclei of the cells on the nuclear membrane; this is a female nucleus pattern dependent on there being two X chromosomes, one of which is genetically active and the other inactive and constituting the nuclear sex chromatin body, according to the Lyon hypothesis.

Other variants with similar physical characteristics have been detected, mostly among institutionalized mentally retarded. Their sex chromosome pattern shows a wide range of aberrations, such as

XXXY, XXXXY, and XXYY. There are frequent mosaics and associations with autosomal trisomies.

The degree of mental retardation in all these patients may vary from mild to severe, but many of them have normal intelligence. The patients are generally cooperative but may develop serious social and body image difficulties, leading sometimes to social withdrawal, serious difficulties in adjustment, especially in adolescence, and paranoid tendencies.

b. Ovarian dysgenesis (Turner's syndrome): The main clinical features of this disorder are small stature, webbed neck, and cubitus valgus. The chromosomal pattern is usually XO, and only a minority of the patients are mentally retarded.

A greater preponderance of mental retardation of mild to moderate degree is found among the so-called super females, most of whom have no physical abnormalities, but they do have three X chromosomes, giving them a total of 47. A smaller group exists with four X chromosomes, for a total of 48.

Neuropathological aspects of prenatal developmental anomalies. The exact nature of the damage or malformation of the central nervous system underlying mental retardation is often difficult to assess. The reaction of the immature nervous tissue differs from the reaction of adult tissue to injury and disease, and the telltale signs of previous destruction in the form of an overgrowth of neuroglial and connective tissue are often missing. The effects of endogenous genetic disturbances may be indistinguishable from those of exogenous origin. The remarkable recovery potential of the immature brain may account for the often striking discrepancy between the degree of retardation and the relative paucity of neuropathological finding. Conversely, intellectual function may be normal in the presence of significant brain damage.

The time of the insult to the CNS, the nature of the injurious agent, and the extent of tissue recovery are the decisive factors in determining the ultimate extent and effect of the CNS damage. However, its final form, available to investigation, may not give precise clues as to the time and duration of the injury. In fact, it is often difficult to distinguish between an abrupt arrest of development and a more gradual delay in maturation.

Structural damage may vary a great deal in response to the same noxa. For instance, the effects of German measles on the fetus may range from deafness through microcephaly and hydrocephalus to fetal death. In addition to the stage of embryogenesis at the time of maternal infection, there are still many largely unexplored factors responsible for these wide variations.

Present knowledge is still limited as to the cause of most intrauterine malformations of the brain, the incrimination of X-ray radiation and German measles being the only exceptions. The mechanism of brain damage in the neonatal period is more predictable, with a characteristic response of the brain tissue to ischemia and asphyxia, which produce structural lesions in the cortical and subcortical tissues. The infant in the neonatal period severs his dependence on the maternal circulation and thus becomes vulnerable to toxic substances that were formerly cleared and removed by the maternal circulatory system. This explains the fact that most of the inborn errors of metabolism do not become manifest until the neonatal period, and structural CNS damage may be prevented by early treatment. The postnatal period is also characterized by a rapid myelination marked by the appearance of various disorders of fat metabolism affecting the central nervous system.

AUTOSOMAL DOMINANT DISORDERS. These anomalies are determined by single dominant genes of variable expressivity and penetrance and are rare, since many of those afflicted are infertile. The clinical picture varies greatly, and mild forms with minimal signs and only mild mental retardation are often seen. In addition to cerebral defects, these disorders involve ectodermal, visceral, and skeletal anomalies.

a. Dystrophia myotonica: Wasting and weakness of muscles of the extremities, face, jaw, and neck are the main characteristics of this disorder. Cataracts, alopecia, and testicular atrophy are found in some cases. All symptoms usually appear in young adults and are often accompanied by moderate to severe mental retardation.

b. Epiloia (tuberous sclerosis): This autosomal disorder may manifest itself with great variability, probably due to the irregularity of the abnormal gene or to the influence of additional modifying genes. The skin lesions consist of sebaceous adenomata, red on the face, and brownish white on the rest of the body. Throughout the cerebral cortex in the lateral ventricles and in the cerebellum, multiple nodules are found, of rubber consistency, composed mainly of glial tissue, with some giant undifferentiated nerve cells. In addition, tumors are found in various parts of the body, such as rhabdomyoma of the heart, mixed kidney tumors, hepatic fibrolipoma, and retinal nerve tumors. (See Figure 4.)

The clinical picture is often complicated by systemic manifestations, such as cardiac failure, respiratory disease due to pulmonary cysts, and retinal involvement. The degree of mental retardation may vary from mild to very severe, and other signs and symptoms show similar variability. Of special interest are cases with psychotic symptoms, often with only moderate retardation.

The prognosis varies with the degree and location of the systemic involvement. Mild forms of the disease may occur with only minimal skin involvement or epilepsy. X-ray of the skull may reveal multiple calcification.

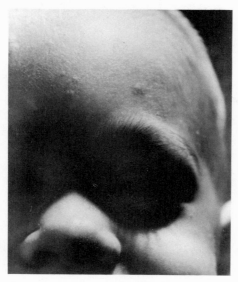

FIGURE 4. Sebaceous adenomata on the face in tuberous sclerosis. (Courtesy of Dr. Richmond S. Paine, Chidlren's Hospital, Washington, D.C.)

Treatment is limited to anticonvulsant medication, which is usually effective in controlling the seizures.

c. Neurofibromatosis (von Recklinghausen disease): The main features of this disorder are small brown patches distributed over the entire body along the course of subcutaneous nerves, autonomic nerves, and nerve trunks. Sensory nerves are usually more affected. Astrocytomas, ependymomas, and meningiomas may be found in the brain. The skin manifestation usually begins in childhood and may include large skin polyps and *café au lait* spots over the trunk and extremities (see Figure 5). Acoustic or optic nerve glioma may also occur. In addition to the skin manifestations, the clinical picture includes epilepsy and, in about 10 per cent of cases, mental retardation as well.

Anticonvulsant medication and neurosurgery may sometimes be effective because of the benign nature of the tumors.

d. Encephalofacial angiomatosis (Sturge-Weber disease): This disorder is believed to be due to an irregularly dominant gene, but the exact mechanism of hereditary transmission is not yet clear. In its classical form, the syndrome includes a facial nevus in the distribution of the fifth cranial nerve, buphthalmos, hemiparesis of the contralateral extremities, convulsions, and mental retardation. The convulsions and mental retardation are due to intracranial angiomata,

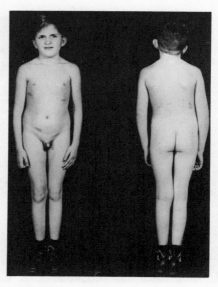

FIGURE 5. Neurofibromatosis. Note the *café au lait* spots over the trunk. (Courtesy of Dr. Richmond Paine, Children's Hospital, Washington, D.C.)

which often become calcified and may be radiologically demonstrated. Neurosurgical intervention has been attempted but is rarely successful.

e. Retinocerebellar angiomatosis (Hippel-Lindau disease): Familial occurrence of this rare disorder has been reported. The pathological findings consist of angiomata in the cerebellum and the retina. The clinical picture includes mental retardation and cerebellar signs.

f. Arachnodactyly (Marfan's syndrome): Arachnodactyly is an inheritable disorder, probably transmitted by a single, dominant gene of variable expressivity. It involves changes in many parts of the body, chiefly in the skeletal, cardiovascular, and ocular structures. The patients are tall, have long extremities with long, spiderlike fingers and toes, coloboma, bilateral lens dislocation, and cardiac anomalies. The accompanying mental retardation is usually mild.

g. Sjögren's disease: This rare disease is transmitted by a dominant autosomal gene. Its clinical features include mental retardation, congenital cataracts, and ataxia.

h. Congenital ichthyosis: Several variants of this skin disorder have been described. The clinical picture is characterized by generalized scaliness, associated with spastic diplegia or epilepsy in the form of generalized motor seizures. The mental retardation varies from moderate in cases with epilepsy to severe in cases with spastic diplegia.

i. Chondrodystrophy (achondroplasia): This disorder is characterized by very short limbs due to a disturbed ossification of the carti-
lage. The head is often large, and the accompanying mental retardation is usually mild.

j. Craniosynostosis: This group includes several conditions characterized by premature closure of cranial sutures, skull deformities, and
brain damage due to increased intracranial pressure. Allen includes in
this group the formerly separate syndrome of Crouzon (craniofacial
dysostosis). The cause of most cases is still unknown, but a dominant
mode of inheritance was reported in some instances, with a familial
tendency to the same type of anomaly. Since not all the cranial sutures are necessarily involved, the shape of the skull may vary greatly.
Its normal growth is inhibited in a direction perpendicular to the
obliterated suture line, and compensatory growth takes place in other
directions. The degree of brain damage may depend on the ultimate
size rather than shape of the skull, but an associated brain anomaly
may exist in some cases. A premature fusion of multiple sutures will
result in increased intracranial pressure during the critical first two
years of rapid brain growth.

The elongated cranium (dolichocephaly) is most common. The
broad skull (brachycephaly) represents another variant. Obliteration
of all cranial sutures results in a pointed skull (acrocephaly). Several
facial and orbital deformities may be associated with various forms of
craniosynostosis, such as hypertelorism, shallow orbits resulting in ex-
ophthalmos, a beak-shaped nose, choanal atresia, and several others.
Syndactyly is often associated with acrocephaly.

The infants may be normal at birth but, during infancy, begin to
manifest a variety of signs and symptoms due to increased intracranial pressure: papilledema, optic atrophy, vomiting, and seizures.
Mental retardation often follows. The severity of the clinical
picture rises in inverse proportion to the time of the fusion. X-rays of
the skull may show digital markings due to increased intracranial
pressure and calcification of the intercranial sutures. Surgical separation of the cranial bones may be effective if done early, before permanent brain damage occurs.

k. Hypertelorism: This disorder is characterized by a very wide
distance between the eyes, which may be seen in several other disorders. Familial occurrence of this disorder indicates a dominant mode
of inheritance in most cases, but some cases with a recessive mechanism have been reported.

In addition to the ocular feature, the patients manifest a flat nasal
bridge, external strabismus, and sometimes a vertical midline groove
in the forehead. The mentality ranges from normal to moderate retardation. Some retarded patients with this anomaly have hyperamino aciduria. Convulsions may occur.

l. Nephrogenic diabetes insipidus: This disorder is usually restricted to males and is counted by some among the sex-linked dominant genetic disorders. The defect lies in the renal tubules and leads to periodic dehydration. Mental retardation and delay in growth are frequent.

DEVELOPMENTAL ANOMALIES DUE TO RECESSIVE OR UNKNOWN GENETIC MECHANISM. a. Anencephaly: The cause of this lethal anomaly is unknown, but it is believed by some to be an autosomal recessive disorder. It is one of the most common congenital brain malformations, and its incidence ranges between 0.5 and 3.7 per 1,000. The anencephalic fetus usually succumbs during delivery or shortly thereafter. The pathological findings include an absence of the cranial vault and most of the central nervous system or at least the absence of both cerebral hemispheres.

b. Hydranencephaly: This condition of unknown cause is characterized by the absence of the cerebral cortex but intact meninges and cranium, the latter filled with clear fluid. The infant may live for several weeks or even a few months and may appear normal at birth. Shortly thereafter, however, he develops convulsions and rigidity of the extremities, and the head enlarges rapidly. Pneumoencephalogram and transillumination of the head are usually diagnostic.

c. Porencephaly: This disorder is characterized by cystic formations in the cerebral hemispheres, communicating sometimes with the ventricular system or subarachnoid space. The defects vary in size and shape, and the clinical picture depends on the amount of remaining functional cortical tissue. The patients who survive early childhood are usually bedridden, have bilateral hemiplegia or tetraplegia, and are either severely or moderately retarded.

d. Microcephaly: Microcephaly is a purely descriptive term, covering a variety of disorders whose main clinical feature is a small, peculiarly shaped head and mental retardation (see Figure 6).

Microcephaly may be found in 20 per cent of the institutionalized mentally retarded population. The cause varies greatly and includes a hereditary group, one due to intrauterine influences, and one due to insults in the perinatal or postnatal period.

The hereditary group is relatively uncommon and includes several varieties, all with an autosomal recessive mode of transmission with one exception—that described by Paine, which follows a sex-linked recessive pattern and is associated with generalized hyperamino aciduria. The clinical picture of the hereditary microcephalics varies but generally is milder than in acquired microcephaly. The patient's small head and birdlike face contrasts with an undersized but relatively well-developed body. Only a minority in this group have disturbance in motor functions, and they are usually severely retarded. The rest fit into the moderately retarded group.

Microcephaly due to intrauterine influences comprises a far larger

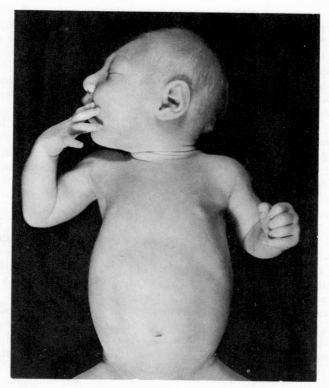

FIGURE 6. Infant with microcephaly. (Courtesy of Dr. Richmond S. Paine, Children's Hospital, Washington, D.C.)

group. The causes include X-ray radiation during pregnancy, maternal rubella, toxoplasmosis, maternal diabetes, and cytomegalic inclusion body disease. These variants often have severe neurological abnormalities in the motor and sensory area that range from a mild spastic paralysis with general delay in development to a spastic tetraplegia or blindness, associated with profound mental retardation. Convulsions occur in this group with great frequency. The cause is often indicated by associated pathological findings, characteristic of the causative agent. These include deafness, microphthalmia, cataracts, cardiac anomalies, and hepatosplenomegaly.

In the perinatal and postnatal group the microcephaly is caused by fetal anoxia, episodes of cardiac arrest, or uncontrolled seizures.

The brain in all types of microcephaly is very small and presents a generalized maldevelopment of the cerebral convolutions and disorganization of the cortical structure of varying degrees. Some cases show intracranial calcifications and cortical atrophy.

e. Macrocephaly: The unusually large size of the brain in this disorder is due primarily to the proliferation of the glial tissue in the white matter of the hemispheres. The clinical features include mental retardation, epilepsy, and disturbances of vision.

In agyria and pachygyria, the convolutions of the brain are absent or maldeveloped. Both anomalies are associated with a severe degree of mental retardation.

f. Hydrocephalus: This name covers a number of conditions having in common an increase in the cerebrospinal fluid, resulting in the enlargement of the head or the ventricles. This group of disorders is listed here because one of its variants, usually due to atresia of the aqueduct, has a sex-linked recessive mode of inheritance. Many cases, however, are due to developmental malformations of undetermined origin, including atresias of the foramina of Magendie and Luschke and of the aqueduct Sylvii, and Arnold-Chiari malformation. The latter is a medullary-cerebellar anomaly, often associated with spina bifida, meningomyelocele, displacement of the medulla into the cervical canal, and occasionally cortical defects. The cases of hydrocephalus that follow viral, bacterial, or aseptic meningitis are due to obstructing fibrosis of the arachnoid tissue.

The abnormality is seldom noted until the second or third month of life, when a rapid enlargement of the head circumference makes its first clinical appearance. The fontanelle becomes tense, and the cranial sutures widen. The head enlarges in all directions. Symptoms of increased intracranial pressure, such as vomiting, papilledema, and rigidity, soon follow. Progressive hydrocephalus leads to dilation of the lateral ventricles, cortical atrophy, and many severe neurological symptoms; it often ends in complete mental and physical deterioration. In milder cases the condition may become spontaneously arrested, and the afflicted children may be only mildly retarded and even have normal intelligence in some cases (see Figures 7 and 8).

g. Agenesis of the corpus callosum: This rare disorder is characterized by the partial or total absence of the great commissure connecting the cerebral hemispheres. This anomaly may be associated with other cerebral defects, such as porencephaly, microgyria, and hydrocephalus. The cause is unclear, but some cases are believed to be genetically determined.

The clinical picture varies with the extent of associated brain anomalies. Mental retardation of varying severity and major, minor, or focal seizures are common. Other neurological disturbances may occur, such as spastic diplegia, hemiparesis, athetosis, and optic atrophy. The pneumoencephalogram shows several characteristic features, of which the marked separation of the lateral ventricles is one.

h. Congenital mental retardation: This large group includes a

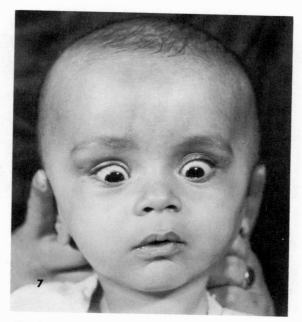

FIGURE 7. Setting-sun sign in hydrocephalus. (Courtesy of Dr. Richmond S. Paine, Children's Hospital, Washington, D.C.)

great variety of mentally retarded children who do not fit into any known clinical category. In addition to mental retardation already evident in early infancy, they may display a variety of nonspecific neurological signs, but many are asymptomatic. Autopsies may reveal many neurological changes, which do not follow a regular pattern.

The cause of most of these cases is obscure and probably includes genetic influences, developmental arrest, and toxic infectious agents. It is to be hoped that, with increased knowledge, this wastebasket group will rapidly dwindle. The last two decades witnessed a good start in this direction.

i. Laurence-Moon-Biedl syndrome: This disorder usually follows an autosomal recessive mode of transmission, but some sex-linked tendency may be suspected from a higher frequency in males. The main features include mental retardation, retinitis pigmentosa, obesity, hypogenitalism, polydactyly, and deaf-mutism.

Maternal infections during pregnancy. SYPHILIS. Syphilis in pregnant women used to be a major cause of a variety of neuropathological changes in their offspring, including mental retardation. Today the incidence of syphilitic complications of pregnancy fluctuates with the incidence of syphilis in the general population. Some recent alarming statistics from several major cities in the United

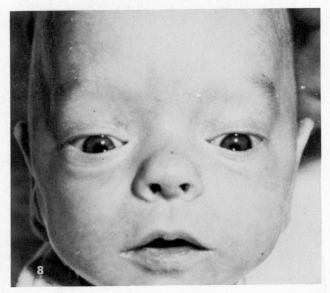

FIGURE 8. Setting-sun sign in a normal premature infant. (From Paine, R. S. Neurological conditions of the neonate. Pediat. Clin. N. Amer., 8: 578, 1961. Reproduced with the permission of the author and the W. B. Saunders Company.)

States indicate that there is still no room for complacency.

RUBELLA (GERMAN MEASLES). This disease has replaced syphilis as the major cause of congenital malformation and mental retardation due to maternal infection. The children of affected mothers may present a number of abnormalities, including congenital heart disease, mental retardation, cataracts, deafness, microcephaly, and microphthalmia. Timing is crucial, since the extent and frequency of complications are in inverse proportion to the duration of pregnancy at the time of maternal infection. When mothers are infected in the first trimester of pregnancy, 10 to 15 per cent of the children will be affected, and the incidence rises to almost 50 per cent when the infection occurs in the first month of pregnancy. The situation is often complicated by subclinical forms of maternal infection, which often go undetected.

OTHER DISEASES. Brain damage due to toxoplasmosis and cytomegalic inclusion body disease transmitted from the pregnant mother to the fetus is another universally recognized but relatively rare complication of pregnancy that often results in mental retardation and a variety of brain malformations. Damage to the fetus from maternal hepatitis has also been reported.

The role of other maternal infections during pregnancy—such as influenza, cold viruses, pneumonia, and urinary tract infections—in the etiology of mental retardation is at present under extensive investigation. The results are as yet inconclusive.

COMPLICATIONS OF PREGNANCY

Toxemia of pregnancy and uncontrolled maternal diabetes present hazards to the fetus and may sometimes result in mental retardation. Maternal malnutrition during pregnancy often results in prematurity and other obstetrical complications. Vaginal hemorrhage, placenta previa, and premature separation of the placenta may be damaging to the fetal brain by causing anoxia. The same may be said about the prolapse of the cord.

The potential teratogenic effect of pharmacological agents administered during pregnancy was widely publicized after the thalidomide tragedy. So far, with the exception of metabolites used in cancer chemotherapy, no usual dosages of drugs are known to damage the central nervous system of the fetus, but caution and restraint in prescribing drugs to pregnant women is certainly indicated.

PERINATAL FACTORS

Prematurity. Many studies point to prematurity as a major cause of disorders of the CNS that are often associated with mental retardation. Paradoxically, improvements in obstetrical techniques result in a higher survival rate of low-birth-weight infants, who are likely to be damaged, since there is an inverse relationship between the degree of damage and the weight at birth. Similarly, there is now a higher survival rate of brain-damaged children who are salvaged by improved obstetrical and pediatric methods.

Prematurity may result in intellectual deficits, sensory and motor handicaps, convulsive disorders, and learning and emotional difficulties. Only a minority of infants weighing less than 1,500 gm. (3 lb. 4 oz.) escape these sequelae.

Prematurity is more prevalent in low socioeconomic segments of the population. Its causes are many and include inadequate prenatal care, with resulting obstetrical complications, such as toxemia and pretoxemic states; multiple births and illegitimate pregnancy; poor maternal nutritional status; mothers' smoking habits; and urinary infections.

Birth injury. This broad term covers all types of brain damage resulting from complications of labor or delivery. Some are due to mechanical trauma, others are due to anoxia, but most cases result from an interplay between these two factors.

TRAUMATIC CEREBRAL INSULTS. These include cephalo-pelvic disproportion, breech delivery, abnormal presentations necessitating the use of mid-forceps and high forceps, and prolonged labor. They may result in subarachnoid and intraventricular hemorrhage, the latter occurring chiefly in prematures.

ANOXIC FACTORS. Anoxemia may occur before, during, and after delivery. Caesarean section and some of the obstetrical complications mentioned under prenatal factors may result in fetal anoxia due to a fall in systemic blood pressure. Changes in fetal heart rate, especially bradycardia, are the best indicators of fetal distress. Respiratory difficulties may be caused by mechanical factors, such as intratracheal mucus plug, or by fetal respiratory depression due to analgesic and anesthetic drugs administered to the mother during labor.

The neuropathological changes after birth injuries are varied and may be found in the cortex, the cerebellum, and the basal ganglia. The most common sequelae include destruction of cortical tissue, with resulting sclerosis, gliosis of white matter, calcification, and cystic cavitation.

Kernicterus. This name refers to yellow staining of the basal ganglia. cerebellum, and brain stem, resulting frequently in cerebral palsy, mental retardation, and hearing deficit. The pigmentation is caused by the excess of nonconjugated (indirect) bilirubin, which is neurotropic, while the conjugated (direct) bilirubin does not enter the nerve cell, for still unexplained reasons. The conversion of indirect to direct bilirubin is effected through conjugation with glucuronic acid, mediated by the enzyme glucuronyl transferase.

Kernicterus follows some cases of neonatal jaundice because of the low enzymatic activity of the newborn, especially the premature infant. It seldom develops unless the level of indirect bilirubin in the blood exceeds 20 mg. per 100 ml. The jaundice usually begins shortly after birth and becomes progressively more extensive, leading to hepatosplenomegaly, apathy, and neurological signs, such as rigidity, inactivity, sometimes flaccidity, a high-pitched or feeble cry, poor Moro's reflex, downward deviation of the eyes, and poor feeding. These signs usually appear on the third to fifth day after birth.

Erythroblastosis fetalis. This is the most common cause of nonphysiological jaundice and is due to mother-child incompatibility regarding the Rh factor, A or B, or (rarely) Kell, Kidd, and Duffy factors in the blood. The resulting breakdown of the infant red cells causes bilirubinemia and anemia. Stillbirth due to a generalized edema, hydrops fetalis, occurs in some cases.

Other causes. Neonatal sepsis, glucose 6-phosphate dehydrogenase deficiency, prematurity, administration of vitamin K, sulfonamides, salicylates, some antibiotics, and caffein and sodium benzoate may all result in indirect hyperbilirubinemia. Exchange transfusion represents the most effective treatment and should be done repeatedly, if necessary, to keep the indirect bilirubin level in the blood below the critical 20 mg. per 100 ml. level. Exchange transfusion carries some risk to the infant, and the risk is greater in prematures. More judicious use of vitamin K, sulfonamides, antibiotics, and salicylates in newborn infants is definitely indicated.

POSTNATAL FACTORS

Advances in antibiotic therapy that permit a higher survival rate of children with infections of the CNS have as a corollary a high frequency of neurological sequelae in the survivors. The extent of the damage varies from mild learning or behavioral disorders to severe dementia, and it depends on several factors, such as the severity of the infection, the nature of the micro-organism, and the age of the child.

Purulent meningitis. This may be successfully treated in most cases if recognized early, but drug-resistant cases may lead to extensive destruction of brain tissue. Subdural effusion is one of many complications that may cause brain damage if unrecognized and untreated. Meningitis caused by pneumococcus usually results in the highest frequency of brain damage, and meningococcus meningitis is the most benign. Tuberculous meningitis also leaves many survivors with extensive chronic encephalopathy.

Viral meningoencephalitis. This group includes poliomyelitis, ECHO virus, Coxsackie virus, herpes simplex, and arthropod-borne encephalitis, still prevalent in some geographic areas. The clinical course varies a great deal, as does the extent of damage to the CNS. Infants run the greatest risk of permanent sequelae, but recovery in even very severe cases is spectacular at times.

Aseptic meningoencephalitis. Aseptic meningitis is seen with the Coxsackie and ECHO viruses, mumps, and herpes simplex. It is usually benign and without residue. An exception is that, due to the herpes-simplex virus in the newborn period, which produces encephalohepatomyocarditis with a high fatality rate and usually damaged survivors.

Parainfectious encephalomyelitis involves small areas of perivenous demyelination but has a lesser inflammatory reaction and does not involve a demonstrable direct viral invasion of the central nervous system.

There is a major possibility of preventing many of these complications by immunization against measles and by performance of smallpox vaccination at the age when the statistical likelihood of involvement of the central nervous system is least—between 1 and 2 years of age. Steroid therapy may be of value in treatment, but this is still uncertain. The sequelae of these complications may include sensory and motor disabilities, convulsive disorders, and mental retardation.

Lead poisoning. This condition, which frequently leads to chronic encephalopathy and mental retardation, is still quite common in large cities among the disadvantaged population. Old houses in numerous slums, coated with lead-containing paints, and a faulty mother-child interaction, characteristic of children with pica, result in the still appallingly high number of permanently damaged children. Treatment with chelating agents such as Versene, followed by removal of the source of lead, may prevent residual damage.

Many other toxic substances accidentally ingested by infants and children may cause brain damage and are seen most frequently in chaotic households where children lack supervision and mothers are overwhelmed by their family obligations.

Another type of toxic influence in the postnatal period is presented by metabolic disorders, previously discussed, which often do not produce mental retardation and neurological disorders until after birth.

Traumas. Head injuries in children seldom produce serious brain damage and mental retardation.

Convulsive disorders. Although most convulsive disorders probably result from prenatal or perinatal influences, they make their appearance in the postnatal period, and their cause often remains unclear. The underlying pathology of the central nervous system is usually responsible for the epilepsy and the associated mental retardation. This association is seen with great frequency among the moderately and, especially, the severely retarded. It is estimated that as many as 20 to 25 per cent of the population in institutions for the mentally retarded have epilepsy. Failure to treat status epilepticus promptly and vigorously may also lead to progressive mental deterioration. Major motor and mixed or unclassifiable seizures account for the majority of convulsive disorders among the mentally retarded.

Infantile spasms. This condition, also known as hypsarrhythmia or massive myoclonic seizures of infancy, usually affects infants between 3 and 12 months of age. The illness is characterized by brief lapses of consciousness with abrupt symmetrical flexion of the head, trunk, or extremities. The EEG is characterized by grossly disorganized slow background frequencies associated with diffuse random high-voltage spike activity.

The condition leads to progressive mental deterioration, and mental retardation has been reported in close to 90 per cent of the cases. The cause is unclear and probably includes a variety of mechanical (birth) and biochemical insults to the central nervous system. The majority of cases occur suddenly and for no apparent reason in a previously normal child.

Recent reports about the beneficial results of ACTH are promising, although they must still await the verdict of time.

Febrile convulsions. Convulsions accompanying nonspecific febrile illness in infancy are harmless in most cases. Sometimes, however, they are a forerunner of an epileptic disorder. Rare cases have been reported of mental retardation after such convulsions.

Cerebral palsy. The estimates of intelligence of patients with cerebral palsy vary greatly, but all agree on the high incidence of mental retardation in this group. This incidence seems related to the type of cerebral palsy. The patients in the spastic tetraplegic group are most affected, and less than 15 per cent possess normal intelligence. In the hemiplegic category, the patients who acquired the handicap postnatally, especially in infancy, do worse than patients with hemiplegia due to prenatal or perinatal causes.

The incidence of mental defect in the hemiplegic group ranges between 40 and 50 per cent. Of the remainder, about half are of borderline intelligence.

Patients with the extrapyramidal type of cerebral palsy are more intelligent than the spastic group, and as many as 50 per cent may fall in the normal or superior range of intelligence. The intelligence of patients in the extrapyramidal category is sometimes underestimated due to hearing and speech disorders frequent in this group.

Heller's disease. This condition was first described by Heller, and, since the time of its original description, there has been a heated controversy. The lines are sharply drawn between those people who accept it as a legitimate disease entity and those who regard it as a meaningless label covering a variety of neuropathological and psychotic conditions. In his original report, Heller described children who developed normally in all respects until their third or fourth year, when, without any apparent reason, they began to show signs of progressive deterioration. The changes began with restlessness, stereotyped and anxious behavior, and loss of already learned speech and led to complete dementia. The children retained an intelligent facial expression and had no localizing neurological signs.

Since the original description by Heller, a number of clinical reports from various countries have appeared in the literature, and some give details of neuropathological findings that include nonspecific structural alterations in various areas of the brain. These authors prefer to consider Heller's disease as a *syndrome* of progressive mental deterioration beginning in early childhood and due to a variety of yet undetermined insults to the central nervous system. These may include traumatic, infectious, and biochemical influences occurring postnatally, or they may be genetically determined. Further systematic research may break down this global concept into several separate clinical units.

SOCIOCULTURAL FACTORS

It was mentioned previously that the overwhelming majority of the mentally retarded in the United States come from the lowest socioeconomic group. These are the indigent, dependent, helpless, hopeless, and often illiterate members of racial minorities, inhabitants of backward rural communities and urban slums. Exact statistics are not available, but the estimates of the frequency of mental retardation in this segment of the population range between 10 and 30 per cent, as contrasted with about 3 per cent in the total population. Many factors contribute to this sad picture, which was brought into sharp focus by the report of the President's Panel on Mental Retardation.

Medical problems.   The medical problems of the disadvantaged group are many and are often related to the problem of mental retardation. The prospective mother is frequently malnourished and shorter than her more fortunate suburbanite sister. She is likely to have either poor, little, or no prenatal care. Consequently, pretoxemic and toxemic states are seen in the disadvantaged group in much higher proportions. The diet often lacks the necessary minimum of vitamins, iron, and minerals. Maternal infections during pregnancy, including lues, are treated with delay or not at all. Many of these factors may result in grave hazards to the fetus. Infant mortality is higher than usual, and so is the rate of prematurity. Diabetes in the mother is often uncontrolled. Each of the many fetal risks may result in brain damage and mental retardation. As demonstrated by Pasamanick and others, this group's contribution to the continuum of reproductive casualty is extremely high.

The baby continues to be exposed to many health hazards after birth. He may never have regular postnatal care, including routine check-ups and immunizations, and his contacts with medicine may be limited to occasional emergency visits to the hospital. As a result, he is more likely to have serious bacterial and viral infections. He is treated relatively late in the course of illness for conditions such as meningitis or dehydration, often when permanent damage has already been done. The same may be said of conditions potentially amenable to surgical treatment that may go unrecognized for a long time.

Where there is mild brain damage that could be expected to be compensated for by appropriate handling and experience, such damage often persists because of understimulation or overstimulation.

The infant's nutrition is often inadequate and consists chiefly of milk, resulting in frequent iron deficiency anemia. Actual starvation is not frequent in the United States, but there are many families with little income and many children, whose members subsist on a substandard diet. Several studies in Central and South America indicate that chronic protein depletion in infants and young children may produce irreversible mental retardation of mild to moderate degree.

As the child grows older, other health hazards are added, such as pica, which often ends in lead poisoning, encephalopathy, and mental retardation. Mothers of children with pica are often immature, overwhelmed by their family duties, and unavailable to their children. Old paint used on the walls of dilapidated slum houses provides a steady supply of lead for children who eat plaster. The frequency of the battered-child syndrome, burns, serious accidents, and ingestion of toxic substances, with inherent risks to the central nervous system, is disproportionately high in this group.

Emotional and social problems. These problems of the disadvantaged group have been widely discussed recently. There is always danger in describing a heterogeneous population. It is easy to oversimplify matters, to generalize, to think in stereotypes. The majority of disadvantaged families are upwardly mobile, have sound ambitions for their children, and have not given up the struggle to help themselves. This discussion concentrates on the lowest 15 to 20 per cent of this group, which produces the majority of the culturally determined retardation. Family cohesion is often missing, the children are often illegitimate and reared by a variety of care-takers in addition to the mother, who is frequently working. These polymatric families often lack a father, and sometimes a grandmother assumes the role of head of the household. More often the roles of the family members are ill-defined, resulting in a chaotic, disorganized household, where things are not planned but just happen. In such an environment, the dependency needs of the growing infant, toddler, and young child may not be met, and he is forced to fend for himself long before he is ready. Having many care-takers—grandmothers, aunts, neighbors, a 2-year-old sister—may result in distorted pictures of human attachments and object relations, so vital to future personality development and social interaction. Because of lack of proper limits and because of the behavior standards they are exposed to, the children may identify themselves with patterns of poor impulse control and are apt to act out rather than sublimate their aggressive and sexual drives. As a result of living in a world that seems hostile, without encouragement and praise, the child's self-concept, including his body image, may be faulty. The fatalistic, hopeless attitudes of the slum environment can stifle initiative and motivation. The defenses necessary to allow the individual child to learn how to survive in this environment, where violence is not unusual, may also interfere with intellectual progress, particularly by emphasizing the need to deal with concrete realities, often ending in lack of flexibility in thinking.

Environmental deprivation. Recent research in sensory deprivation and studies of children in institutions have provided the main impetus for the study of the role of environmental factors in the cause of sociocultural mental retardation. Appropriate sensory stimulation of the young infant to facilitate his intellectual development is being widely explored for utilization in preventive approaches. There are still many unanswered and controversial questions in this area, but there are already many areas of agreement.

The importance of a stable, focal care-taking person in the intellectual and emotional development of an infant and toddler is undisputed. Young children need routine and predictability in their environment as well as variety, offered in proper balance. For example, a range of verbal stimulations that begins to elicit response from the infant by the age of two months is crucial in the development of language, the foundation of abstract thinking.

The disadvantaged socioeconomic environment confronts a growing child with several hazards to his intellectual development. The level of sensory stimulation may be too low or too high, or it may vacillate between the two extremes, with many possible outcomes, including the passive, unresponsive, or highly irritable child. Life may be drab and monotonous, with a paucity of new people, new toys, and new experiences, or it may be very chaotic and violent, devoid of any regularity, with new people coming and going without a predictable pattern. The available verbal stimulation is frequently deficient, resulting in a meager vocabulary, poor sentence structure, and concrete reasoning—a poor basis for a school learning experience. Nonverbal language, particularly body language, is often the chief communication medium, which deprives the child of more complex verbal skills, hindering his transition to more abstract thinking. The care-taking figure, even if regularly available, may at best attempt to satisfy the child's physical wants but will have little or no opportunity for playing with the child or providing him with new pleasurable experiences.

It is particularly in the institutional setting for infants and young children that the greatest hazards exist for environmental deprivation. There, preventive measures should be applied. Hospital nurseries, too, must provide a stimulating environment for babies.

Familial mental retardation. It was the usual practice in the past to begin the classification of the mentally retarded with the large category of familial retardation, also known as garden variety, physiological retardation or poor protoplasm. It is currently fashionable to dismiss this group as an artifact rather than a medical or biological entity. The main difficulty in resolving these opposing viewpoints lies in the lack of objective, observable, genetically determined characteristics of this group, which leaves the field open for speculation.

There is fairly wide agreement as to some characteristics of children in this category. Its members constitute about 75 per cent of all the mentally retarded in this country and usually come from the lowest socioeconomic group. In addition to being mentally retarded, they are the chief contributors to the ranks of juvenile delinquents, the jobless, and the mentally ill. They have no neurological signs, neuropathological abnormalities, chromosomal or known biochemical characteristics to distinguish them from the rest of the population. In borderline to mild retardation there is usually a consistency in I.Q. among members of the same family.

It may be assumed that intelligence or, rather, its multiple components are, in part, genetically determined. The distribution of measurable intelligence in the general population may be represented by a bell-shaped

Gaussian curve skewed to the left, since there are far more people falling in the below-average category than those in the above-average or superior range. But the statistical speculations cited in support of the hereditary nature of intelligence are subject to considerable distortions. Nobody will dispute the high correlation between the I.Q. of members of the same family. This is, however, complicated by the usually equal exposure of all the family members to identical or similar environmental influences.

The studies of Skeels on the remarkable effects of a stimulating environment in enhancing the intellectual level of retarded institutionalized children and experiences in the Head Start program indicate that, with appropriate experience, gains can be made by children from deprived families. Even more startling were the experiences during World War II with illiterate recruits, who were taught to read and write in crash programs of only three months' duration.

PSYCHIATRIC FACTORS

Personality development in mentally retarded children. Differences in the degree of intellectual functioning in the mentally retarded are compounded by the divergence of causative factors, ranging from clearly demonstrable brain damage—occurring in all phases of prenatal and postnatal development from a multitude of causes—to emotional and cultural deprivation. The resulting extreme heterogeneity of the mentally retarded group is probably responsible for the often conflicting and confusing views about the personality development and frequency of psychopathology of its members. What contributes to the existing confusion in this field is the paucity of well-conducted studies and surveys that use similar standardized methods of investigation. Most assumptions are often based on studies using residents in state institutions or patients in psychiatric clinics and hospitals. No wonder the views on the personality development of the mentally retarded range widely from the assumption of little or no difference from the normal population in the frequency of emotional disturbance to the contrasting opinion that assigns to the mentally retarded a very high risk of psychotic illness—up to 40 per cent in some studies.

Most people agree that there is, at present, no solid objective body of evidence to support a definitive opinion in this matter, and only well-detailed, well-designed studies of the course of personality development in well-defined uniform groups of mentally retarded will provide the answer in the future. Fortunately, similar studies of normal infants and children are being conducted with increasing frequency. They contribute very useful clues to the field of mental retardation in addition to providing good research models. Until the results of such systematic studies become available, clinical experience, coupled with cautious speculation, will have to be relied on.

Many borderline, mildly retarded, and even severely retarded persons are capable of having as normal a personality development as those with normal intelligence. Given an accepting and adequately stimulating family environment and appropriate educational and vocational training facilities, the majority of retarded children can develop good social and vocational adjustment and capacity for appropriate interpersonal interactions and attachments. However, in the process, they face hazards along the way that exceed the ones facing the normal population. Such hazards seem to increase in direct proportion to the degree of retardation.

Emotional vulnerability

FACTORS WITHIN THE CHILD. Modern research in child development stresses the degree of intellectual functioning as a factor of overriding importance in the timetable but not as the essence of the child's successful negotiation of progressive phases of emotional maturation. To give one example: Most people agree on the fundamental role of early attachments in infancy, manifesting themselves in recognition and preferential treatment of the mother by the infant (about 4 to 6 months) and in the phenomenon of separation anxiety and fear of strangers (about 6 to 8 months). The infant's recognition of his mother as an entity, separate from himself and clearly distinguishable from others, is an intellectual process that precedes or parallels its affective counterpart. This process of self-differentiation depends, in turn, on intact sensory and perceptual mechanisms, memory, and the ability to organize bits and pieces of experience into a meaningful whole. The infant's failure or delay in the recognition of his mother, for whatever reason, will delay—if severe, it may even preclude—the development of these vital early attachments, thus slowing down and disrupting the timetable of emotional development. One such distortion is the longer duration and greater intensity of the child's dependency period, requiring a delay in developing independence of thought and action. It is particularly important to ensure proper resolution of the dependency needs. If they are not properly solved, the child can remain preoccupied with having these needs met throughout his life.

The phase of negativism often starts later in infancy in the retarded and lasts longer than usual, which may interfere with the attainment of autonomy and mastery. The child's responsiveness to people in his environment is often reduced because of perceptual difficulties and lack of alertness. This, in addition to delay or failure in the mastery of spoken language, interferes with the intricate problems of interpersonal communication, causing a breakdown in the reciprocal exchange of meaningful messages between the child and his environment.

The mentally retarded child often has difficulties on a constitutional basis in handling anxiety and frustration, postponing gratification, handling disappointments, and accepting substitutes. This weakens his emotional resilience and lengthens the period of recovery from an emotional crisis, however small. As the child grows older, his lessened adaptability interferes with the general processes of socialization, which requires cooperation, compromise, and a capacity to give.

The retarded child's self-image, closely related to his self-acceptance, is often unfavorable, due to his frequent frustrations, failures, mistakes, and distortions in body image.

Play is of crucial importance in the development of a healthy personality. It permits experimentation and the finding of solutions to problems, represents a medium of expression of feelings and ideas, and provides a model for social interactions. The mentally retarded child may lack originality in his play. He may lean toward repetition and stereotype, particularly if there are organic bases for his difficulty. Such children use a minimum of toys and are often unable to play in larger groups or imitate play without help. All this potentially deprives them of yet another vehicle of emotional growth unless programs are set up to help overcome these handicaps.

In spite of the hazards, it is possible for the vast majority of the retarded to develop personality patterns as normal as compatible with their level of mental functioning. Developmental stages must be properly handled. To function as an individual, a child needs self-help skills and the motivation to use them. To function in society, he needs adequate control over impulses, a sense of responsibility, a good conscience, a reciprocal interest in and participation with others, and habit and character patterns (especially work patterns) that allow for productivity, even though at a limited level.

Since the most important components of personality development are evolved in the first five years of life, it is essential to provide the optimal setting and conditions in which this can take place. Most often this is in the home, if the presence of the retarded child is not decompensating for the family.

ROLE OF THE FAMILY. The role of the mother and other family members in the personality development of a young child is crucial. The parent-child interaction passes through several predictable stages, leading from a very close mother-child union to a gradual loosening of the emotional ties. Usually, the early closeness between mother and child is promoted by the mother's feeling of pride and acceptance and is continually reinforced by the child's predictable responses, such as smiling, cooing, cuddling, and playfulness. Delay in such responses and knowledge of the child's mental retardation often induce parental inner turmoil, grief, a sense of disappointment, shattered hopes, and sometimes feelings of guilt and failure. These feelings, if unresolved, make it difficult for many parents to accept the child, to be proud of him, and to give him affection and recognition.

Ignorance of the fact that the child is mentally retarded is equally hazardous, since parental expectation of normal behavior may be frustrated, leading to tension, confusion, and often estrangement between parent and child. The parents sometimes respond by vacillating between denial, overprotection, infantilization, and overt or covert rejection. The resulting tensions and conflicts may present definite handicaps in the emotional development of the growing child. Where there are brighter siblings, the inability to compete can be traumatic for the retarded child.

INFLUENCE OF THE COMMUNITY. The community may affect the personality development of the retarded child directly and indirectly. To begin with, the prevailing general attitudes toward mental retardation will profoundly influence the parents' reaction to having a retarded child. The more technologically advanced, sophisticated communities, which put a premium on education and intellectual achievement, have been less accepting and tolerant than the more primitive, underdeveloped ones.

As the child grows older and his social world widens, he comes to depend more on his peers for emotional support and stimulation. His acceptance by other children in the neighborhood, on the playground, and in school will largely depend on the personal attitudes, tolerance, and compassion of their parents. The retarded child, because of his inability to compete, is frequently excluded from neighborhood groups, leading to further frustration and feelings of inadequacy.

The various hazards to normal personality development in the mentally retarded make it difficult but not necessarily impossible to achieve normal adjustment. The intellectual capacity plays an important but not deciding role in this process, and it would be a fallacy to equate the level of emotional maturity with mental age. An adolescent mongoloid with a mental age of 4 or 5 years can be trained to perform a set of simple tasks, permitting him to hold a regular job in a supervised setting, which would hardly be expected from a normal 4- or 5-year-old child. The recent visibility given mental retardation tends to create a more enlightened community with more special services and facilities for the retarded, which in turn preserves and enhances their acceptance of themselves.

Maternal deprivation. The undisputed risks that maternal deprivation present to the emotional and intellectual development of a normal child are certainly far greater in a mentally retarded one. The retarded child needs more than the usual amount of mothering, affection, and stimulation. Denial of these results in an often irretrievable loss of whatever inner resources the child possesses. This matter is of particular importance in the problem of early institutionalization.

A more subtle form of maternal deprivation may result from the child's inability to respond to normal mothering because of sensory or perceptual difficulties. The mother's depression, self-preoccupation, or rejection may lead her to neglect the child's emotional needs.

Impact of retarded children on the family. The parents of retarded children represent the total spectrum of human personality variations, and yet there is often a tendency to treat them as a homogeneous group, beset by overwhelming feelings of guilt, anxiety, hostility, and insecurity. There is no doubt that many parents respond to having a retarded child with some degree of emotional disorganization, but the intensity and quality of their reactions vary greatly. Most of them experience considerable tension and anguish at the time of initial diagnosis, causing a weakening of the habitual defense system and a temporary breakdown of adjustment patterns. Most studies of families with mentally retarded children indicate that the period immediately after the diagnosis is extremely crucial and may have a deciding influence on the parents' handling of the child in the future.

The ultimate impact of the retarded child on the family depends on several factors, such as the degree of retardation, personality development and life adjustment of each parent preceding the arrival of the retarded child, the degree of their professional and social success, the adequacy of the marital adjustment, other children in the family and their intellectual progress, and the parental socioeconomic status. Reasonably well-adjusted parents with a positive self-image are usually able to absorb the retarded child without upsetting the family balance or jeopardizing the well-being of other family members. A marriage based on mutual support and free communication and the presence of other normal children help cushion the blow to the parents' self-esteem.

If, however, the parents are emotionally immature and beset by neurotic conflicts, the arrival of a defective child may precipitate a crisis that sometimes leads to family breakdown. The difficulty of managing a retarded child may contribute to this, particularly if management is complicated by hyperactivity, excessive irritability, or other distressing and hard-to-control manifestations. As a result, the child may be cast in the role of the family scapegoat, destined to drain off family tensions. In such cases, the removal of the child to an institution is often followed by an increase of marital tensions and sometimes by divorce or separation.

The social life of these families frequently becomes limited, leading to a feeling of isolation. The siblings' acceptance of the retarded child depends largely on parental attitudes and gratification of their own dependency needs.

The degree of family turmoil rises in direct proportion to the parents' social status. In this regard, the disadvantaged members of society fare better than the privileged ones.

The predominant defenses of the family may help or hinder their adjustment to the presence and handling of their retarded child. Denial, which may frustrate the physicians involved, may also allow the family to work usefully with the child. The danger is in overprotection and unrealistic pressure on the child for achievement. Projection, with the parents concentrating on blaming others for the child's situation, can lead to losing sight of the child's needs. Displacement can be useful if properly directed, such as involvement of the parents in community action on behalf of the retarded. Withdrawal can be destructive if it leads to the whole family's isolating itself and hiding from the rest of the world or concentrating all its investment in the retarded child to the neglect of the other children in the family.

Role of the physician. An informed and interested physician may play a pivotal role in preventing family tensions. An effective intervention on his part includes clarification, support, and reassurance. Bluntness, disinterest, or lack of caution in prognostication only adds insult to injury. The physician's empathy and flexibility help bring the parents' feelings and attitudes to the surface. Patience and flexibility are of particular importance in dealing with parents from low socioeconomic strata. Paying attention to their difficulties in verbalizations and to cultural and ethnic variations in attitudes toward mental retardation greatly increases the physician's effectiveness.

An extensive psychiatric intervention is superfluous for most parents, but many profit greatly from counseling by an experienced social worker, and some may need psychiatric treatment. Group therapy for parents of retarded children has also been useful. Above all, the physician should move to relieve the parents' helplessness in the face of the diagnosis of retardation. He needs to give them appropriate things to do, especially in the area of helping the child be as normal as possible in personality and adjustment.

PSYCHOLOGICAL FACTORS

Nature and development of intelligence. The problem of the nature and determinants of intelligence has baffled people from time immemorial. The controversy continues unabated in our century and has assumed renewed significance with the current interest in mental retardation. It is generally agreed that intelligence represents a man's problem-solving capacities, his adaptability to new situations, his ability to form concepts and to profit from experience. Thus, intelligence may be viewed not as static but rather as forever changing according to the individual's life circumstances.

The difficulty in even defining intelligence in a general acceptable way may explain in part the never-ending controversy about the causative factors in the development of intelligence. In the early part of this century, the lines were sharply drawn between the proponents of the theory of fixed and genetically predetermined intelligence and those who considered environmental factors the most decisive ones. This nature versus nurture controversy was perpetuated by many developments and discoveries, providing support for both factions. Mention can be made of the rapid advances in genetics and increased knowledge of the cell processes, the conceptual model for brain activity provided by information theory and cybernetics, studies of identical twins reared in dissimilar environments, the recognition of the relevance of obstetrical complications to the functioning of an individual, and the interest in maternal and cultural deprivation.

Today there is a movement away from the extreme positions and a gravitation toward the center. Thus, intelligence is most commonly viewed as resulting from interaction between biological and sociocultural factors. The former include genetic characteristics, prenatal and perinatal factors, favorable and unfavorable influences. The sociocultural factors are experiential and operate on the psychological level. Mental retardation often results from disturbances in all these areas: a genetically vulnerable individual may suffer obstetrical complications and be exposed to a culturally deprived environment. Such cases present a challenge to the most skillful diagnostician. To quote Pasamanick:

> The biological determinants serve primarily to establish physiological limits and the floor of potential in the organism. The sociocultural factors are like the soil in which the plant is nurtured. By enrichment or impoverishment, human intellectual potential can be made to blossom or to wither, to achieve its limits or to *fall far short of them.*

Such a general description of intelligence fits many current theoretical approaches. There is disagreement, however, as to the best methods of tapping or measuring intelligence. The several intelligence tests in common use, which assign to an individual a numerically expressed intelligence quotient (I.Q.), are very useful in predicting school performance. They are, however, less reliable in predicting future social adjustment and problem-solving ability. In addition, the test scores may be lowered by abnormal character traits, overwhelming anxiety, distractibility, and many other factors.

In the past, reliance on the I.Q. often led to keeping a child back in school, since the score was believed to be immutable. The studies of Bayley and others convincingly proved the fallacy of this assumption. There is also a growing realization that intelligence, seen as a sum total of all intellectual processes, is inadequately reflected in the conventional tests. The variety of these processes is far greater than had been thought previously.

The majority of the mentally retarded come from the low socioeconomic segment of society, and their intellectual potential is inadequately measured by the culturally biased conventional tests. There have been several attempts to devise culture-free tests, none of which has gained general acceptance as yet.

The work of Piaget and of the Pavlovian psychologists suggests a possible solution. They place the emphasis on the *nature* of the thinking process rather than on the performance during a defined test period, which may fail to demonstrate the individual's actual intelligence potential.

Some basic defects in cognitive development. There is general agreement about the reduced ability of the mental retardate to learn, to acquire knowledge at the same rate and in the same quantity as normal children. The differences are small in the simple forms of learning, but the gap widens in direct proportion to the complexity of the learning process. The many existing theories that attempt to define and analyze in detail the process of cognition have been related with varying success to the learning deficits of the mentally retarded.

The difficulty of directing attention to relevant cues has been recently stressed. Short-term retention seems deficient in the mentally retarded, but long-term retention is not disturbed. This may partially explain the fact that the retarded individual does not profit from a previous single learning experience as much as a normal child with a comparable mental age. The retarded person requires much more repetition and practice.

The sensory and perceptual handicaps found in many of the mentally retarded may significantly contribute to their learning difficulties. Where such defects exist, their responsiveness to various stimuli of normal intensity and duration differs from that of the normal child, making learning difficult without appropriate modification, repetition, and other forms of reinforcement of the stimuli.

The inability to inhibit already learned responses hinders the broadening of the available repertoire of responses in the same situation.

The main handicap is represented by the diminished capacity in abstracting and generalizing from experience, due to the deficit in verbal ability. The lessened permeability between cognitive functions results in monotonous thinking and lessened flexibility and inventiveness, as compared with normal children of the same mental age.

Jean Piaget's developmental psychology.   The work of Jean Piaget in Switzerland is compared by some to Freud's monumental contribution. Almost singlehandedly, over a span covering half this century, Piaget evolved a comprehensive theory of intelligence and the process of acquiring knowledge. Although his work shares many ideas with the learning theory, the Russian theory of intelligence, and ego psychology, to mention just a few, it remains a unique, unparalleled study of the function and development of the human mind. Although Piaget was chiefly concerned with the workings of the normal mind, his theory and methods of investigation are of great potential use in the study of the defective or subnormal mind as well. A brief description of the basic aspects and terminology of Piaget's work must necessarily precede any explanation of the possibilities of its application to the field of mental retardation.

Piaget views the evolving intelligence as a result of a continuous interaction between the individual and his environment. The active attempt on the part of the individual to mold and adapt the external environment to his own needs is called assimilation. The process of adjusting oneself to the external environment is called accommodation. The continuous reciprocal interaction between the individual and his environment, if harmonious, leads to an equilibrium or adaptation. This, in turn, gives rise to a new advance in the ever-unfolding process of intelligent functioning, characterized by a specific behavior pattern or schema. These schemata do not remain static but undergo further changes and differentiation as the interaction between the individual and his environment continues, leading to new equilibria and new and increasingly complex schemata. The interplay among the individual schemata leads to gradual integration and generalization of behavior and the thinking process.

In this ever-expanding dynamic process of evolving intelligence, Piaget distinguishes several stages, characterized by distinct types of behavior and thinking. The progression from one stage to the next more complex one is an orderly, predictable process, although the rate of this progress varies with the child's basic neurophysiological endowment, maturation, experience, and appropriate social interaction. The major periods in Piaget's model of intelligence development are: (1) the sensorimotor stage (birth to ½ years), (2) preoperational stage, subdivided into the preconceptual stage (1½ to 4 years) and the intuitive stage (4 to 7 years), (3) the stage of concrete operations (7 to 11 years), and (4) the stage of abstract operations (11 years onward). The stages represent a detailed analysis of the developing thought process, from the reflex behavior of the infant to the abstract thinking of the adolescent.

Unlike most psychologists, Piaget is not primarily interested in the content of the child's performance, which permits measuring and quantification. Rather, he is interested in the thought process underlying the child's functioning. Viewed from this vantage point, each behavioral item, even if functionally meaningless, assumes importance as representative of the child's thinking, however primitive. For instance, the seemingly bizarre repetitious hand movements of an infant are seen as attempts to substitute a magic, ritualistic procedure for a desired act, such as reaching for a favored toy that is unavailable at that time.

Piaget's concepts have already been applied to the study of the mentally retarded. They represent a more fruitful approach, especially to the severely and moderately retarded, than the traditional testing methods, which become unreliable below the I.Q. of 50. Rather than describe a retarded individual in terms of a magic number that implies a defined store of knowledge, it is easier and more useful to describe his functioning in terms of his arriving at a certain stage of his intellectual development, characterized by a specific behavior and reasoning process. Thus, the profoundly retarded individual may be viewed as arrested or fixated at the sensorimotor stage of development; the moderately retarded person is capable of reaching only the intuitive and preconceptual stages; the mildly retarded person does not advance beyond the stage of concrete operations; and the borderline retarded individual stops at the simpler levels of abstract thinking.

The mannerisms so often seen in profoundly retarded children, which baffle students of human behavior, become clearer when compared with the very similar behavior of a 7- to 8-month-old infant and may be regarded as quite purposeful in Piaget's framework of the developing mind. Since this manneristic behavior of the profoundly retarded is used so often to obscure and obfuscate the problem of childhood psychosis and infantile autism, it is to be hoped that, in time, Piaget's concepts will shed some light on the still very dark no-man's-land bordering childhood schizophrenia, infantile autism, and mental retardation.

DIAGNOSTIC FACTORS

History. Although caution is indicated in taking history from a parent, it often remains the only source of information. The history of pregnancy, labor, and delivery, the consanguinity of the parents, and the presence of hereditary disorders in their families deserve particular attention. The parents may also provide information about the child's developmental milestones. This area is especially subject to distortions, due to parental bias and anxiety. History is particularly helpful in assessing the emotional climate of the family and their sociocultural background, which play an important part in the evaluation of clinical findings.

Physical examination. This has to include a careful observation of the child's behavior level of activity and the quality of his interaction with his parents, other people, and inanimate objects. Various parts of the body may have certain characteristics commonly found in the mentally retarded due to prenatal causes. The configuration and size of the head offer clues to a variety of conditions, such as microcephaly, hydrocephalus, and Down's syndrome. The patient's face may have some of the stigmata of mental retardation, which greatly facilitate the diagnosis. Some of the facial signs are hypertelorism, flat nasal bridge, prominent eyebrows, epicanthal folds, corneal opacities, retinal changes, low-set and small or misshapen ears, protruding tongue, and disturbance in dentition. Facial expression, such as looking dull, may be misleading and should not be relied on without other supporting evidence. Color and texture of the skin and hair, high arched palate, the size of the thyroid gland, the size of the child and his trunk and extremities are further areas to be explored. Measurement of the head circumference is an essential part of the clinical investigation.

Dermatoglyphics, handprinting patterns, may offer another diagnostic tool, since uncommon ridge patterns and flexion creases are often found in retarded children. Abnormal dermatoglyphics may be found in chromosomal disorders and in children who were infected prenatally with rubella.

Neurological examination. The incidence and severity of neurological signs generally rise in inverse proportion to the degree of retardation, but there are many cases of severely retarded children without neurological abnormalities. Conversely, about 25 per cent of all children with cerebral palsy have normal intelligence.

The disturbances in motor areas manifest themselves in abnormalities of muscle tone (spasticity or hypotonia), reflexes (hyperreflexia), and involuntary movements (choreoathetosis). A lesser degree of disability in this area manifests itself in clumsiness and poor coordination.

The sensory disturbances may include hearing difficulties, ranging from cortical deafness to mild hearing deficit. Visual disturbances may range from blindness to disturbances of spatial concepts, design recognition, and concept of body image.

Paine advanced the knowledge of the evolution of postural reflexes in infants, which may help the examining physician in his prognosis. Caution, however, is indicated, since some children who initially present various motor abnormalities later show no abnormal motor signs and may not be mentally retarded.

Hyperirritable infants, jittery or convulsing with asymmetrical neurological signs, need careful attention, since about half of them may be brain-damaged in later life. The infants with the poorest prognosis are those who manifest a combination of inactivity, general depression, and exaggerated response to stimuli.

In older children, hyperactivity, short attention span, distractibility, and a low frustration tolerance are further hallmarks of brain damage.

In general, the younger the child at the time of investigation, the more caution is indicated in prediction of future ability, since the recovery potential of the infantile brain is very good. Following the child's development is probably the most reliable approach.

Pneumoencephalogram is somewhat hazardous and seldom indicated in the evaluation for mental retardation. The occasional findings of internal hydrocephalus, cortical atrophy, or porencephaly in a severely retarded, brain-damaged child are not considered very contributory to the general picture.

Skull X-rays are usually done routinely but are illuminating only in a relatively few conditions, such as craniosynostosis, hydrocephalus, and several others that result in intracranial calcifications. These include toxoplasmosis, tuberous sclerosis, cerebral angiomatosis, and hypoparathyroidism.

The electroencephalogram (EEG) is best interpreted with caution in cases of mental retardation. The most notable exceptions are patients with hypsarrhythmia or *grand mal* seizures, where the EEG may help establish the diagnosis and suggest treatment. In most other conditions, one deals with a diffuse cerebral disorder that produces nonspecific EEG changes characterized by slow frequencies with bursts of spikes and sharp or blunt wave complexes. The confusion over the significance of the EEG in the diagnosis of mental retardation is best illustrated by the reports of the frequency of EEG abnormalities in Down's syndrome that range from 25 per cent to the majority of patients.

Laboratory procedures. These include examination of the urine and blood for a host of metabolic disorders. The recently described enzymatic abnormalities in chromosomal disorders, notably Down's syndrome, promise to become useful diagnostic tools. The determination of the karyotype in a suitable genetic laboratory is indicated whenever a chromosomal disorder is suspected.

Hearing and speech evaluations. These should be done routinely. The development of speech may be the most reliable single criterion in the investigation of mental retardation. Various hearing impairments are often present in the mentally retarded; on the other hand, they may, in some instances, simulate mental retardation. Unfortunately, the commonly used methods of hearing and speech evaluations require the patient's cooperation and are often unreliable in the severely retarded.

Psychiatric examination. The psychiatric examination of mentally retarded children does not differ essentially from such examination of children with normal intelligence. The similarity decreases, however, in direct proportion to the severity of the mental defect. In no other category, except perhaps with psychotic children, is nonverbal communication and careful observation of the patient and his activity of greater importance.

The psychiatrist's contribution should always include study of the interpersonal aspect of the retarded patient's personality development. The way he reacts to both human and inanimate objects and how he relates to the examiner and to his mother or care-takers may tell most about his social maturity. Just as with infants and young children, it may be useful to examine even the older retarded patients with and without a parent or a parent substitute in evaluating dependency status and response to separation.

The child's control over motility patterns should be ascertained, and clinical evidences of distractibility and distortions in perception and memory may be evaluated. The use of speech, reality-testing, and the ability to generalize from experiences are important to note.

The nature and maturity of the child's defenses—particularly the exaggerated or self-defeating uses of repression, denial, introjection, and isolation—should be observed. Sublimation potential, frustration tolerance, and impulse control—especially over motor, aggressive, and sexual drives—should be assessed. Also important is self-image and its role in the development of self-confidence, as well as assessment of tenacity, persistence, curiosity, and the willingness to explore the unknown.

The severely retarded child presents the greatest challenge to the examiner. Bizarre, primitive, and seemingly purposeless behavior is often difficult to interpret. Categorizing the patient's observable behavior in response to the examiner's interaction with him or independent of it, using as a model the developmental examination of infants, may help to systematize observations and provide a reasonable estimate of the patient. It is helpful for the psychiatric examiner to combine appropriate components of neurological and psychological examination methods with his own approaches.

In general, in the psychiatric examination of the retarded child, there should be a picture of how the child has solved the stages of personality development. From the areas of failure or regression, it is possible to develop a personality profile of a type that allows for more logical planning of management and remedial approaches.

Psychological examination. The examining physician may avail himself of several screening instruments—such as those developed by Gesell, Caldwell, Illingworth, and Knobloch—that are useful for infants and toddlers. As in so many areas of mental retardation, there is a heated controversy over the predictive value of infant psychological tests. The correlation of abnormalities during infancy with later abnormal functioning is reported by some authors as very low and by others as very high. It is generally agreed that the correlation rises in direct proportion to the age of the child at the time of the developmental examination.

Copying geometric figures may be used as a quick screening test of visual-motor coordination. The same can be said of the Goodenough Draw-a-Person Test, Kohs Block Test, and geometric puzzles.

Psychological testing, performed by an experienced psychologist, must be considered a standard part of an evaluation for mental retardation. The Gesell, Bayley, and Cattell tests are most commonly applied in infants. For children, the Stanford Binet and the Wechsler Intelligence Scale for Children (WISC) are most widely used in this country. Both of these tests have been criticized for penalizing the culturally deprived child, for testing mainly potential for academic achievement rather than for adequate social functioning, and for their unreliability in children with an I.Q. of less than 50. Some people have tried to overcome the language barrier of the mentally retarded by devising picture vocabulary tests, of which the Peabody Vocabulary Test is the most widely used.

The tests often found useful in detecting brain damage are the Bender-Gestalt and the Benton Visual Retention Tests. These tests are also applicable in mildly retarded children.

THE NEED FOR NEW TEST METHODS. There is a need reported from many quarters for new, unconventional appraisal methods of the mentally retarded that would allow the examination of the child's strengths and handicaps in a number of areas of functioning with greater precision. Most of the existing tests give only an inaccurate, global, and somewhat amorphous picture in children with severe intellectual handicaps, in whom a precise appraisal is of paramount importance. Only the knowledge of small units of functioning may help in creating suitable specific educational programs that take advantage of the child's assets. One such approach is utilized in the Illinois Test of Psycholinguistic Abilities, which tests auditory, vocal, and motor responses, both alone and in combination. The recent application of Piaget's theory to mental retardation may represent another possible approach to this diagnostic dilemma.

SOCIAL FUNCTIONING. This important area, which reflects the patient's adaptive behavior, has been relatively neglected. The most popular test that measures social functioning is the Vineland Social Maturity Scale. Based on the observations of the patient and the description of his care-taker, it assigns to him a social quotient (S.Q.). The test taps the individual's competence in meeting life contingencies and dealing with his environment. It is especially useful in the severely retarded who are untestable by other methods. The social quotient (S.Q.) should not be considered synonymous with the intelligence quotient (I.Q.).

Differential diagnostic problems. A variety of conditions may simulate mental retardation. Children who come from very deprived homes that provide inadequate stimulation may manifest motor and mental retardation that is reversible if an enriched, stimulating environment is provided in early childhood. A number of sensory handicaps, especially deafness or blindness, may be mistaken for mental retardation if, during testing, no compensation for the handicap is provided. Speech deficits and cerebral palsy often make a child appear retarded, even in the presence of borderline or normal intelligence.

Chronic, debilitating diseases of any kind may depress the child's functioning in all areas. Convulsive disorders may give an impression of mental retardation, especially in the presence of uncontrolled seizures.

Chronic brain syndromes may result in isolated handicaps—failure to read (alexia), failure to write (agraphia), failure to communicate (aphasia), and several others—that may exist in a person of normal and even superior intelligence.

Emotional difficulties may often lead to an apparent retardation. Emotionally disturbed children do poorly in school and often perform far below their actual mental level.

An alert psychiatrist or pediatrician experienced with normal and abnormal children is usually able to assess properly the child's mental status in most of the above-mentioned conditions.

The most controversial differential diagnostic problem concerns children with severe retardation, brain damage, early infantile autism, childhood schizophrenia, and, according to some, Heller's disease. The confusion stems from the fact that details of early history are often unavailable or unreliable, and, by the time they're evaluated, many children with these conditions manifest similar bizarre and stereotyped behavior, mutism, or echolalia and function on a retarded level. By the time these children are usually seen, it does not matter from a practical point of view whether the child's retardation is secondary to a primary early infantile autism or schizophrenia or whether the personality and behavioral distortions are secondary to brain damage or retardation on other bases. When ego functions are delayed in development or are atrophic on any other basis, the physician must first concentrate on overcoming the child's unrelatedness. The child must be reachable before one can successfully apply remedial educational measures.

Several differentiating diagnostic criteria have been suggested, such as neurological signs, EEG, withdrawal, obsessiveness, better relation to objects than to people, and retention of an intelligent physiognomy. Since these conditions may be interrelated, the diagnosis may be very difficult without an adequate follow-up. Some people use the term "atypical child," implying a common organic matrix for all these conditions. This approach has inherent dangers that always accompany the grouping of medical conditions according to one or several common symptoms. It invites diagnostic complacency and discourages efforts to find more precise diagnostic criteria.

PREVENTION

PRIMARY PREVENTION

Public education. A preventive approach to mental retardation can only succeed in an educated, enlightened community. Without wholehearted support of the people for whom it is intended, the best-conceived plan is doomed to failure. Public education is of particular importance in enforcing preventive measures against mental retardation, since one has to sweep away a cobweb of superstition, inertia, and revulsion that has developed over the ages, compounding and perpetrating the ignorance in this area.

The public has to be educated that mental retardation is a symptom producing a handicap and not a curse or visitation; that, as in many other illnesses, its causes can be studied, treatment found in some of its variants, and amelioration found in most; that mentally retarded people have feelings of love and hate, anger and compassion, and have a need for affection, comradeship, and a sense of belonging, like all of us; and that, as citizens, they have inalienable rights, which include the best that medicine and education have to offer and the right to the pursuit of happiness, which, in the case of the mentally retarded, means a right, inasmuch as possible, to a productive existence and humane treatment.

Only when such basic issues are clarified and become common knowledge and conviction can people begin to think in preventive terms and take preventive measures seriously. As experience with mass vaccinations, venereal diseases, and prenatal care in this country clearly showed, merely to offer the means of prevention, however perfect, will be useless unless people avail themselves of existing facilities. The public attitude is of even greater importance in the prevention of mental retardation. In addition to concrete, relatively easily administered measures, such as vaccinations and screening examinations of blood and urine, the main hope lies in far more complicated measures, such as ensuring an appropriately stimulating environment for a young infant or providing an emotionally stable environment for the growing child.

Public education has to proceed on several levels—impressing school children with basic facts about mental retardation, reaching their parents through communication media and through patient personal efforts of interested professionals, going out among those of the underprivileged who are at greatest risk and trying to win their cooperation. Isolated examples of such personal crusades and their sometimes spectacular success make headlines, but, unless they become a formalized mass phenomenon, there is little hope of finding a solution to the problem of familial culturally determined retardation, which accounts for the majority of all mental retardation in the United States.

All members of the community, regardless of their socioeconomic status, have to be kept abreast of the new developments and insights, ranging from the importance of preventing measles to the modern concepts of institutional care. Significant strides have been made in the last decade or two in this field of public enlightenment, both in the awareness of various causative factors and in the need to create and support measures to prevent them. But only small inroads have been made in the most disadvantaged group.

Improvement of socioeconomic standards.   Basic to any real improvement in this area is the raising of the standards of living and education among disadvantaged, forgotten citizens. There is little value in preaching about the value of proper nutrition to people who lack bare necessities or in explaining the virtues of verbal stimulation and a great variety of toys to a husbandless mother of eight, living on public assistance. One has to attack the basic social and economic conditions that give rise to all the secondary phenomena, such as malnutrition, prematurity, obstetrical hazards, understimulation, and overstimulation. People who are given good vocational training that permits them to compete successfully in the labor market and be economically secure are much more inclined to think in terms of securing good health and education for themselves and their families. But half measures and superficial palliative solutions cannot be effective in interrupting the vicious self-perpetuating cycle of poverty.

Unlike the inborn errors of metabolism, in which the abnormality can be successfully treated by measures concentrating on one point in the metabolic pathway, the pathway of poverty has many defects or blocks. Only a concerted, simultaneous, vigorous effort that attacks all these points at once may drastically alter the total picture. Improvement in employment opportunities presents one such strategic point. The reform of welfare practices, to permit more than bare survival, represents another. A coordinated effort by social agencies, government authorities, and community leaders, including representatives of the poor, to strengthen family stability in slums through vigorous case work, financial aid, and rehabilitation of individual family members is of equal importance.

Only a cohesive, economically and emotionally secure family can offer the proper soil for both intellectual and emotional growth. To reach and to stabilize the family units in the slum culture requires new, bold approaches, often departing from the traditional ones in psychiatry and social work.

The securing of proper housing is another aspect of rehabilitation that is important for medical as well as social reasons. One cause of mental retardation, lead poisoning, is fostered by pica. The newly acquired knowledge about the psychodynamics of pica may be useless in the prevention of lead poisoning unless decent dwellings, free of lead paint, are provided.

Providing vigorous programs of adult education and vocational retraining and wholesome recreation for people of all ages may help to overcome the inertia and fatalistic attitudes that present the major obstacles to the implementation of preventive and corrective measures. In helping people adopt and accept modern principles of prenatal or infant care, group discussions and group lectures in small circles are far more effective than official sermons by cold, impersonal authorities who fail to bridge the gap separating the rich from the poor. Only a reawakening of a sense of dignity can provide the proper motivation for self-improvement and self-help, which are far more effective than paternalistic spoon-feeding.

School buildings, school personnel, and school programs have to be improved and enriched to reach the young. Preschool training in the early formative years needs more vigorous community assistance. Whenever possible, this should be done in close cooperation with the child's family, impressing them with its importance and patiently teaching them the principles of healthy diet and verbal and nonverbal stimulation.

Whenever a mother is working or is unavailable, a community-supported infant and child care center, staffed by well-trained educators and aided by volunteer members of the community, may provide an appropriate program. Many less affluent countries have social laws that protect the working mother by the provision of generous, paid prenatal and postnatal leaves and adequate day care centers for their infants and children located near their homes or places of work. Practices in this country are still quite antiquated and need urgent revisions.

Preventive medical measures. Improvement of prenatal care is a recognized cornerstone in all efforts to prevent mental retardation. To begin with, restricting the number of pregnancies in adolescence and after the age of 40 will reduce the risk of chromosomal aberrations and obstetrical complications. Prevention of prematurity; detection of Rh and other blood incompatibilities; adequate nutrition during pregnancy, including vitamin and mineral supplements; control of maternal diabetes, pretoxemic states, syphilis, and other infections by appropriate medication and diet—all these no doubt help reduce the number of reproductive casualties that Pasamanick et al. showed to be responsible for a host of disorders associated with mental retardation.

Preventive obstetrical measures include good technical preparation of the delivering physician, not always available in overcrowded city and rural hospitals; reduction of the amounts of anesthetic and analgesic drugs given to women in labor, since they often have a depressing effect on the baby; a less lackadaisical obstetrical attitude toward neonatal transient apnea, which can produce lasting brain changes, despite its short duration; better monitoring of the vital fetal signs during labor; caution in the use of new drugs during pregnancy, unless their lack of harmful effects on the baby is proved beyond a reasonable doubt; and standardization of delivery records by the universal adoption of the Apgar scoring system, which may become the first *reliable* information in the natural history of mental retardation.

Pediatric preventive measures cover acute and long-range problems. The measures covering acute problems include improvements in infant resuscitation techniques; early recognition of hemolytic diseases of the newborn and their vigorous and early treatment by skillful exchange transfusions and the still experimental intrauterine transfusions; early recognition of transient convulsive disorders caused by such factors as hypoglycemia, hypocalcemia, and pyridoxine deficiency and their prompt treatment. A close cooperation between the obstetrician and the pediatrician and their respective departments is indispensable in securing improvements in neonatal care.

The long-range pediatric measures involve prevention of acute illnesses potentially dangerous to the central nervous system. In addition to already available vaccinations against many viral and bacterial diseases, new ones may be expected shortly. Further, the supervision and, if necessary, improvement in the infant's nutritional status—especially his intake of protein, vitamins, and other essential food ingredients—are very important. Recognition and early treatment of various diseases potentially affecting the central nervous system—such as meningitis, hypernatremia, lead poisoning, and convulsive disorders—will help to reduce the number of sequelae resulting in mental retardation.

Obstetricians and pediatricians are doing a creditable job of primary prevention in their private practices, but this care is not universally available for the indigent and most vulnerable population. This opinion is best supported by reliable statistics indicating that in the rate of infant mortality the U.S. is in tenth place, having a worse record than far less affluent and technologically advanced nations. Another statistic indicates that, in many big-city slums, as many as four-fifths of all pregnant women never have any prenatal care. Human social factors explain the failure to use existing free prenatal and well-baby clinics. Several measures could help remedy this paradoxical situation. Providing a continuity of doctor-patient relationship in the clinics by having the same physician see a patient over a span of at least one year, instead of providing the prevailing impersonal assembly-line atmosphere, would certainly be a major incentive to the continuity and regularity of medical care. The impersonal use of "Mother," "Miss," etc., without the addition of the family name, hardly inspires confidence or induces a resolve to follow the physician's directions or to return for the next scheduled appointment.

The role of other specialized personnel is vital to the success of any preventive mass program. The public health nurse, the social worker, the nutritionist—all can maintain a warm contact with their patients and their families, facilitating communication and ensuring a follow-up. Latest innovations in this field include a traveling well-baby clinic on wheels, operating literally on the principle of reaching out into the community, and child-care counselors recruited from among middle-aged, intelligent women, trained intensively in infant development and well-baby care, who help spot potential distortions in the baby, in the mother, or in the mother-baby interaction and who work intensively with the mothers to help them in child-rearing.

These measures may help, no doubt, but the real key to the dilemma of improving physical and mental health in indigent populations may well be in the new concept of comprehensive health programs, based at head-quarters in a multipurpose community health center or hospital and branching into the community through the use of satellite preventive clinics. Each such program encompasses a delineated part of the city, the inhabitants of which and their health status will become known to the program staff. A thorough knowledge of the community permits the early spotting of hard-core multihandicapped families and other potential risks and permits zeroing-in on a troubled family in a very intensive way. This kind of network will help reduce greatly the number of stragglers, the ones who skip appointments or who are too inhibited or depressed to seek help on their own. Such programs, if successful in winning over the community and its leaders, are the main hope at present for the effective prevention of much of the mental retardation in this country.

Genetic counseling. Genetic counseling, which usually involves the question of the desirability of future offspring by the parents, siblings, and sometimes more distant relatives, can be done by private practitioners and staff physicians in clinics and hospitals. Knowledge in this area is still limited, and precise data are available in only a few condtions. Thus, the amount of presently available information can be acquired and usefully applied by any practicing physician. This use has to be preceded, however, by an exact diagnosis, which may require biochemical and cyto-genetic studies.

In many cases of mental retardation, the problem of genetic transmission is either unknown, unresolved, or very complex. Counseling of such cases is better left to mental retardation evaluation centers staffed by specialists in this area and equipped with a cytogenetic and biochemical laboratory, permitting the performance of specialized tests.

In the counseling of parents of patients with Down's syndrome, it is of greatest practical importance to differentiate between the cases resulting from translocation and those caused by trisomy. In the former, the risk of having a second child with Down's syndrome is 1 in 3; in the latter, it averages 1 to 2 per cent.

With some exceptions, conditions known to be caused by a dominant recessive gene are quite predictable, in that the children of affected persons have a 1 in 2 chance of inheriting the same disorder, but the asymptomatic relatives do not carry the deleterious gene.

In cases of autosomal recessive genes, the accurate prognosis is more complicated, but certain fundamental facts are known and may be used in practice. The parents of one child with such a condition run a 1 in 4 risk of having a second affected child. This is true in PKU and galactosemia. The siblings of PKU patients are heterozygous carriers in two-thirds of all the cases that can be confirmed or ruled out by a phenylalanine tolerance test, but their chance of having a PKU child is only 1 in 250, provided they marry outside their own family. Equally predictable are the sex-linked diseases, in that half the sons of a carrier mother are affected, and half the daughters are carriers.

In stating the likelihood of a second defective child, the counselor is doing nothing more than making a statement of mathematical statistical probabilities. There may be a statistical risk of 1 in 4 of two heterozygous carriers having a phenylketonuric child, for example, but the couple may be lucky or unlucky and may have either four normal or four affected children in a row. The physician's role is to present the known facts and also the uncertainties to the parents frankly and openly, to tell them what the chances are insofar as these are known, but to recognize that what to do in the presence of any particular set of odds is a parental rather than a medical decision.

Counseling the family about the procreation of the mentally retarded themselves presents several legal, ethical, and scientific problems. The severely retarded are seldom fertile, and the proof of genetic inferiority of the majority of the mildly retarded is still lacking. Regional approaches to this problem are reflected in differing state laws affecting sterilization and abortion. An increased interest in this question can be anticipated with the present trend to keep the mentally retarded within the community. An appointed panel of medical specialists and lawyers acquainted with the intricacies of this problem would seem most suitable to examine each case on its own merit and to pay attention to possible hardships to the family, the community, and the patient himself. Judicial sterilizations and abortions may be very helpful in individual cases, but their influence on the prevalence of mental retardation in the population is negligible.

SECONDARY PREVENTION

Early identification and treatment of hereditary disorders. Despite considerable progress in this area, there are still only a few conditions in which early detection and treatment may prevent mental retardation. Mass screening for inborn errors of metabolism is recommended at present only for PKU, galactosemia, and possibly maple syrup disease, but several other conditions may be added shortly to this list.

The simple urinary tests for PKU (ferric chloride) do not become reliable until the baby is 4 to 6 weeks old. The Guthrie bacteriological method of blood examination may help detect the condition in the first week of life, which is of importance, especially in indigent patients, who may not be readily available for testing after their discharge from the obstetrical unit. Dietary treatment with a low phenylalanine diet is effective in preventing at least the severe degrees of retardation and the behavioral manifestations if it is started in the first six months of life. This treatment carries certain hazards, and its administration requires the teamwork of several specialists—physician, nutritionist, social worker, nurse—to assist the parents and to evaluate the child at frequent intervals. Such supervision is probably best carried out in specialized centers.

Galactosemia can be readily screened by using Clinitest and examining the urine for reducing substances. Treatment requires the omission of milk from the diet; several milk substitutes are readily available. Early detection and institution of treatment is effective in preventing mental retardation and other manifestations of this disease. Milk may be reintroduced into the diet in moderate quantities at the age of 4 or 5 years, since by that time the child apparently develops alternative metabolic pathways for handling galactose, but these are not sufficient to handle a quart of milk a day.

The third condition in which early diagnosis is crucial is hypothyroidism. Although diagnosis is not always easy in early infancy, careful examination, coupled with a high index of suspicion, helps the physician detect the disorder in most cases. His suspicion aroused, the physician has several tests available with which to confirm the diagnosis, such as radioactive iodine uptake, protein-bound iodine (PBI), and butanol extractable iodine (BEI) in the blood. On confirmation of the diagnosis, it is essential to institute immediately vigorous treatment with thyroid extract, preferably during the first six months of life. Treatment started after that time seldom prevents mental retardation, although it may still mitigate the results of thyroid deficiency.

There is now dietary treatment available for a number of amino acidurias, such as maple syrup disease, but, despite recent developments of several diagnostic methods, mass screening for most of these conditions does not seem justified at present.

Medical and surgical treatment of other conditions. Prompt diagnosis and treatment of bacterial meningitis with antibiotics and occasionally with steroids may prevent neurological sequelae, including mental retardation. The sequelae of viral meningoencephalitis are best prevented by immunizations, since at present only supportive therapy is available, although there is some promising research in the area of antiviral therapy.

Lead poisoning, caused by the chronic ingestion of lead, should be suspected, especially in indigent populations, in cases of unexplained vomiting, abdominal pain, irritability, failure to thrive, and encephalitic signs. At Children's Hospital of the District of Columbia, interest in the pica phenomenon led to a high index of suspicion in the staff, resulting in a rate of detection of plumbism in the clinic population exceeding by far the frequency in other pediatric centers. Prompt deleading with Versene is usually effective, but relapses are frequent, due to the personality difficulties of the mothers and continued availability of lead paint in dilapidated slum dwellings. Each relapse increases the risk of permanent central nervous system damage. Effective prevention must include provisions of decent, lead-free housing and intensive parental counseling.

Surgical treatment that is effective in preventing mental retardation is limited to only a few conditions. Evacuation of a subdural hematoma after a trauma or meningitis is a simple procedure that has to be supplemented in some cases by the excision of the membrane from the subdural space. If untreated, the condition may result in irreversible brain damage and mental retardation.

The surgical treatment of hydrocephalus is far less satisfactory. Several procedures for shunting the excess cerebrospinal fluid to various areas of the body are employed with varying success in different centers, but the overall results are still rather disappointing.

Craniosynostosis, premature closure of the suture lines, may be corrected by a craniectomy. If performed early in infancy, the operation will allow the rapid brain development of this period and prevent damage caused by its restriction. It is important not to confuse this condition with congenital microcephaly, in which surgical measures are useless.

Excision of the epileptogenic focus in temporal lobe epilepsy may be effective in cases that fail to respond to anticonvulsant medication.

The results of various experimental procedures designed to increase the blood flow to the brain and thus improve mentation have not been very promising to date.

Early recognition and handling of children with isolated handicaps. There is a growing recognition of the existence of a large number of infants and children with isolated motor, sensory, perceptual, behavioral, and intellectual difficulties. By some estimates, the number comes to about 5 per cent of the general school population. Causes vary from hereditary factors to mild brain damage due to obstetrical insults. The early history in many of these children suggests some prenatal, perinatal, or postnatal difficulties, and the resulting variety of symptoms gives support to the concept of a continuum of reproductive casuality. In as many as half of these patients, the early history is noncontributory, and one could think, in mild cases, in terms of delay of maturation of the CNS.

The perceptual difficulties may manifest themselves in disturbances of body image, spatial relationships, and design recognition. These are often accompanied by EEG changes and give rise to many learning problems. Perceptual training aimed at overcoming these difficulties is still in the experimental stage, but it is to be hoped that practical methods in this area will emerge shortly, with specific recommendations as to appropriate play materials and play methods.

In frank sensory deficits, such as deafness or blindness, the child can be helped by intensive use of the remaining normal sensory pathways, which enables the developmental and socialization process to progress along normal lines by maintaining communication between the child and his environment. Failure to recognize these handicaps early and to employ compensatory avenues of sensory imput often results in preventable mental retardation and withdrawal.

Deficiency in the motor area may manifest itself as general clumsiness and poor coordination, which interfere with the mastery of motor skills, such as writing. Making allowances for this will prevent penalizing the child and holding him back in school. Early recognition of this handicap in a younger child helps the parents delay introduction of such activities as bicycle-riding or ice-skating to spare the child the sense of failure.

Isolated scholastic difficulties may involve number concepts, reading, handwriting, or abstract thinking. Help in these areas by way of small groups or individual tutoring may make it possible for the child to keep up with his age-mates. There are a number of teaching methods available to deal with these learning problems, and it is incumbent on school officials to provide such specialized services.

Distortions in reactivity patterns, such as hypersensitivity and hyposensitivity to various sensory stimuli, may be overcome if recognized early and treated appropriately. An infant or young child with a low arousal threshold does better with a lowered intensity of environmental stimulation. The reverse holds true for children with a high arousal threshold.

Distractibility and hyperactivity due to mild brain damage or to unspecified constitutional factors present stumbling blocks to learning and are starting points of child-parent and child-teacher conflict, resulting in a behavior problem. Effective medical measures include the use of amphetamines, phenothiazines, and some antihistamines. The educational measures usually employed aim at increasing the child's attention span by limiting his visual field to only a few items essential to the task at hand. Small classes for such children allow the teacher more flexibility and a more liberal behavior policy than is possible in a regular large classroom. The parents' attitude toward the child improves as they are better able to understand the causes of his erratic behavior.

The problem of aphasia in children is the most difficult and controversial of all manifestations of minimal brain syndromes. The difficulty is primarily on the receptive level and may occur at any point of the central auditory pathways, resulting in a variety of disorders in the reception of auditory stimuli. Expressive aphasias, which prevent the child from expressing his thoughts while allowing him to perceive and interpret sounds correctly, are relatively rare in children. Aphasias may often be masked by mental retardation or autistic withdrawal and, if not recognized and treated early, may well result in these conditions. The training of aphasic children, aiming chiefly at maintaining communication, requires highly specialized personnel and is done best under the aegis of a hearing and speech department in an academic center.

All these handicaps, regardless of cause, are very taxing to the child, his parents, and his teachers. The resulting conflicts may contribute to the development of serious psychiatric difficulties, such as uncontrollable aggressive behavior, difficulties in group adjustment, withdrawal, and passivity. Despite a normal intellectual potential, the children may function on a retarded level if continued in an unsuitable school program. The emotional difficulties and the retardation are best prevented by an early diagnosis followed by long-term parental counseling and guidance by the physician or appropriate paramedical or educational specialists. Psychotherapy is required for only those few patients who have already developed serious school difficulties. Environmental adjustments—such as the establishment of a routine, flexible but firm limit-setting, appropriate regulation of the sensory input, and opportunity to burn excess energy—often result in a rapid, striking improvement, particularly in infants and young children.

Early identification and treatment of the culturally deprived child. Infants from disadvantaged, deprived backgrounds are indistinguishable from their more fortunate age-mates in the first year of life. They often score even higher than middle-class children on infant development tests, which are all heavily weighted with sensorimotor items. However, in the second year they begin to fall behind, and by the age of 2 or 3 years they show delay in speech development, less originality and spontaneity in play, and a constriction, rigidity, and general impoverishment of the thinking process. It is estimated that, by the time deprived children begin their school career, the gap separating them from more privileged children widens to about 1 to 2 years.

The early recognition of environmental deprivation by the physician requires his knowledge of both normal and deviant child development. Periodic developmental examinations or screening by physicians or other trained professionals is the best guarantee of early detection.

The treatment of culturally determined retardation aims at filling the gap by providing more sensory, verbal, and emotional stimulation and by the introduction of new, pleasurable experiences and useful skills to widen the child's intellectual horizon. Appropriate counseling and guidance may make it possible to conduct such enrichment programs at home, but often a well-staffed child-care day center provides the most appropriate setting for the mental rehabilitation of these children. There is reason to believe that an intensive, systematic application of such enrichment programs throughout the country may reduce the number of mentally retarded by at least 50 per cent.

The environmental hazards for children from deprived backgrounds are not limited to the preschool age. They enter school under serious handicaps, and only a rich program conducted by experienced teachers in small classes may bring them up to the expected grade level. Unfortunately, these children often attend schools housed in dilapidated buildings, in crowded classes conducted by inexperienced teachers overwhelmed by the magnitude of their task. As a result, the prevailing standards are below the national average, and the initial gap widens, leading to a relative retardation.

The detection and treatment of emotional difficulties in young children may prevent serious learning difficulties in the future. This requires more attention being paid to the child's personality development in the course of well-baby and child health care. The emphasis on detection has to be coupled with a greater availability of facilities and staff for parent counseling and psychotherapy.

TERTIARY PREVENTION

Treatment of behavioral and personality difficulties. The emotional problems of the mentally retarded differ in many ways from similar ones of children with normal intelligence. Consequently, they often require methods of treatment not commonly employed with the latter group. This applies particularly to the moderately or severely retarded; the mildly retarded may profit greatly from conventional play and activity group therapy.

The chief obstacle to effective psychotherapy is the difficulty in establishing communication with the child. Meaningful verbal interchange is difficult or impossible, due to faulty language development and impairment of concept formation. The latter often interferes with the use of toys and play situations as symbolic representations of the child's concerns. The therapist has to operate on a very concrete level in order to reach the child and, above all, has to be flexible and pragmatic. Methods used with disturbed infants and young children may be usefully applied, aiming toward making the child comfortable and relatively free of anxiety. Physical contact may be indicated in some children, but others react to it with panic and disorganization. Repeated clarification of situations and the therapist's reactions and intentions is very reassuring. Engaging the child in shared activities is probably the most effective way to establish a meaningful relationship. Unlike that in conventional psychotherapy, firm limits have to be established and adhered to consistently, particularly in children with difficulty in impulse control. Verbal and nonverbal reassurance and praise should be used generously, and situations should be set up that permit the patient to succeed. In addition, concrete evidence of affection in the form of small gifts, toys, and candy is very helpful, as are such pleasurable activities as trips to the drugstore, park, playground, etc. Many would call it relationship therapy or good mothering, but it certainly is psychotherapy in the broad sense of the word.

Countertransference problems may be serious and often resemble those encountered in the course of treatment of psychotic children. The patience and ingenuity of the therapist are taxed much more in cases of mental retardation associated with psychosis. As in the treatment of adult schizophrenics, the therapist, in order to be effective, may require certain personality attributes that are yet to be determined but that probably include spontaneity, flexibility, and tolerance.

Individual and group psychotherapy may be effective only if it is an integral part of a structured program involving the total milieu of the child, including his home and day or residential school. Establishing an appropriate school program, matching the child with suitable teachers and child-care workers, establishing order and consistency at home, and building an appropriate recreational program are all essential components of such a total program, which has to be coordinated and unified. One may see the psychiatrist's role primarily as that of coordinator and guide of such programs.

Drugs play an important role in the psychiatric treatment of the mentally retarded. Many reports of institutionalized children describe excessive drug dosage, often ten to twenty times higher than is usually recommended. Since most of the ataractic drugs are not without hazards, caution is indicated, and excessive dosage should be discouraged. This is especially true of children living at home or in institutions without constant medical supervision. Phenothiazines are the most widely used and probably the most effective drugs. Hyperactive, restless children often profit from amphetamines. Antihistamines have also been applied by some with good results. Barbiturates are usually contraindicated, since they often produce the unexplained paradoxical effect of increasing the restlessness and tension.

Parent counseling. Parent counseling is of paramount importance. The approach to parents has to be flexible and pragmatic. Some parents need help only in coming to grips with their feelings about the child and require a conventional dynamic casework approach. Judiciously used support, reassurance, guidance, and practical advice as to the management of the child are often indicated. Homemaking services, temporary placement of the child in institutions, and similar arrangements increase the parents' effectiveness by giving them periodic relief. Group therapy, which permits the sharing of burdens and getting reassurance from similarly afflicted parents, is especially effective with parents of retarded children, and this explains the rapid proliferation, success, and popularity of parents' groups in the last two decades.

The problem of institutionalization is probably the most difficult aspect of counseling and guiding parents of retarded children. The huge, impersonal, understaffed state institutions for the retarded are the outgrowth of the nihilistic and pessimistic thinking about mental retardation in the past. The physicians who then recommended immediate hospitalization after the diagnosis were in accord with the contemporary medical thinking and community attitudes. Today the public's philosophy in this area is undergoing a radical change; it was given impetus by the research on maternal deprivation and the new community orientation on mental retardation.

Early institutionalization, before age 6, is seldom indicated and takes a heavy toll in the social and the intellectual development of the child. Many parents might keep the retarded child at home, at least for the first few formative years, if they have the appropriate guidance, support, and interest of the physician. There are instances, of course, where the family equilibrium is so shaky and the emotional balance of the family members so precarious that early removal of the child from the home is necessary in the interest of the family. This, however, is the exception rather than the general rule.

Effective parent counseling by the physician requires his thorough knowledge of the appropriate community agencies and resources in his area, such as educational facilities, institutions, vocational rehabilitation, public school classes for the retarded, and sheltered workshops.

Modern concepts of institutional care. The early pioneers of residential care for the mentally retarded stressed education and training. The failure of early exaggerated hopes to materialize caused a shift of emphasis. Institutions took on a custodial character, protecting the retarded individual and isolating him from the community. Today the thinking in this field has come full circle. Training, education, treatment, and rehabilitation are once again the primary goals. This radical change in orientation closely parallels a similar revolution in the concept of mental hospitals. Both areas now share similar goals of intensive treatment and reintegration of the patient into the community. The main obstacle to this goal is the large size of most state institutions and their inclusion of patients of all ages with all degrees of mental and physical handicaps, which precludes individual attention except for the most promising patients—that is, the least retarded.

The realization that mentally retarded people have need of affection, approval, and dignified treatment prompted the current gradual change of institutional settings. Instead of huge, sterile barracks with endless rows of beds and little else, a homelike setting is advocated, planned around smaller units that include living rooms, playrooms, separate kitchens and dining rooms, and attractive bedrooms. The homelike atmosphere is underscored by the careful choice of personnel for such units or cottages. Their emotional stability and motivation guarantee their effectiveness as substitute parents. Dealing with a relatively small stable group of children and adults helps the retarded child, especially in his social maturation, in the areas of impulse control and the development of meaningful human relationships. The small group concept is extended to classrooms, workshops, and recreational facilities. Children are grouped according to age, degree of retardation, and type of handicap. Only such grouping permits the tailoring of the program to fit the needs of the individual child.

Contact with the child's family should be maintained primarily by the location of residential care centers within the community, by liberal visiting hours, and by the encouragement of regular, frequent home visits whenever feasible.

In addition, a number of other facilities may serve the needs of mildly retarded individuals who cannot be cared for at home and yet do not require a full-time residential center. These facilities are best located in the vicinity of a larger institution or health care center, where needed services may be obtained without delay. The half-way house or hostel originated in Western Europe and proved very useful in the handling and rehabilitation of chronic schizophrenic patients. It also seems ideally suited for adolescent and adult mildly retarded individuals who require a minimum of supervision and can work in the community. Patients of the same age group who require more guidance may do well in sheltered workshops, where they are engaged in productive work geared to their skills, under close supervision. Recreational day centers for children of all ages give parents a welcome relief and an opportunity to lead a normal life and may enable them to keep even a disturbed child at home. The parent can be assisted in home care by a number of specialized services—such as visiting nurses, social workers, and visiting housekeepers—and by an opportunity for temporary short-term placement of the retarded child in an institution or summer camp in times of crisis and increased family tension.

At present, there are about 200,000 mentally retarded individuals in residential care, which amounts to about 4 per cent of the estimated total retarded population. Recent experience clearly shows that the introduction of modern diagnostic, treatment, and training facilities into the community reduces the need for long-range institutional placement, which in time will probably be limited to bedridden, profoundly retarded patients and those with severe emotional disturbance.

Vocational rehabilitation. The area of vocational training and rehabilitation has been neglected in the overall educational program for the mentally retarded. The stress has been on academic skills, leading to frequent disappointments because of negligible gains, despite intensive and patient efforts. Since recent experience indicates the capacity of almost all mentally retarded to be productive, the emphasis is gradually shifting to vocational and prevocational training, especially within the adolescent group.

To be effective, such programs have to include a variety of training possibilities tailored to the individual's skills and previous experiences. A detailed assessment of the patient's strengths and defects in functioning must precede any sensible program planning. As in all other phases of education and training, the success of such programs depends largely on a small instructor-trainee ratio, on the amount of individual attention available, and on the support of the community. Vocational services should include counseling of the trainees and their families and an employment placement service.

Physical rehabilitation. The mentally retarded, especially those in the moderate or severe group, are often afflicted with a variety of physical handicaps that further reduce their potential for normal functioning. Sensory deficits, especially of vision and hearing, require correction whenever possible and special training if the damage is irreversible. Blind, deaf, or aphasic children do better as a rule in specialized centers, with special training and educational facilities. Children with motor difficulties often require orthopedic services as well as physical therapy. For such children, the unavailability of crippled children's programs to the retarded is particularly to be deplored.

Awareness of the unfavorable body image of the mentally retarded has recently prompted some consideration of the role of plastic surgery in correcting some of the stigmata of the mentally retarded for cosmetic reasons.

Special education. The education of the mentally retarded shares, with the education of normal children, the goal of preparing the student for future satisfactory life adjustment and helping him develop his full potential. There is often disagreement among educators, however, as to what presents a reasonable objective for a given child and the best way to achieve it. This has resulted in many rival theories and curricula, which can confuse rather than guide the educator.

It may help bring the controversy into historical perspective to remember that the principles of special education laid down by the early pioneers over a century ago are still among the best guidelines available. Recent knowledge of the importance of neurophysiological, cultural, and affective factors in the learning process confirms rather than detracts from their validity.

Itard's five objectives in the management of the wild boy of Aveyron were, as Kanner reports:

(1) To render social life more congenial to the boy by making it more like the wild life he had recently kept. (2) To excite his nervous sensibility with varied and energetic stimuli and supply his mind with the raw impressions of ideas. (3) To extend the range of his ideas by creating new wants and expanding his relations with the world around him. (4) To lead him to the use of speech by making it necessary that he should imitate. (5) To apply himself to the satisfaction of his growing physical wants, and from this to lead on to the application of his intelligence to the objects of instruction.

Guggenbühl stressed "(1) the development of sensory perceptions beginning with primary excitations and progressing to more refined complex stimuli, (2) attempts to awake the soul through habituation to regular routine, memory exercises, and speech training" (Kanner).

And Séguin, in his classic textbook, published in 1846, said, as Kanner notes:

To be physiological, education must at first follow the great natural law of action and repose, which is life itself. To adopt this law to the whole training, each function in its turn is called to activity and to rest; the activity of one favoring the repose of the others; the improvement of one reacting upon the improvement of others; contrast being not only an instrument of relaxation but of comprehension also. The general training embraces the muscular, initiative, nervous, and reflective functions, susceptible of being called into play at any moment.

The preceding passages sound surprisingly modern and seem in perfect accord with our views concerning sensory stimulation; the value of a familiar, stable environment; the intersensory organization as a precursor of intelligence; the role of motivation; the value of routine and of stimulus variation; the importance and promotion of speech; and the Pavlovian bipolar view of the higher nervous activity, oscillating between the states of excitation and inhibition, to mention just a few.

The role of emotional ties between the student and the instructor is not explicitly stated by these pioneers but is implicitly conveyed by their conduct. Itard devoted five years exclusively to the training of the wild boy of Aveyron, and Séguin spent eighteen months on the treatment of an idiotic child.

The present system of special education employs the division between the educable—those capable of grasping the rudiments of academic skills —and the trainable—those capable of acquiring only basic social habits. The general characteristics of the retarded group, particularly where there is also brain damage, include rigidity and concreteness of thinking, distractibility, and poor motivation. The methods applied to overcome these handicaps vary, but they all share several general principles strikingly similar to those mentioned above: limiting the number of available stimuli; gradual introduction of new, more complex experiences; emphasis on success to bolster motivation; and utilization of several mutually reinforcing approaches—visual, auditory, tactile, kinesthetic, and verbal—in the teaching of a single concept.

A few of the new trends in special education may be mentioned here: (1) the lessened emphasis on academic performance and greater stress on prevocational and vocational training and on practical life experiences; (2) the attempt to recognize small rather than global units of the child's functioning, permitting the precise identification of his assets and building an individual program around these assets; (3) the introduction of operant conditioning techniques in the training of the severely retarded, based on the principles of reinforcement of desired behavior by reward, reported as less effective in retarded children than in animals but useful in the habit training of this group; (4) the recognition of the value of psychiatric guidance and consultation by teachers and instructors.

The current emphasis on preschool education may be considered as the most important innovation in the field of special education. It is now generally recognized that early intervention may accelerate mental and social development and break up or correct faulty learning habits. Some people advocate such intervention in infancy, regarding this age group as most malleable and responsive to environmental changes.

LEGAL ASPECTS

The more humane approach to the mentally ill and the mentally retarded in the nineteenth century had a strong impact on the law throughout the civilized world. Concern for the weak, minors, and the naturally disabled is increasingly reflected in changing laws and statutes.

Many inherent difficulties greatly complicate the legal issues of mental retardation. The most formidable obstacle to the uniformity of opinion and procedures has to do with the lack of clarity in the areas of definition and classification. It is still controversial as to what criterion should be used by the legal authorities to classify a person as mentally retarded and to determine the degree of his handicap and legal responsibility. The common use of the intelligence quotient is being challenged by many lawmakers who prefer to consider the current degree of social adjustment and competency. Regardless of the choice of criteria, the issue is further complicated by the realization that mental retardation is not a static condition but rather one that is subject to change in response to environmental and maturational factors. The most expedient and just approach to the definition of mental retardation for legal purposes has to include the individual's level of present functioning and his intellectual potential as measured by various standardized tests, which may project the individual's functioning in the future.

Civil Law

One of the most important legal issues in mental retardation has to do with residential care. Whenever possible, one prefers a voluntary admission to an involuntary commitment. This is often complicated, however, by the degree of retardation or emotional upheaval that precludes a conscious choice on the part of the retarded individual. In the case of a minor, the parents usually assume the responsibility for the decision, and in cases of parental neglect or absence, the child falls under the general jurisdiction of the juvenile court and other official protective services. In the case of an adult patient, a legal procedure to determine his incompetency is often necessary before an involuntary commitment takes place.

Until recently, a patient admitted to a state institution for the mentally retarded often remained there for the rest of his life. Under the impact of new knowledge, however, an increasing number of residential patients are released into the community. Since permanent institutionalization is no longer considered beneficial or necessary for most mentally retarded, it is important to retest the mentally retarded patients in institutions at regular intervals to guarantee their basic right to live in a normal community if their general level of functioning improves sufficiently to permit it. This is obviously one of the many areas in which lawmakers will look for assistance from the medical and behavioral sciences.

Recently it became obvious that most people in state institutions are there for two reasons: (1) the lack of proper educational, vocational, recreational, and counseling facilities in most communities, and (2) emotional difficulties. To guarantee the rights of the mentally retarded, the law would have to oblige the communities to create and improve appropriate facilities, including opportunities for psychiatric treatment.

The problems of guardianship and legal competency are often complicated, and a highly individualized approach by the legal authorities is most desirable. It is of great importance to determine the degree to which mental retardation interfered with the exercise of good judgment by the given individual. This will then be decisive in delineating the areas of social incompetency requiring decisions by third parties. It is preferable for the court to specify the areas to be included in the guardianship. A flexible plan may prevent the mentally retarded individual from administration of his property without restraining him from decisions concerning his person. Specific decisions may be required in matters such as signing of legal documents, voting, driving, marriage, adoption, and eugenic sterilization. The court will have to rely in all these matters on professional opinion, and the role of the psychiatrist as an expert in the area of human behavior is of crucial importance in helping the legal authorities arrive at a just solution. The usefulness of psychiatrists and of other members of a professional team—psychologists, social workers, vocational specialists—will largely depend on their acquaintance with mental retardation in all its complexity.

To safeguard the rights of the mentally retarded, a protective government agency is needed to supervise individual cases, especially when the immediate family fails to assume the responsibility. Such an agency might help a retarded person challenge court decisions through ordinary legal channels and should be available for consultation to the patient, the family, or other legally approved guardians.

CRIMINAL LAW

This area is even more controversial than that of civil law because, in addition to the rights of the individual, public safety and the rights of the community are of great concern. Since the middle of the nineteenth century, there has been a growing awareness in the Anglo-Saxon law of emotional and intellectual handicaps reducing the criminal responsibility of some members of society. Another growing trend is to view the sentence as a therapeutic and rehabilitative rather than a punitive process.

The paramount issue is that of competency to stand trial. Here again, the court will have to rely on professional, expert opinion, and the role of the psychiatrist in this context is quite obvious. His testimony will help the court to determine the defendant's capacity to exercise sound judgment, to highlight the circumstances leading to and surrounding the crime, and to decide on appropriate measures designed to be therapeutic. The psychiatrist will also be called on to help determine what degree and extent of isolation of a mentally retarded criminal is necessary for the protection of the community.

The previously mentioned protective government agency should attempt to ensure the legality of the judicial proceedings, the validity of the defendant's confessions, and the availability of proper legal counsel. This agency should also supervise the existing therapeutic rehabilitative facilities in state institutions, prisons, and the open community. A wide range of facilities within a state—including foster homes, half-way houses, and vocational training—will help the court reach a just decision.

The actual implementation of these measures varies greatly in the United States, with some striking differences between states and communities. Further improvement requires a general public enlightenment to help overcome some deeply rooted fears and prejudices. In addition, it requires a greater involvement and cooperation in the problem of mental retardation on the part of the legal, medical, and paramedical professions. The perfect law will be useless without a trained interdisciplinary team familiar with all the facets and ramifications of mental retardation. The growing awareness of the need for change and reform of legal statutes in accord with contemporary knowledge of the nature of mental retardation found expression in several studies addressing themselves to this complex but necessary task, of which the most publicized was the Report of the Task Force on Law of the President's Panel on Mental Retardation.

ROLE OF THE PSYCHIATRIST

In the past, when organic approaches dominated the field of psychiatry, mental retardation was considered an integral part of mental illness; *dementia* and *amentia* were viewed as not very far apart. The predominantly dynamic orientation of the early part of our century was one of several factors responsible for the present dichotomy between the two disciplines. The change in psychiatric thinking—which now stresses the interplay among biological, psychological, and cultural factors in the shaping of human personality—permits the reintegration of mental retardation into psychiatry, the latter seen broadly as a science concerned with human behavior. The behavior of the majority of the mentally retarded shares many features with that of people with normal intellectual endowment. The problems are often similar, except for the timetable of their occurrence. The methods applied for the prevention of emotional difficulties in normal children seem to be equally effective in the mildly retarded group, which constitutes about 85 per cent of the retarded. The behavior disorders of the severely retarded often resemble those presented by psychotic children and may call for similar therapeutic measures.

Increased understanding of personality development and its many biological and environmental determinants can be usefully applied to the study of personality development in the mentally retarded. Psychiatrists, especially child psychiatrists, seem uniquely equipped to contribute to the clarification of our basic thinking in this still controversial field. Conversely, the detailed study of the mentally retarded may increase our general knowledge of the reciprocal interaction of cognitive and affective factors in the process of learning and of the biochemical and neurophysiological corollaries to the adaptation of the human organism to stress.

The many hazards in the process of personality development faced by the mentally retarded point to the pivotal role of the psychiatrist in the prevention of retardation; as a consultant to other physicians, educators, and rehabilitation programs; and as a direct participant, when indicated, in the treatment, care, and rehabilitation of the retarded. His training helps him recognize the innate developmental forces and environmental influences. By timely intervention, he may direct the handling of distorted personality patterns so as to identify and help interrupt patterns of pathological interaction between the retarded patient and his family or his caretakers. His training in identifying sources of anxiety and the nature of defensive maneuvers helps him in bringing about a reduction of tension, thus promoting emotional maturation and motivation for learning.

The study of the theoretical and practical aspects of mental retardation will greatly benefit the psychiatric trainee by offering him a unique exercise in nonverbal communication; an opportunity to study the evolution of defenses in their primitive forms, rarely seen in normal children and adults; and a dramatic demonstration of the interplay of dynamic and organic factors in human behavior. The strong feelings of countertransference often provoked by working with mentally retarded patients permits the trainee to identify and come to grips with the regressive forces within himself in the early stage of his career, thus increasing his general therapeutic effectiveness.

The psychiatrist's role as an interdisciplinary coordinator, currently emphasized in psychiatric training, seems especially applicable to the field of mental retardation. The complexity of the problem calls for cooperation of many medical and nonmedical specialties. His knowledge of group dynamics and training in recognition of and dealing with the interaction of social, biological, and psychological factors places the interested psychiatrist on at least a par with the other candidates for leadership in many areas of service and community planning. Furthermore, as an expert in human personality development, he should play an important role in the training and education of physicians, psychologists, social workers, and educators in the field of mental retardation. His clarification of the sometimes bizarre behavior of the mentally retarded and the intrafamily tensions provoked by a retarded family member will greatly increase the effectiveness of all disciplines.

The role of volunteers in the field of mental health and mental retardation is of great practical importance in view of the acute shortage of trained personnel. Psychiatric guidance and supervision may increase the volunteers' competence and permit maximal utilization of their services, particularly in the process of social rehabilitation.

The reasons behind the institutionalization of the majority of the retarded are the behavior and attitudes that make it difficult or impossible for the individual to function in the community. The retarded child has as much right to have help with such personality disturbances as his brighter brothers and sisters. Thus, the psychiatrist has an obligation to be equally available to the retarded child and adult.

ROLE OF PHYSICIANS IN OTHER COUNTRIES

All the pioneers in the beginning of the nineteenth century came from within the medical profession. They provided the leadership in medical matters of diagnosis and treatment and laid the foundation for the educational and training endeavors as well. The end of the nineteenth and the early part of the twentieth century witnessed a gradual withdrawal of interest in the problem of mental retardation on the part of physicians. Diagnostic and therapeutic nihilism replaced the enthusiasm of people like Itard, Howe, and Séguin. Medical research came virtually to a standstill, with only a few notable exceptions. The isolation of the mentally retarded both from the community and from the mainstream of academic learning deterred most physicians from personal involvement. It was left to psychologists and educators to pick up the slack and to make the major contributions to the understanding and the management of mental retardation. This phenomenon was more pronounced in the United States than in Europe.

A renewed medical interest in mental retardation in Western Europe and the U.S.S.R. began in the 1930's and has continued with increased vigor since the end of World War II. In the U.S.S.R., psychiatrists and neurophysiologists provide the leadership in research and in practical management, in close collaboration with the fields of psychology and education. In Western Europe, the impact of postwar social psychiatry led to experimentation with new concepts of community-based facilities for the mentally retarded. Most of the modern facilities that now serve as models for planners in this country are directed by physicians, who usually come from the ranks of pediatrics and child psychiatry. Although nobody in Europe denies the necessity of interdisciplinary cooperation in this complex area, the physician is generally regarded as the one best suited to guide and coordinate such efforts. The excellence of many existing programs in Europe attests to the wisdom of this approach.

NEEDS OF THE FUTURE

EDUCATIONAL PROGRAMS FOR MEDICAL STUDENTS
AND POSTGRADUATE TRAINEES

The recent public interest in mental retardation will be followed by a gradually increasing involvement of the entire medical profession, which will be called on to assume leadership and responsibility in providing maximal help to the mentally retarded. The response to this call will depend largely on the development and expansion of training facilities in mental retardation for medical students and residents. The training programs have to be balanced between the theoretical and the practical aspects of the problem and will require a university-based or -affiliated clinical facility for the mentally retarded.

The training of medical students may be regarded as the most essential step in the process of physicians' education in mental retardation. The theoretical training should include human development, biochemistry, genetics, and social aspects of mental retardation. The student should also become acquainted with the problems of community resources and planning, with emphasis on prevention. The practical training is best done in a diagnostic and treatment clinic or in a residential facility that provides opportunity for observation and participation in medical management, parent counseling, contact with other such disciplines as psychology and social work, and some interaction with public agencies. In addition to this basic, mandatory program, selected students should be encouraged to explore the field of mental retardation in greater depth through participation in research projects and prolonged clerkship in a clinical setting.

Education in mental retardation must continue in postgraduate programs on several levels. Certain disciplines—such as pediatrics, psychiatry, obstetrics, and neurology—are most involved in the diagnosis, treatment, and prevention of mental retardation. Pediatricians are most strategically situated to detect and combat mental retardation. It is essential, however, to impart some fundamental knowledge of the problem to all physicians, especially to future general practitioners, the primary physicians. Such knowledge about mental retardation may be obtained during internship and residency programs and in postgraduate courses and is best provided by addition of specialists in mental retardation to the hospital staffs.

One may predict an increased need of physicians capable of assuming leadership in the field of mental retardation. This need becomes more apparent as the state plans for comprehensive mental retardation programs are emerging. Future leaders will best be recruited from pediatrics, psychiatry, and neurology. Their intensive training should cover the entire spectrum of problems relevant to mental retardation, such as diagnosis and treatment, placement, administration, research, and community relations. It is to be hoped that a variety of such programs will be developed to provide a cadre of versatile specialists, capable of meeting the different needs in this rapidly expanding field.

COMMUNITY PLANNING

The diversity of the handicaps associated with mental retardation requires a variety of services to meet all needs. They must include diagnosis, treatment, training, recreation, rehabilitation, and protective supervision, and they require a combination of medical specialties, social work, special education, and vocational training. These broad areas of service may be provided by private physicians and agencies, various state facilities and university clinics, public and private schools and hospitals. At present, there is an acute shortage of such services, but as various programs emerge, waste and duplication can be best prevented by careful community planning. The planning body should use existing facilities and support the creation of new ones. It should also pay attention to the training of professional personnel, without which not even the most modern facility can operate.

Recently, the concept of a comprehensive multipurpose center has gained in popularity. Such centers constitute a fixed referral point in the community. Here, a thorough evaluation and treatment of the entire range of problems is provided, and there is also the most suitable place for parent counseling, with emphasis on proper placement. Such a facility could cover a defined geographic area, and its usefulness might be increased by strategic location of satellite clinics in its vicinity. In such centers, a risk registry of high-risk children would permit early identification of mentally retarded individuals in the area and an early start of treatment if available.

The recognition of the need for coordination of community services has brought forth the concept of life-planner. Such an individual would be intimately acquainted with the contribution of different professions relevant to the field of mental retardation. His background and skills would enable him to provide life consultation and guidance to the retarded person and his family.

AREAS OF FUTURE RESEARCH

The present research effort will no doubt become intensified with the establishment of university-based multidisciplinary research centers throughout the country. Several avenues of such future efforts are listed below.

Biochemical research. The inborn errors of metabolism will continue to present a most challenging field. In addition to the recognition of specific blocks of metabolism processes, the interplay between enzymes and the problem of cellular metabolism still await elucidation. The parallel discoveries in chromosomal and enzymatic research may permit the mapping of chromosomes. A breakthrough in the understanding of storage diseases seems imminent. Better understanding of brain metabolism represents another fruitful area, as does the elucidation of the structure of chromosomes.

Other organic factors. There is a pressing need for a better understanding of fetal metabolism and the placental function. The effects of the normal and abnormal birth process on the brain of the newborn and the role of maternal viral disease during pregnancy need to be elucidated further.

Educational research. Basic and applied research will be required to improve present teaching methods. Better knowledge of cognitive processes, application of motivational research, and emphasis on practical life adjustment may bring about radical changes in special education. Introduction of new testing methods may permit a better assessment of the student's strengths and weaknesses. This will obviate the present global approach and would permit the tailoring of individual curricula. The study of language development of the mentally retarded needs urgent attention.

Psychiatric and neuropsychiatric research. Correlation of organic factors with the mental status and personality development represents an area likely to be shared by psychiatry and neurology. Longitudinal personality studies of mentally retarded children will permit better planning for prevention of emotional difficulties and may contribute to a better understanding of early infantile autism and other childhood psychoses.

REFERENCES

American Association on Mental Deficiency. A *Manual on Terminology and Classification.* American Association on Mental Deficiency, Willimantic, Conn., 1961.

Begab, M. The mentally retarded and his family. In *Prevention and Treatment of Mental Retardation,* T. Philips, editor. Basic Books, New York, 1966.

Bowman, P. W., and Mautner, H., editors. *Mental Retardation.* Grune & Stratton, New York, 1960.

Crothers, B., and Paine, R. S. *The Natural History of Cerebral Palsy.* Harvard University Press, Cambridge, 1959.

Efron, M. L. Aminoaciduria. New Eng. J. Med., 272: 1058 and 1107, 1965.

Eisenberg, L. If not now, when? Am. J. Orthopsychiat., 32: 781, 1962.

Ellis, N. R., editor. *Handbook of Mental Deficiency.* McGraw-Hill, New York, 1963.

Farmer, T. W., editor. *Pediatric Neurology.* Hoeber Medical Division, Harper & Row, New York, 1964.

Ginzberg, A. M., and Butler, A. J. *The Un-educated.* Columbia University Press, New York, 1953.

Greenfield, J. G., Blackwood, W., Meyer, A., McMenemey, W. H., and Norman, R. M. *Neuropathology.* Edward Arnold, London, 1958.

Hunt, J. McV. *Intelligence and Experience.* Ronald Press, New York, 1961.

Inhelder, B. *Le Diagnostic du Raisonnement chez les Debiles Mentaux.* Delachue Nestle, Neuchatel, 1944.

Jervis, G. A. The mental deficiencies. In *American Handbook of Psychiatry,* S. Arieti, editor, vol. 2, p. 1289. Basic Books, New York, 1959.

Kanner, L. *A History of the Care and Study of the Mentally Retarded.* Charles C Thomas, Springfield, Ill., 1964.

Knobloch, H., et al. The neuropsychiatric sequelae of prematurity. JAMA, 161: 581, 1956.

Lourie, R. S., et al. A study of the etiology of pica in young children, an early pattern of addiction. In *Problems of Addiction and Habituation*. Grune & Stratton, New York, 1958.

Luria, A. R. *The Mentally Retarded*. Macmillan, New York, 1963.

Masland, R. L., Sarason, S. B., and Gladwin, T. *Mental Subnormality*. Basic Books, New York, 1958.

National Clearinghouse for Mental Health Information. *Mental Retardation Abstracts*. National Institutes of Health, Bethesda, 1964–1966.

Paine, R. S., and Oppe, T. E. *The Neurological Examination of Children*. Heinemann, London, 1966.

Pasamanick, B. Determinants of intelligence. In *Conflict and Creativity*, S. Farber and R. Wilson, editors. McGraw-Hill, New York, 1963.

Pasamanick, B., et al. Association of maternal and fetal factors with the development of mental deficiency. JAMA, 159: 155, 1955.

Penrose, L. S. *The Biology of Mental Defect*. Grune & Stratton, New York, 1963.

Piaget, J. *The Origins of Intelligence in the Child*. Routledge and Kegan Paul, London, 1953.

Presidents' Panel on Mental Retardation. *National Action to Combat Mental Retardation*. United States Government Printing Office, Washington, 1962.

Proceedings of the International Copenhagen Congress on the Scientific Study of Mental Retardation, vols. 1 and 2. Copenhagen, 1964.

Robinson, H. B., and Robinson, N. M. *The Mentally Retarded Child*. McGraw-Hill, New York, 1964.

Rosner, F., Ong, B. H., Paine, R. S., and Mahanand, D. Biochemical differentiation of trisomic Down's syndrome (mongolism) from that due to translocation. New Eng. J. Med., 273: 1356, 1965.

Woodward, M. The behaviour of idiots interpreted by Piaget's theory of sensori-motor development. Brit. J. Educ. Psychol., 33: 123, 1960.

AREA D

*Psychiatric Treatment
of Children*

CHAPTER SIXTEEN

Individual Psychotherapy

SAUL I. HARRISON, M.D.

HISTORY

R E C O N S T R U C T I N G the history of psychotherapy for children is complicated by uncertainties in delineating the limits of what processes should be labeled psychotherapy. This difficulty is greater with child psychotherapy than with adult psychotherapy because of the superficial resemblance between some child psychotherapeutic techniques and many of the usual practices employed in rearing and educating children. As a consequence, there is a risk that something may be designated as psychotherapy not because of the nature of the process but as a consequence of the child's emotional disturbance and the professional's preference to consider his interventions to be psychotherapy, regardless of their substance.

Evidence of direct therapeutic contact with children prior to the twentieth century is rare. Until this century, formal efforts to cope with emotional and mental disturbances in children generally took the form of advising the parents about alternate means of handling their children. The experts rarely confronted the child directly in an effort to alter his clinical course. A noteworthy exception was the celebrated efforts of the French otologist Jean Marc Gaspard Itard in the latter part of the eighteenth century. Itard adopted Victor, a prepubertal boy who was assumed to have lived the bulk of his life as a savage with animals in the forests of Aveyron. Itard undertook to civilize and educate Victor in a manner that conceivably might be considered psychotherapy.

The modern era of child psychotherapy is generally thought to begin with Sigmund Freud's famous case report of little Hans, a five-year-old phobic child. Though the approach employed with little Hans should unquestionably be labeled psychotherapy, it is of historical significance to note that it was the young patient's father, a physician, who, under Freud's direction, was the psychotherapist.

Sandor Ferenczi, in the second decade of this century, reported the first attempt at direct psychoanalytic treatment of a child without the use of an intermediary, such as little Hans's father. Ferenczi found that the psychoanalytic method, as then used with adults, was not feasible with his young patient, who readily became bored with this approach and wanted to return to his toys.

It was only after it was recognized that a child's play could be considered a valid means of communication that child psychoanalysis was developed as a direct psychotherapeutic approach to the child. The central role of play in the development of modern child psychotherapy has been compared to the historical significance of hypnosis in adult psychiatry. Each has contributed considerably to the understanding of unconscious mental phenomena.

Women who had the advantage of experience with children as well as backgrounds in psychoanalysis devised the means of utilizing play in treating emotionally disturbed children without the use of an intermediary. Hermine von Hug-Hellmuth published the first such report eight years after Ferenczi described his abortive attempt. The major credit, however, for the subsequent development of child psychoanalysis belongs to Anna Freud and Melanie Klein. Melanie Klein's theoretical assumptions about the similarity of the child's and the adult's personality structure were expressed in the development of a therapeutic technique that considered the child's free play as a substitute for the adult's free associations. Anna Freud, giving more credence to the child's inevitable dependence on his parents, evolved a different technique. As she observed, the early days of child analysis were marked by a prestigious tendency to emphasize the similarity between the processes of analysis with children and adults. The principal differences recognized then were the absence in child analysis of free association and transference neuroses. In recent years, as the development of a transference neurosis has come to be considered the *sine qua non* of classical psychoanalysis, transference neuroses have been observed during the course of child analysis. Concurrently, there has been a paradoxical decrease in the insistence of child analysts that there is no distinction between the processes of child and adult analysis.

In the United States, the development in the 1920's of the child guidance clinic movement under the aegis of the National Committee for Mental Hygiene and the Commonwealth Fund gave much impetus to widening the scope of child psychotherapy, enabling it to reach its current status in this country. Lawson Lowrey credits David Levy with giving the first report, never published, on play therapy at the 1925 meeting of the American Orthopsychiatric Association.

TYPES OF PSYCHOTHERAPY

Psychotherapy, regardless of the age of the patient, has evolved so that practitioners tend to think either that there are several different psychotherapies based on varying frames of reference or that there is only one psychotherapy with the potential for a variety of different emphases. In either event, psychotherapy can be classified in several ways, based on various features of the process.

A common frame of reference for classification is the global one, which takes into account the general aim and mode of the treatment, resulting in supportive-suppressive-directive and expressive-exploratory-ventilative types of psychotherapy. Focusing on the therapist's attitude or the influence that he endeavors to exert, psychotherapy can be classified as being abreactive, interpretive, suggestive, persuasive, educative, etc. It is possible also to describe psychotherapy in terms of its depth, duration, and intensity. Emphasizing the theoretical concepts favored by the practitioner results in labeling therapy with eponyms such as Freudian, Kleinian, Rankian, and Rogerian.

Probably one of the most commonly used bases for classification of child therapy is the identification of the factor that is presumed to be the most helpful for the young patient. The history of psychotherapy has been punctuated by different factors or processes being emphasized at one time or another as the vitally essential element without which psychotherapy would not be effective. Suggestion, persuasive exhortation, and reassurance were the most prominent psychotherapeutic techniques prior to the ascendancy of psychoanalysis. In the infancy of psychoanalysis, symptomatic relief was attributed to the fact the patient had rediscovered a lost memory. Shortly thereafter, abreaction, the release of dammed-up emotions, was highlighted. With further development of psychoanalytic thinking, the emphasis shifted to modification of superego standards, identification with the therapist, development of increased emotional discipline in the working-through process, the development of insight, and expansion of ego functioning.

Concurrently, there has been a waxing and waning of prominence accorded conditioning factors, such as motivating needs, stimulating cues, and the reinforcement of reward and punishment. Similarly, improvement has been perceived as developing from a deconditioning process that may involve systematic desensitization or a manipulation of the therapeutic relationship so as to provide a corrective emotional experience.

Clearly, many of these factors overlap, and many are comparable with others, despite the fact that they are articulated in different conceptual frameworks. For example, subtle persuasion, operant conditioning, and fostering identification with the therapist probably entail similar processes. Efforts to attribute therapeutic progress with *all* patients to a single factor are unconvincing. It is likely that all the factors mentioned assume varying degrees of significance under different circumstances. Although none of these factors is specific for any particular age group, it is evident that with children the relationship and corrective emotional experiences exert a greater influence than they do with adults.

Isolating a single therapeutic element as the basis for classification is somewhat artificial, as each of these factors is present, in varying degrees, in every child psychotherapeutic undertaking. For example, there is no psychotherapy in which the relationship between therapist and patient is not a vital factor; yet child psychotherapists commonly talk of relationship therapy to describe a form of treatment in which a positive, friendly, helpful relationship is viewed as the primary if not the sole therapeutic ingredient. Probably one of the best examples of relationship therapy is found outside a clinical setting in the work of the Big Brother organization, highlighting again the difficulty encountered in drawing a fine line between psychotherapy and child-rearing and educational practices.

Remedial, educational, and patterning psychotherapy endeavor to teach new attitudes and patterns of behavior to children who persist in using immature and inefficient patterns. Often, though not invariably, these are presumed to be due to a maturational lag resulting from some organic deficit that is difficult to define.

Supportive psychotherapy is designed primarily to enable a youngster to cope with the emotional turmoil engendered by a crisis.

Release therapy, described initially by David Levy, facilitates the abreaction of pent-up emotions. It is this factor in psychotherapy that is publicized in the popular news media, probably because it is easy for laymen to grasp the idea of a youngster deriving benefit from venting a feeling such as hostility in a play situation. Although abreaction is an aspect of almost all therapeutic undertakings, in release therapy the treatment situation is structured to encourage only this factor. It is indicated primarily for preschool-age children who are suffering from a distorted emotional reaction to an isolated trauma.

Psychotherapy with children is often psychoanalytically oriented, which means that it endeavors through the vehicle of self-understanding to enable the child to develop his potential further. This is accomplished by liberating for more constructive use the psychic energy that is presumed to be expended in defending against fantasied dangers. The child is generally unaware of these unreal dangers, his fear of them, and the psychological defenses he uses to avoid both the danger and the fear. With the awareness that psychoanalytically derived psychotherapy facilitates, the patient is in a position to evaluate the usefulness of his defensive maneuvers preparatory to relinquishing the unnecessary ones that constitute the symptoms of his emotional disturbance.

This is to be distinguished from child psychoanalysis, a more intensive treatment, in which the unconscious elements are interpreted systematically in the sequence of affect-defense-impulse. Under these circumstances, transference manifestations may mature to a full transference neurosis.

Though interpretation of dynamically relevant conflicts are emphasized in these psychoanalytic descriptions, this does not imply the absence of elements that have been the basis for naming other types of psychotherapies. Indeed, in all psychotherapy, the child should derive support from the consistently understanding and accepting relationship with the therapist, and varying degrees of remedial, educational guidance and emotional release are inevitably present.

DIFFERENCES BETWEEN CHILDREN AND ADULTS

It is often assumed that therapy with children should consume less time than therapy with adults. Experience, however, does not confirm this expectation. This observation has been explained by a relative deficiency in children of many of the qualities that are prerequisites for successful psychotherapy.

For instance, a child typically begins psychotherapy because some adult in his environment has decided he should have it. As a consequence, one of the first tasks for the psychotherapist is stimulation of the child's motivation for treatment. In fact, children are often brought to psychotherapy not only against their wishes but also without the benefit of parental support because the parents may be blind to the child's needs and seek help only because of pressure from educational and legal agencies. Thus, the child in psychotherapy, in contrast to many adult patients who see advantages in getting well, may envision therapeutic change in terms of conforming to a disagreeable reality.

Furthermore, children tend to externalize internal conflicts in search of alloplastic adaptations. This causes the child's view of therapy to diverge from the therapist's. Although many adult patients anticipate solutions resulting from internal change, children find it difficult to conceive of doing anything other than altering an obstructing environment. It is inconceivable to the passive masochistic boy, who is the constant butt of his schoolmates' teasing, to rectify this situation by altering his mode of handling his aggressive impulses rather than by controlling his tormentors. This view may be reinforced by parental agreement.

The tendency of children to immediately reenact their previous feelings in new situations facilitates the early appearance of spontaneous and global transference reactions that often prove troublesome. Concurrently, the eagerness that children have for new experiences, coupled with their natural developmental fluidity, tends to limit the intensity and therapeutic usefulness of subsequent transference developments.

Children have a limited capacity for self-observation, with the notable exception of some obsessive children who resemble adults in this ability. These obsessive children, however, isolate the vital emotional components.

In the exploratory interpretative psychotherapies, development of a capacity for simultaneous emotional involvement and self-observation is most helpful. Only by means of identification with a trusted adult and in alliance with that adult are children able to approach such an ideal. Furthermore, the age-appropriateness of primitive mechanisms such as denial, projection, and isolation hinders the process of working through, which relies on a patient's synthesizing and integrative capacities.

Though children compare unfavorably with adults in the above qualities that are generally considered desirable in therapy, they have the advantage of active maturational and developmental forces. The history of psychotherapy for children is punctuated by efforts to harness these assets and to overcome the liabilities cited above. Recognition of the importance of play constituted a major forward stride in these efforts.

THERAPEUTIC TECHNIQUES

THE PLAYROOM

Scott has discussed the structure, design, and furnishing of the playroom suitable for child psychotherapy. He favors Klein's suggestion that the number of toys be few, simple, and carefully selected, so as to facilitate communication of fantasy. This contrasts with Axline's view that a wide variety of playthings be available, so as to increase the range of feelings that the child may express. These contrasting recommendations have been attributed by Brody to differences in therapeutic methods. Axline tends to avoid interpretation, even of conscious ideas, whereas Klein, at the other extreme, recommended interpretation of unconscious content directly and quickly. In teaching a flexible technique emphasizing neither of these extremes, the author has observed that therapists tend to change their preferences in equipment as they accumulate experience and develop confidence in their ability. Inexperienced therapists seem to derive a sense of security from having a large variety of playthings available. They stock their playrooms, for example, with many competitive board games, which they subsequently regret because these games can be so absorbing that they readily serve the purposes of resistance to therapy.

INITIAL APPROACH

There is no standard initial approach to children in psychotherapy. Variations are derived from perception of the child's needs and the therapist's individual style. The range extends from those in which the therapist directs the child's thought content and activity, as in release therapy and certain educational patterning techniques, to those exploratory methods in which the therapist endeavors to follow the child's lead. Even though the child determines the focus, it remains the therapist's responsibility to structure the situation. By encouraging a child to play freely and to say whatever he wishes, the therapist in exploratory psychotherapy establishes a definite structure. He has created an atmosphere in which he hopes to get to know all about the child. He may communicate to the child that it is not the therapist's task to get angry or to be pleased in response to what the child says or does but rather that he is in the business of understanding children. This does not mean that therapists do not react emotionally, but it assures the young patient that the therapist's personal feelings and standards are subordinate to his wish to understand the youngster.

A child whose disagreeable behavior has typically evoked a negative reaction from everyone may be threatened by this new apparently unconcerned person, the therapist. It may seem unbelievable to a child that a strange adult he is seeing only because of his bad behavior appears to like the child with no knowledge of him other than the bad behavior. The more benign the therapist's attitude, the more horrid are the punishments the child may fantasy. When this is the case, it is incumbent on the therapist to communicate his understanding of the child's apprehensions about the neutral therapeutic approach.

An inhibited, neurotic child who is the product of a rigid home and a highly organized school may experience mounting anxiety in response to the apparent absence of structure in the psychotherapeutic situation. From his superego-oriented view of the world, such a constricted child feels that the neutral therapeutic situation invites forbidden instinctual expression. Once again, the therapist's verbalization of his understanding of the child's anxiety helps to clear the air.

Nothing induces a child to participate in therapy so readily as the therapist's demonstrated understanding of him. This may take the form of clarifying the child's reaction to the therapeutic situation, as described above, or it may entail interpretation of affect and defense preparatory to subsequent interpretation of impulses. Experience has dictated that such activity often precludes the necessity for the introductory phase that used to be considered a vital preparation for child analysis and other exploratory psychotherapies with children. This introductory phase involved risky devices, such as promising the child a cure, joining the child in criticism of his parents, courting the child's affections in all conceivable fashions, exaggerating the gravity of a symptom and thereby frightening the patient, making oneself interesting to and useful to the patient. Such methods are rarely used today except with extremely regressed and withdrawn children. The demonstration of understanding that has replaced these introductory maneuvers should not assume an aura of magical mind-reading. Rather, it should convey to the child that the therapist knows something about emotionally disturbed children, that he likes to help them, and that he has great faith in the value of understanding.

COMMUNICATION

Some children participate in play activities immediately and verbalize spontaneously without assistance from the therapist; others appear to require considerable help. Responsive to the child's apparent needs, the therapist assumes either a relatively passive, observing role or a more active, intervening one.

Children generally are not as verbal as adults, making it vital that the child therapist appreciate and accept the importance and value of nonverbal communication. The child's facial expressions, gestures, posture, and motility and the content, form, and configuration of his play and art may say more than his words. Adopting this attitude, of course, essentially reverses the value placed on language in adult communication.

Furthermore, the child therapist must be prepared to adjust to the varying connotations attached to the same words and phrases by people of different ages. One of the most striking examples is the word "why," probably the most commonly used word in psychotherapy with adults. As such, it is expressive of the therapist's effort to understand. Children, however, often seem to react to the question "Why?" as if it were an accusation. Thus, even if the child's capacity for abstract thinking is sufficiently mature to enable him to appreciate that the therapist is interested in determining causal relationships, the child may regard an evasive "Because" as a suitable response. In all likelihood, whenever the child was asked to explain his actions or thoughts in the past, the questioner was not so much interested in establishing causal relationships as he was in being assured that whatever questionable thing the child had said or done would not be repeated. To test this assertion, the reader should observe queries directed by parents to children as to *why* something was said or done. This question rarely, if ever, inquires about approved deeds or thoughts. It is phenomenal how infrequently children, whether emotionally disturbed or not, are exposed to an interest in the motivational forces underlying *valued* thoughts and deeds. It is no wonder that sensitive children in psychotherapy automatically translate the word "why" into criticism and disapproval. The result is that the message sent by the therapist is not the same message that the child receives.

THERAPEUTIC INTERVENTIONS

Therapeutic interventions with children encompass the same range as those employed with adults in psychotherapy. If one regards the amount of therapist activity as the basis for a continuum, at the lower end are the questions posed by the therapist regarding the patient's statements or behavior. Closely aligned is the process of clarification of the patient's manifest productions by means of questions, recapitulation, or reorganization. Next, there are exclamations and confrontations in which the therapist directs attention to some data of which the patient is cognizant but which the therapist thinks the patient should attend to at the time. Then there are interpretations designed to expand the patient's conscious awareness of himself by making explicit those elements that have previously been implicitly expressed in his thoughts, feelings, and behavior. Beyond interpretation, the therapist may offer the patient new information, information that is new because of the patient's lack of experience. At the most active end of the continuum, there is advising, counseling, and directing, designed to help the patient adopt a course of action or a conscious attitude.

There are, however, some vital differences in the ways these interventions are employed with children and adults. The probable fate of broad, open-ended questions is illustrated vividly by citing the book title *Where Did You Go? Out. What Did You Do? Nothing.* To avoid such responses and to encourage verbal and nonverbal associations, the child therapist needs to be far more specific, focusing his questions on what the child is just about ready to express. The best clues, of course, come from what the child has already communicated. In essence, the therapist asks the child to elaborate on what he has already said or done. The therapist should not sound as though he is quizzing the child and invading his privacy. The more the therapist can imply curiosity, not unlike that of another interested youngster, the greater the likelihood of fruitful response.

This apparent naiveté should be tempered with awareness of the risk of asking questions that may seem devious to the child, such as those to which the therapist obviously knows the answer. For example, if the therapist, in his initial contact with the child, inquires about the reasons for the consultation, the child, who assumes rightfully that his parents have already told the therapist, may wonder whether the therapist is being dishonest. It can make a great deal of difference to the child if the therapist states that he aleady knows the parents' reasons for consulting him but that he is interested in the child's ideas. Similarly, the therapist who inquires as to what dolls are doing, in an effort to have the child elaborate on the fantasy underlying the doll play he is observing, will very likely get a minimal return, since, from the child's point of view, what the dolls were doing should be obvious to the therapist. It would be more productive for the therapist to make running comments describing the dolls' activities, like a television announcer at an athletic event. Under those circumstances, the child often responds by elaborating on the therapist's description, thereby facilitating the approach to the underlying fantasy.

Certain interventions that are vital with children are generally superfluous if not insulting to most adults. For example, to tell an adult who is consciously angry that he is angry would be a confrontation that could readily prove offensive to most adults. With an angry child, however, the same intervention may be a necessary interpretation of affect, inasmuch as everyone may know about the child's anger except the child himself. Also, there are many more occasions with children than with adults where clarification of misconceptions can be helpful.

Many psychotherapists are convinced that it is wise to deal with defenses and resistances before interpreting impulses. With children, however, there is an important exception to this general guideline. It is often unwise to undo the projection into play that is so characteristic of child therapy.

Thus, when a child with adequate reality-testing causes two dolls to fight, the therapist's running commentary might be limited to a description of the dolls' affect—namely, that the dolls are angry with one another. Though the displacement of the child's own feelings to one or both dolls may be obvious, it may be wisest to communicate about the anger without attributing it to the child, thereby dealing with the impulse without interpreting the defensive projection into play. Under these circumstances, projection is viewed as an age-appropriate, adaptive mechanism rather than as a pathological, defensive maneuver. If the therapist told the child that he had the dolls fight because of his own anger, the child's resistance and defensiveness might be increased to the extent that he would stop the activity, interrupting the communication. It is as if the therapist and the child with adequate ego strength have tacitly agreed to the significance of play without spelling it out specifically each time. Bornstein noted other disadvantages in interpreting play directly. Repeated interpretation of the symbolic meaning of play can impede the child's use of play in the service of the development of sublimations, since such interpretations may facilitate libidinization of play.

Treating children whose ego functioning is so defective that they confuse play and reality calls for caution in dealing with impulses displaced in play. In such instances, the therapist may have to devote his efforts to educating the child about the distinction between play and reality before it is judicious to deal with the content of the play. This type of educational intervention, however, is not supportive for those children who do not have difficulty in distinguishing fantasy and reality and who are generally alienated by such interventions. At the risk of oversimplification, it is comparable to the situation when the therapist interprets to an adult patient that he feels as though the therapist were his father. If the adult patient's ego functioning were borderline, the therapist might add, "And I am not your father." To add this comment with a patient whose reality-testing is not impaired would not only be unnecessary but also insulting and clearly not therapeutic.

Children can derive ego strength out of any activity that produces gratification as a consequence of making progress in lieu of attention-seeking devices. The dependent child who, for instance, repeatedly states or shows that he cannot perform a simple task, such as putting his shoes on the wrong feet more frequently than is possible by chance, needs to discover that there can be more gratification in an accomplishment than in getting the assistance of an adult. Similarly, psychic growth is promoted by the development of internal controls rather than reliance on the adult's external controls and by deriving gratification from work as opposed to accomplishing the same tasks by cheating.

PARENTAL INVOLVEMENT

Psychotherapy with children is distinguished by the necessity for parental involvement. This does not necessarily reflect parental culpability for the youngster's emotional difficulties; it is a factor of the child's dependent state.

In practice, there are varying degrees of parental involvement in child psychotherapy. With preschool-age children, it is common for the entire psychotherapeutic effort to be directed toward the parents without any direct psychotherapy of the child. The rationale is that helping the parents results in environmental alterations that will be beneficial for the child.

At the other extreme, children can be seen in psychotherapy without any parental involvement beyond the payment of fees and perhaps transporting the child to the therapeutic sessions. Most therapists agree that only those relatively rare neurotic children who have reached the oedipal phase of development can sustain therapy by themselves. Even in such instances, however, the majority of practitioners prefer to maintain at least an informative alliance with the parents for the minimal purposes of transmitting information about the child.

Probably the most common arrangement is the one that has been stressed in child guidance clinics—that is, involving both child and parents in therapeutic relationships either with the same therapist or with different therapists. In recent years there have been efforts to shift the focus from the child as the primary patient to the family as the patient. In such family therapy, all or selected members of the family are treated simultaneously as a group.

CONFIDENTIALITY

Consideration of parental involvement highlights the important question of confidentiality in psychotherapy with children. There are advantages to creating an atmosphere in which the child can feel that his words and actions are viewed by the therapist as both serious and tentative. In other words, the child's communications do not bind him to a commitment; nevertheless, they are too important to be communicated to a third party without the patient's permission.

Ordinarily, such an attitude is conveyed implicitly and does not require explication. However, there are occasions when a child patient insists on discussing the issue of confidentiality. It is unwise, particularly with those children who are inclined to make an issue of it, to promise a child patient that the therapist will not tell parents what transpires in his therapeutic sessions. Though the therapist has no intention of disclosing such data to the patient's parents, the bulk of what children do and say in psychotherapy is common knowledge to the parents. Therefore, should the child be so motivated, it is easy for him to manipulate the situation so as to produce circumstantial evidence that the therapist has betrayed his confidence. Accordingly, if confidentiality requires specific discussion during treatment, the therapist is best advised not to go beyond indicating that he is not in the habit of telling parents what goes on in therapy, as his job is to understand children and to help them understand themselves.

It is important also to try to enlist the parents' cooperation in respecting the privacy of the child's therapeutic sessions. Needless to say, this is not always readily accomplished. Parents quite naturally are curious about what transpires and may be threatened by the therapist's apparently privileged position.

THEORETICAL ASSUMPTIONS

Brody has characterized child psychotherapy as a "theoretical orphan." This refers to the fact that child psychotherapy does not have its own readily identifiable body of theory. Currently, three major theoretical systems underlie the bulk of child psychotherapeutic work: (1) psychoanalytic theories of the evolution and resolution of emotional disturbance, (2) social-learning-behavioral theories of psychopathology and treatment, and (3) developmental theories.

PSYCHOANALYTIC THEORY

Psychoanalytic theory conceives of exploratory psychotherapy, with patients of all ages, as working by reversing the evolution of psychopathological processes. The principal difference noted with advancing age is a sharpening distinction between psychogenetic and psychodynamic factors. The younger the child, the more difficult it is to distinguish between genetic and dynamic forces.

The development of these psychopathological processes is usually thought to begin with certain experiences that have proved to be particularly significant to the patient and that have affected him adversely. The reason for this may reside in the nature of these experiences or their intensity or both. Their influence may have been exaggerated because of their occurrence in the early, impressionable years of the patient's life or under special emotional or physical circumstances that rendered him vulnerable. Though in one sense the experiences were real, in another sense they may have been misinterpreted or imagined. In any event, for the patient they were traumatic experiences that have caused unconscious complexes to which the patient reacted in a manner analogous to the body's organic reaction to irritating foreign bodies. Being inaccessible to conscious awareness, these unconscious elements escape rational adaptive maneuvers. They are subject, instead, to a pathological misuse of his adaptive and defensive mechanisms. The result is the development of distressing symptoms, character attitudes, or patterns of behavior that constitute emotional disturbance.

The therapist can design various therapeutic programs to interrupt this evolution. Expressive and exploratory psychotherapy facilitates a reversal of this evolution through a reenactment and desensitization of the traumatic events by free expression of thoughts and feelings in an interview-play situation. Ultimately, the therapist helps his patient understand the warded-off fears, feelings, and wishes that have beset him. As the therapist leads the patient toward his goal, he helps him realize that he has been defending himself, points out the nature of these defenses and the reasons for these maneuvers.

Though the patient may have varying degrees of desire to learn about himself and thus gain conscious control over automatic processes, he invariably manifests resistances. These are paradoxical tendencies that oppose therapeutic progress. For instance, patients invariably manifest an inertia that is grounded in the fact that what has been repressed tends to remain forgotten and what has been repeating itself for years tends to perpetuate itself endlessly. Also, there are usually advantages, real or imagined, in remaining emotionally disturbed, and certain people, greatly burdened by conscience, develop a need to suffer, which opposes psychic health.

At the center of these resistances to treatment are the psychic functions that facilitate forgetting and repetition, which lead the patient to reexperience certain feelings out of context without recalling their relevancy. In the therapeutic setting, it is the therapist who becomes the object of these reexperienced thoughts, feelings, and reactions, known as transference. Their origins are found in the past and in relation to other people, notably parents. In such transference, the therapist becomes the target of desires, loves, hates, or suspicions that make sense only when viewed in terms of relationships the patient has experienced with other people. With the therapist's recognition that the patient misunderstands the relationship, he attempts to use these transferred reactions to discover the genesis of the patient's problems and to formulate interpretations that will help the patient understand his enigmatic stance. The goal of these interpretations is to enable the patient to increase conscious control over heretofore automatic mental processes. The desired result is a rearrangement of his personality structure and enhanced ability to realize his potential.

Whereas such an expressive-exploratory-interpretive approach seeks improvement by exposure and resolution of buried conflicts, suppressive-supportive-educative psychotherapy works in an opposite fashion, aiming to facilitate repression. Capitalizing on the patient's desire to please him, the therapist encourages the patient to substitute new adaptive and defensive mechanisms. In this type of therapy, the therapist uses interpretations minimally, emphasizing suggestion, persuasion, exhortation, counseling, education, direction, advice, abreaction, environmental manipulation, intellectual review, gratification of the patient's current dependent needs, and similar supportive techniques.

LEARNING THEORIES

Stimulated by developments in experimental psychology, several theories of learning that have relevance for all psychotherapeutic undertakings have been developed. Recently, they have received increased attention as the basis of an allegedly new therapeutic method, most commonly referred to as behavior therapy. Regardless of the type of treatment, however, the theoretical assumptions, derived primarily from laboratory experiments, assert that, since disturbed behavior is acquired, its evolution and treatment can be understood within the framework of established theories of learning, such as Hull's reinforcement theory, Pavlov's conditioned reflex theories, and Skinner's operant conditioning.

This framework may be summarized by citing Watson and Raynor's classical demonstration almost a half-century ago of the development of a phobia in 11-month-old Albert. After determination that Albert was not afraid of furry objects and that he had had no previous experience with white rats, he was given a rat to play with. Whenever Albert made an overture to the animal, the experimenters made a loud noise. After a short period of time, Albert appeared fearful whenever he saw the white rat. This phobia then generalized to similar stimuli, such as white rabbits, cotton, and other furry objects. Albert's experimentally induced phobic reactions reportedly persisted several months later. This was not the invariable response of all infants; some turned to scowl at the source of the noise while they continued playing with the animal. Four years later, Jones demonstrated that another infant who had been conditioned to fear furry objects could be relieved of the fear by means of both social imitation and direct reconditioning.

As a consequence of coupling such observations with clinical experience, concepts encompassing the learning and reinforcement of maladaptive behavior have always been implicit in the rationale underlying all child psychotherapy. Only recently, however, has there been a resurgence of interest outside the laboratory in behavioral techniques specifically designed to eliminate symptoms. Systematic symptom-oriented efforts to induce unlearning, inhibition, and extinction of maladaptive behavior by means of desensitization, operant conditioning, aversive conditioning, avoidance learning, etc., have been applied primarily to phobias, enuresis, sexual disorders, tics, and anxiety-tension states. Eysenck suggested that those treatment approaches that explicitly employ behavior in an effort to change habits ostensibly rooted in the nervous system should be designated behavior therapy and distinguished from psychotherapy, which employs psychological methods.

DEVELOPMENTAL THEORIES

Underlying child psychotherapy are a variety of psychosociobiological developmental schemata. The employment of this vital frame of reference distinguishes child psychotherapy from adult psychotherapy. It entails more than knowledge of age-appropriate behavior derived from studies, such as Gesell's descriptions of the morphology of behavior. It must encompass more than psychosexual development with ego psychological and sociocultural amendments. It extends beyond familiarity with Piaget's sequence of intellectual evolution as a basis for knowledge of the level of abstraction in which children of various ages may be expected to function.

It is more than recognizing that children of various ages do not react to hunger, other frustrations, injury, illness, and death in some uniform fashion that resembles adult behavior but rather in ways that are characteristic of their stages of development.

Such information may be derived from a number of descriptions of child development; however, it is essential that it be supplemented by personal knowledge and observation of children, with the resultant view of the child as fluid instead of static, as a maturing and developing organism who is not complete. The child's personality must be viewed in the perspective of the interrelationships of his past, present, and future; the focus must be on questions of regression-progression and transience-permanence rather than only on static assessments, even if they are articulated in psychodynamic terms.

Special mention should be made of the developmental line, as Anna Freud conceptualizes it, from play to work. Children do not play solely for the recreational purposes that adults prefer to attribute to their own games and sporting activities. Play serves a number of important purposes, such as facilitating the mastery of many of children's inevitable developmental crises through playful transformation of what was passively experienced into activity. As a consequence, play has been assigned a special position in child psychotherapy, as both a medium of communication and a means of sublimation.

USE OF PSYCHOTHERAPY

INDICATIONS FOR PSYCHOTHERAPY

The present level of knowledge does not permit the compilation of a meaningful list of the multifaceted indications for child psychotherapy. Existing diagnostic classifications cannot serve as the basis for such a list because of invariable deficiences in nosological specificity and comprehensiveness. In general, psychotherapy is indicated for children with emotional disorders that appear to be sufficiently permanent to impede maturational and developmental forces. Psychotherapy may be indicated also when the child's development is not impeded but appears to be proceeding in such a fashion that he inevitably induces reactions in the environment that are considered pathogenic. Ordinarily, such disharmonies are dealt with by the child with his parents' assistance; however, when these efforts are persistently inadequate, psychotherapeutic intervention may be indicated.

CONTRAINDICATIONS

Psychotherapy is contraindicated if the emotional disturbance is judged to be an intractable one that will not respond to treatment. This is an exceedingly difficult judgment but one that is essential, considering the marked excess of the demand for psychotherapy over its supply. Because the potential for error in such prognostic assessments is so great, therapists should bring to them both professional humility and a readiness to offer a trial of therapy. There are times when the essential factor in intractability is the therapist. Certain patients may elicit a reaction from one therapist that is a contraindication for psychotherapy with that therapist but not necessarily with another therapist.

Another contraindication is evidence that the therapeutic process will interfere with reparative forces. A difficult question is posed by evidence that the forces mobilized as a consequence of psychotherapy may have dire social or somatic effects. An example is the circumstance where psychotherapy may upset a shaky family equilibrium and cause more difficulty than the original problem posed.

SELECTION OF THE APPROPRIATE TECHNIQUE

Most contraindications to psychotherapy really relate to complications that are not so much absolute contraindications as they are factors that influence choice of the appropriate form of therapy for the particular child. Matching the child and his disturbance with a specific treatment is a worthwhile goal that is difficult to achieve because of limited precision in diagnosis and uncertainty about the curative factors in psychotherapy. Clearly, there is no single, effective therapeutic element in treatment. Though therapists may attempt to predict in advance which factor will be the most influential, experience demonstrates that such predictions have limited reliability. Therapists need to guard against developing rigid preconceived ideas that will interfere with flexible sensitivity.

Certain elements in psychotherapy with specific children induce complications that militate against that particular variety of psychotherapy for that child. Many children, for instance, respond to a positive, constructive interaction with a neutral adult, thereby necessitating no more than relationship therapy. However, there are many instances where such treatment is so insufficient that it is contraindicated because its chance of success is so negligible.

With most neurotic children, a form of interpretive psychotherapy aimed at uncovering intrapsychic conflicts is indicated. However, if the youngster's ego functioning, particularly in the area of reality-testing, is borderline, such an approach may prove to be so deleterious as to precipitate a frank psychotic adjustment. A minimal prerequisite for interpretation of the significance of doll play to a child is that the child appreciates that the doll play is different from real life. When the child's capacity for such reality-testing is impaired, therapeutic interventions should be designed to strengthen this defective function. If, on the other hand, this function is not impaired, efforts aimed at strengthening a child's intact reality-testing by helping him to distinguish doll play from reality are insulting and not beneficial.

Though there are many hyperactive children, there is no standard psychotherapeutic approach to the child with this distressing symptom. If, for example, the hyperactivity seems to represent a means of expressing anxiety resulting from an intrapsychic conflict over aggression, one would be inclined to approach that child with interpretive psychotherapy, exposing the child's conflicts over aggression to rational scrutiny. On the other hand, if the hyperactivity is presumed to be due to organic processes, the therapist's primary task is to supply externally the controls that are lacking internally. This may require medication, regulation of the child's life, isolating him from distressing stimuli, and similar supportive, suppressive measures.

These markedly different approaches to hyperactivity are not interchangeable. Though regulating the life of the anxiously hyperactive child may result in relief of the symptom of hyperactivity, this is done by inducing passivity as a means of handling the unconscious aggression—in essence, a new handicap. Approaching the child who is hyperactive due to organicity with accurate interpretations of underlying conflicts may be perceived by the child as increased stimulation, to which he will react with greater hyperactivity. It is not the underlying conflicts that are primarily pathogenic so much as the deficiency in internal controls.

The fact that symptomatic treatment may be beneficial requires no elaboration. However, symptomatic treatment is not invariably innocuous; there are times when it may be harmful. Consider the youngster with the symptom of reading retardation, secondary to underlying emotional factors, who does not respond to tutoring. The tutoring could result in more than a mere waste of effort if the child takes his failure to respond to these special efforts to be further evidence of his stupidity and hopelessness. Furthermore, such a symptomatic approach may be unwittingly repeating a pertinent trauma for the child.

Eight-year old John was unable even to begin to learn the alphabet in his three years of schooling. Intensive tutoring only seemed to increase his resistance to learning. It was subsequently uncovered during the course of psychotherapy that John's sister, three years his senior, used to play school with him. During this game, which started when she was 5 and he was 2, she played the role of the teacher and he the pupil. His inability to learn the alphabet in this game prompted his 5-year-old teacher to be extremely punitive and threatening. She warned John repeatedly that he would never be permitted to go to school unless he learned. This game and these warnings persisted until John's entry into school, when he terminated the game. However, in reconstruction during the course of psychotherapy, it appeared that John's expectation of school had been such that he was sure he would hate it. Unconsciously, he was determined not to learn so that he would not be permitted entry into school. Only after these experiences and their resultant ideas and attitudes were uncovered and worked through was John able to dismiss them as inappropriate to his current situation and to benefit for the first time from tutoring. Until that point, he had unconsciously viewed tutoring as a punishment that reinforced his determination not to learn from it.

Psychoanalytically derived individual psychotherapy is most effective for youngsters who have internal, self-sustaining, neurotic conflicts that have not originated earlier than the phallic stage of development and have resulted in circumscribed, ego-alien symptoms. Such expressive-exploratory-interpretive therapy is generally less helpful to those children whose disturbance has not caused them much immediate discomfort. Such syndromes are often a consequence of conflicts derived from prephallic phases, and the resulting disturbance tends to permeate the child's entire character structure. Psychoanalytically oriented therapy is least effective when the therapist cannot establish a therapeutic alliance with the child, as in the cases where there has been an arrest in ego development resulting in a diminished capacity for abstract thinking and the establishment of object relationships. When the capacity for object relationship is severely limited, as it is in extremely young children or older psychotic children, the treatment needs to be based on a foundation of need satisfaction. In such instances it may be advantageous for the therapist to be the person who cares for the child.

PROGNOSIS

One of the most complex issues in psychiatry is the assessment of change and determination of the factors responsible for the changes. Inevitably, the number of variables is so great that all investigators are cautious in attributing change to any single factor, including psychotherapy.

The amount of time and energy invested in child psychotherapy seems to suggest that clinicians are convinced it is a worthwhile endeavor. As the patient cannot be used as his own control, it is never possible to state with absolute finality what would have happened had that particular patient not had the benefit of psychotherapy. Investigators who have attempted to survey the results of psychotherapy statistically have amassed data suggesting favorable results in 65 to 80 per cent of the cases. Neglecting momentarily the complex issue of the methodology involved in determining success, one is still left with the question as to what would have happened to these children had they not been exposed to psychotherapy. Comparisons have been attempted with different types of control groups, but none of these has been entirely satisfactory. In all these studies there are reasons to question the degree of success of the intensive efforts to select a control group of children with comparable prognoses who had received no therapy. Comparisons of the treated children with these questionable control groups generally fail to demonstrate that the treated patients obtained markedly better results than those who left treatment early or failed to continue after diagnostic study.

Illustrative of the additional difficulties in determining meaningful and measurable criteria of the outcome of psychotherapy is the fact that appearance of anxiety in a delinquent is generally considered a sign of improvement, but a comparable result in a phobic youngster probably represents lack of progress. Although symptomatic considerations alone are an inadequate criterion of the results of psychotherapy, it can nevertheless be anticipated that a youngster with academic inhibitions will demonstrate a better academic performance as a consequence of successful psychotherapy. In contrast, an obsessive-compulsive youngster may demonstrate, after successful psychotherapy, that his academic performance has diminished.

Furthermore, different assessments by different clinicians of the same change in the same patient are common. The tightly controlled obsessive-compulsive patient who, during the course of therapy, demonstrates loosening of his thought processes may be considered by one clinician to be on a progressive road to eventual recovery, whereas another clinician could view this same patient as being on a regressive road to a schizophrenic reaction. The only variables in such instances are the evaluators.

The methodological problems inherent in the evaluative process have proved so great that many investigators have shifted their focus from study of the results of psychotherapy to examining the process of psychotherapy. Temporarily, they are willing to sacrifice a global but imprecise overview in favor of a more intensive investigation of the changes taking place during the course of psychotherapy in an effort to isolate the factors responsible for these changes. Thus, it is not yet possible to articulate meaningfully the results of psychotherapy for a large number of cases. There are currently in progress what appear to be meticulous methodological studies, and these are to be encouraged.

REFERENCES

Allen, F. H. *Psychotherapy with Children*. W. W. Norton, New York, 1942.

Axline, V. *Play Therapy*. Riverside Press, Cambridge, Mass., 1947.

Bornstein, B. Clinical notes on child analysis. Psychoanal. Stud. Child., 1: 151, 1945.

Brody, S. Aims and methods in child psychotherapy. J. Amer. Acad. Child Psychiat., 3: 385, 1964.

Buxbaum, E. Technique of child therapy. Psychoanal. Stud. Child. 9: 297, 1954.

Freud, A. *The Psychoanalytic Treatment of Children*. Imago, London, 1946.

Freud, A. *Normality and Pathology in Childhood*. International Universities Press, New York, 1965.

Freud, S. Analysis of a phobia in a five year old boy. In *Standard Edition of* the *Complete Psychological Works of Sigmund Freud*, vol. 10, p. 1. Hogarth Press, London, 1955.

Hamilton, G. *Psychotherapy in Child Guidance*. Columbia University Press, New York, 1947.

Harrison, S. I. Communicating with children in psychotherapy. Int. Psychiat. Clin., 1: 39, 1964.

Harrison, S. I., and Carek, D. J. *A Guide to Psychotherapy*. Little, Brown, Boston, 1966.

Haworth, M. *Child Psychotherapy*. Basic Books, New York, 1964.

Klein, M. *The Psychoanalysis of Children*. Hogarth Press, London, 1932.

Levy, D. Release therapy. Amer. J. Orthopsychiat., 9: 713, 1939.

Lippman, H. S. *Treatment of the Child in Emotional Conflict*. McGraw-Hill, New York, 1956.

Lowrey, L. G. Therapeutic play techniques (Symposium). Amer. J. Orthopsychiat., 25: 574 and 747, 1955.

Scott, W. C. M. Differences between the playroom used in child psychiatric treatment and in child analysis. Canad. Psychiat. Ass. J., 6: 281, 1961.

Strupp, H. Psychotherapy. Ann. Rev. Psychol., 13: 445, 1962.

Witmer, H. L. *Psychiatric Interviews with Children*. Commonwealth Fund, New York, 1946.

CHAPTER SEVENTEEN

Group Therapy

IRVIN A. KRAFT, M.D.

HISTORY

GROUP PSYCHOTHERAPY of children originated in 1934, when Slavson began to work with latency-age children in what he called activity group therapy. This and subsequent work differed from using children in common activities, such as scouting or group work, by there being a theory of personality and behavior on which were predicated certain actions of the leader in a deliberately designed situation. The children's behavior in the contrived staging of the group constituted their responses to treatment.

Activity group therapy laid the groundwork for further developments in the use of group psychotherapy with children and adolescents. It used classical psychoanalytic therapy consistently, as did play group psychotherapy, which was described in 1937. In the same year, Bender reported using groups in the treatment of children in a hospital ward. During the 1940's, investigators devised different methods to suit the usual age groupings of children, especially latency and adolescence. Techniques were tried for different settings, such as correctional institutions, public schools, hospitals, residential treatment facilities, and pediatric specialty clinics.

BASIC ASSUMPTIONS

The field of group psychotherapy presents a number of theoretical postures and variations of techniques. Client-centered psychotherapy, Adlerian concepts, and classical psychoanalytic principles have dominated the practice of group psychotherapy for children. Despite the particular theoretical background of the therapists, certain assumptions pervade their work. These include the unconscious, some constructs of the mind (such as ego), psychic determinism, and infantile sexuality.

Activity—such as play, gestures, and interactions—is based on inner fantasies of the child that seek expression and resolution in development, family transactions, and other aspects of growth-promoting adaptation. From these and other considerations, a therapist evolves an individualized treatment style that enables him to work comfortably with his patients.

Certain theoretical positions—such as an adolescent's possession of weak self-identity, subjection to strong sexual urges, and action on them— could lead to a definite, concrete mode of thinking about group membership. In this circumstance, few therapists attempted adolescent groups with boys and girls together until Ackerman, in 1955, showed that sexual acting out need not occur. Subsequent efforts by others demonstrated that boys and girls could be treated effectively in groups at any age.

AGE GROUPINGS

The age and developmental stage of the child influenced the growth of group psychotherapy techniques more than perhaps any other factor. Since the standard diagnostic nomenclature for psychiatric disorders of childhood failed to describe adequately the disturbances in children, investigators tended to group children by age and nature of presenting difficulties. They also assumed that the verbalizations of children could not be utilized extensively much before puberty or adolescence, so that play and activity dominated techniques. Psychotic children and severe sexual deviates, such as homosexuals, seemed unsuitable to the groups. The grouping of children fell into about five categories. These categories were: (1) preschool and early-school age, (2) late latency: ages 9 to 11, (3) pubertal: ages 12 and 13, (4) early adolescence: ages 13 and 14, and (5) middle adolescence through late adolescence: ages 14 to 17.

Preschool and Early-School Age Groups

Work with the preschool group is usually structured by the therapist by using a particular technique, such as puppets, or it is couched in terms of a permissive play atmosphere. In therapy with puppets, the children project onto the puppets their fantasies in a way not unlike ordinary play. The main value lies in the catharsis afforded the child, especially if he shows difficulty in expressing feelings. Here the group aids the child less by interaction with other members than by action with the puppets.

In play group psychotherapy, the emphasis rests on the interactional qualities of the children with each other and the therapist in the permissive playroom setting. Slavson stated that the therapist should be a woman who can allow the children to produce fantasies verbally and in play but who also can use active restraint when the children undergo excessive tension. The toys are the traditional ones used in individual play therapy, such as water, plasticene, a doll's house, and toy guns. The children use the toys to act out aggressive impulses and to relive with the group members and the therapist their home difficulties. The children catalyze each other and obtain libido-activating stimulation from this and their play materials. The therapist interprets a child to the group in the context of the transference to her and to other group members.

Ginott aims in group play therapy to effect basic changes in the child's intrapsychic equilibrium through relationship, catharsis, insight, reality-testing, and sublimation. The mechanism of identification affords the child major opportunities for therapeutic gain as he identifies himself with other group members and the therapist. Since the individual child constitutes the focus of the treatment, little attention is given to the group as an entity in itself. Corresponding to ordinary play relationships of children, attachments to peers and toys and the formations of subgroups shift for each child.

Criteria for selection. The children selected for this group treatment procedure show in common a social hunger, the need to be like their peers and to be accepted by them. Usually the therapist excludes the child who has never realized a primary relationship, as with his mother, since individual psychotherapy could better help the child. Ginott also rejects children with murderous attitudes toward siblings, sociopathic children, those with perverse sexual experiences, habitual thieves, and extremely aggressive children. Usually the children selected include those with phobic reactions, effeminate boys, shy and withdrawn children, and children with primary behavior disorders.

Modifications of these criteria have been used by Speers and Lansing, who utilized group therapy for autistic children along with parent group therapy and art therapy. They began with four children under the age of 5 who showed reality withdrawal and severe disturbances in self-identity. Language deficits, lack of bowel and bladder control, severe sleeping and eating disturbances, and stereotyped behavior were prominent in these children. The investigators reported that these psychotic children can change in a group setting by obtaining rudimentary self-identity. The physical and psychological closeness of the group members panicked some of the children, but in time it helped them establish relationships. The group ego, originally described for older children in group therapy by E. J. Anthony, provided part of a therapeutic symbiosis for each patient and developed after the autistic defenses were repeatedly penetrated. Safety in the group fostered emancipation from the sick relationship with the mother.

LATENCY-AGE GROUPS

Activity-interview group psychotherapy combines elements of activity, play, and interview group therapies. It differs from activity group therapy in that the therapist actively interprets to the children their actions and verbalizations as they involve themselves with the usual materials used in play therapy and activity therapy.

The children can be more disturbed than in activity group therapy, since dreams and other dynamically laden verbalizations undergo group discussion. The meetings occur after school hours and last about an hour, with the last ten minutes devoted to refreshments.

In this type of group therapy, as with pubertal and adolescent groups, the children verbalize in a problem-oriented manner with the awareness that problems brought them together and that the group aims to change them. They report dreams, fantasies, daydreams, traumatic and unpleasant experiences. These and their group behavior undergo open discussion.

Composition of the group. In some clinic and private practice situations, where an activity therapy setting may not be feasible, the emphasis in the group treatment of these children can be shifted to an interview type with little toy play and no use made of tools or arts and crafts. Late latency-age children (ages 9 to 11), who usually constitute the majority of referrals to a child psychiatric clinic, utilize this procedure well. The children can be of both sexes, and their selection depends more on the overall structure of the group than on the individual patient's characteristics. The optimum size of the group is six children. If the group contains several withdrawn and taciturn members, for example, it behooves the leader not to include another similar child. The leader can be of either sex, and he utilizes psychodynamic generalizations in verbalizing with and for the children as they relate daily experiences and comments about their parents and discuss their interactions with other group members. Here, as in other forms of group psychotherapy of children, the professional discipline of the therapist may be any of the traditional ones in the mental health field. A co-therapist of the same or opposite sex to the therapist can be useful in these groups.

The patients not usually taken into these groups include the incorrigible or psychopathic child, the homicidal child, and the overt sexually deviant child. The severely threatened, ritualistic, socially peculiar children who cannot establish effective communication at any useful level with the group members fail to do well in these groups.

Intellectual ability should be well distributed, for too many retardates in the group impede interaction and tend to enhance motoric patterns of all the group members. Children with physical deformities, tics, protruding teeth, or behavior based on maturational brain dysfunction find the group situation helpful. Vehement interactions or taunts about their disabilities produce in time a group response of support as the members perceive the victim's sensitivities and feelings.

Since the sex ratio inherent in child psychiatric work with latency children runs 3 to 1 of boys to girls, finding enough girls becomes a problem for these groups. If possible, equal numbers of each sex should be sought.

The girls act as a modulating influence and diminish extremes of behavior.

Parents. In these circumstances, as with most treatment procedures for children, parental difficulties present obstacles. Sometimes uncooperative parents refuse to bring a child or to participate in their own therapy. The extreme of this reveals itself when severely disturbed parents use the child as their channel of communication to work out their own needs. Then the child finds himself in an intolerable position of receiving positive group experiences at the clinic that create havoc at home.

PUBERTAL GROUPS

Similar group therapy methods can be used with pubertal children, who are often grouped monosexually rather than mixed. Their problems resemble those of late latency children, but they are also beginning, especially the girls, to feel the impact and pressures of early adolescence. In a way, these groups offer help during a transitional period.

Activity group psychotherapy has been the recommended type of group therapy for preadolescent children. The children, usually of the same sex and in groups of not more than eight, freely act out in a setting especially designed and planned for its physical and milieu characteristics. Slavson pictured the group as a substitute family in which the passive, neutral therapist becomes the surrogate for parents. The therapist moves about the group as the children work with arts and crafts materials and tools. He assumes different roles, mostly in a nonverbal manner, as each child interacts with him and the other group members.

This freedom of expression and activity instigates responses among the members so that a number of roles emerge. There are the instigators, who enable the group to stay alive dynamically; the neutralizers, who, by greater superegos, keep impulsive acts down and help regulate behavior; the social neuters, who seem impotent to accelerate or impede the flow of group activity; and the isolates, who are so neurotically constricted that they initially find the group too frightening to join in its activities.

These children use the materials, under some control by the therapist, as fixators of such feelings as aggression. They can, however, engage in boisterous and destructive acts, especially with each other. The therapist does not intervene except when realistic danger to the patient or building arises. He helps with tasks when asked. The method assumes that, in time, the children will constructively transfer their energy from the tools and materials to each other.

The refreshment period at the end of the two-hour sessions affords the children stimulation by the food and a family type of situation in which new modalities of behavior eventually assert themselves. The children in this clublike atmosphere also go as groups on self-selected visits to a variety of community offerings, such as athletic events, movies, and museums.

Pattern changes. During these exposures to the group, the child demonstrates his customary and usual adaptational patterns. If, for example, he has utilized his haplessness to elicit dependency fostering and psychological feeding responses from adults and peers, he finds the group and the therapist failing him. The neutrality and passivity of the therapist impede these patterns and create enough frustration to initiate different behavior in time. Similarly, the provocative, extremely aggressive child finds no rejection or punishment for his behavioral distortions. In time, he begins to react differently to the therapist and to his fellow group members.

The therapist needs to be consistently aware of himself and the individuality of each patient. He sees himself as a catalyst for each child in special situations at appropriately timed moments. All these demands confront the therapist with an intense need for appropriate use of himself and nonexploitation of the children.

This therapeutic medium helps children with deficient and distorted self-images, inadequate role identifications, habit and conduct problems, and mild psychoneuroses. Neurotic traits that may be present in behavior disorders diminish in this type of group. Characterological disorders—as shown by the passive, dependent, infantilized child—tend to alter as these personality traits persistently fail to achieve satisfaction and as other behaviors become possible.

ADOLESCENT GROUPS

Boys and girls tend to be divergent in social awareness and responsivity in early and middle adolescence. Nevertheless, with this in mind, the therapist can place them together in interview group psychotherapy. Ackerman described in 1955 his work with members who ranged from 15 to 23 years of age. Each patient had previously undergone individual psychotherapy, and his group therapy experience supplemented it. Ackerman suggested that the group functioned to "provide a social testing ground for the perceptions of self and relations to others." He emphasized the importance of nonverbal behavioral patterns as material for the group.

Subsequent reports tended to agree that group therapy dealt more with conscious and preconscious levels than did an intensive, deeply introspective approach. Hulse listed clarification, mutual support, facilitation of catharsis, reality-testing, superego relaxation, and group integration as ego-supportive techniques.

Composition of the group. Adolescent patients can be treated in an outpatient clinic, private office, hospital, or a special setting, such as a detention home, with modifications appropriate to the setting. The group format is that of an open-ended, interview-interaction, activity organization. The preferred number of adolescents for these groups is 8 to 10, but often circumstances require screening of perhaps 30 or more to produce a group of 15. Of these, about 6 will form a core group with constant attendance and effort, another 3 or 4 will constitute an intermediate group who attend more than they miss, and the remainder will make up a peripheral group who attend occasionally. Attendance and therapeutic output are difficult to predict for the individual patient, since they do not seem to be related to age, presenting problem, and diagnosis. Some therapists suggest separation of patients in early adolescence (ages 13 and 14) from older patients, since boys of 13 and 14 find 17-year-old girls difficult to deal with in these groups. Otherwise, treatment procedures remain the same.

Here again, the diagnostic categories fail to distinguish sufficiently among patients to serve as guideposts to patient selection. Certain behavioral patterns—such as overt homosexuality, a flagrant sociopathic history, drug addiction, and psychosis—contraindicate inclusion in these groups. Group methods for these patients can be used, but they require special considerations.

Aims and techniques. Interview mixed-group psychotherapy offers opportunity for the adolescent to learn peer-relating techniques in a protective and supportive situation. Diminution of anxiety over sexual feelings and consolidation of sexual identification occur. He participates in group interaction in time and feels the pull of group cohesiveness. He also reacts to the group's pace and its changes, as when the group shifts its content level, a phenomenon that occurs frequently and rapidly, often within a single session.

The adolescents employ diversionary tactics to avoid discussing threatening subjects. A favorite maneuver is to change the focus by a question or a comment about an unrelated topic. Sometimes diversion masks itself behind physical activity, such as throwing a gum wrapper at the wastebasket or showing a picture in a textbook to others. These and other behaviors frequently receive comments by group members; if not, the therapist calls attention to them.

Schulman, Kraft, and Duffy commented that the therapist must be active, ego-supportive, and in control of the group situation at all times. He interprets cautiously to avoid the patient's misconstruing interpretation as personal criticism. Interpretations also focus on reality rather than on symbolisms. They are couched in simple, direct references to basic feelings and to unconscious intent of behavior when it lies quite close to awareness.

The therapist can be of either sex. Co-therapists and observers do not deter group movements and interaction. When the co-therapists are of different sexes, differentiated responses to each occur.

The content of the discussions varies tremendously, ranging over school examinations, sibling competition, parental attitudes, difficulties with self-concepts, and sexual concerns. Sexual acting out or impulse eruption rarely occurs. Brief group responses to significant experiences narrated by a patient fulfill his needs, for he can return to the subject later if necessary. The group often prefers short discussions, since the anxiety is too high to dwell at length on a topic.

Therapy for delinquent adolescents. Since children and adolescents require many special care-taking facilities by Western society, group psychotherapy techniques have been adapted to these different settings. Among these, the delinquent has received a good deal of attention, including group work, such as a field worker working directly with a neighborhood gang and group psychotherapy with probationers.

The customary procedures for group psychotherapy of disturbed adolescents require modification to account for contingencies of the character disorders of delinquents. These adolescents differ in their dyssocial patterns from those who, in an adjustment reaction of adolescence or a transitional neurotic acting out incident, violate the legal, moral, and social values of the community. The adolescent with a delinquent character disorder is persistently truant, steals, runs away, or engages in other activities that usually mean removal to an institution.

Institutional group therapy. Schulman pointed out that the complexities of the interactional processes of group psychotherapy become complicated by the characterological pressures for dissent and chronic uncooperativeness. These factors and those inherent in institutional settings create design and procedural difficulties in studies to formulate the role of group psychotherapy for the antisocial adolescent delinquent.

Several reports indicate favorable aspects in this group. In Gersten's study in 1951 of group psychotherapy with male delinquents in an institution, he found that group psychotherapy improved intellectual and school functions, and psychological tests indicated some enhancement of emotional maturity. Another study reported by Thorpe and Smith in 1952 indicated sequential steps in the responses, the first being episodes of testing and the second a series of acceptance operations. Peck and Bellsmith in 1954 used group methods for delinquent adolescents with reading disabilities.

Schulman emphasized a three-fold purpose in integrating group psychotherapy into the totality of care for these patients: (1) Intellectual insight and reality-testing occur in the group milieu; (2) alloplastic symptoms and superego development can be observed; and (3) the group situation readily tests the developmental stage of new attitudes, since the patient continues to perform in a homogeneous group of delinquents.

The character distortions to be dealt with use aggression predominantly to reduce the internalized anxiety. The delinquents show a weak ego structure and a defective superego. Schulman suggested that their inherent difficulty with society and its authority symbols serves as the nidus for a therapeutic relationship. Modifications of the traditional therapist-patient relationship can then develop a shallow emotional attachment in the delinquent. Schulman initially used variations in activity and unexpected refreshments, but later he modified this to focus on the authority-dependency relationship built into the institutional situation. From the beginning, the adolescent knows that his getting out depends on the therapist, who then assumes a greater omnipotence and becomes one with whom he can identify. As the therapist continues to model early life experiences for the adolescent—but without their inconsistencies of feelings, exploitations, and dishonesties—he becomes somewhat of an ego-ideal for an embryonic superego.

Schulman and others described the sexual preoccupation of adolescent female delinquents and the need by the therapist to control it to avoid a deterioration through perseveration. This deterioration occurs in the male group also, often on a scapegoat in the group. Directed discussion by the therapist changes the tone of the session or blocks group disintegration.

Some therapists believe they can adhere to the more traditional leader role of permissiveness and support, contrary as it may be at times to the overall patterns of the institution. The goals of all these efforts seem to fall into two categories. The first is to facilitate the delinquent's adjustment to the institution, and the second is to promote therapeutic readiness. Among the many variables that need to be examined, one of the most pertinent seems to be the duration of the group therapy process. Generally, the longer the group functions, the better are the chances for alterations in the members.

OTHER GROUP THERAPY SITUATIONS

Some residential and day treatment units also use group therapy techniques in their work. Child placement agencies may use group psychotherapy with cottage parents, with the children, and with the foster parents employed by the agency. Unwed adolescent girls who have become pregnant have been placed in groups for counseling and psychotherapy. Children in pediatric hospital settings have been worked with in groups to help them handle their adaptation to disease and the hospitalization. Group therapy has been used in school settings for underachievers, for truants, and for children with behavior disorders.

Children can also be treated by group methods in art therapy, and psychodrama has been used for children at all ages. Lebovici has described psychodrama for adolescents as providing an opportunity for action preparatory for real life and a psychotherapeutic tool if used with the insights of psychoanalysis.

The foregoing has stayed mainly in the channel of group psychotherapy directly with the children. At the same time, most therapists agree that concomitant therapy with the parents is helpful. Some therapists believe that parental psychotherapy, such as a mothers' group, will be sufficient and more than adjunctive to remedying the problems with preschool through latency children. Multiple-impact therapy can serve as both a diagnostic instrument and an intake device in family therapy. It is in these circumstances that one often sees so clearly how the child-patient can serve as the emotional radar of the family.

From the foregoing, one can gather that there are many indications for the use of group psychotherapy as a treatment modality. Some can be described as situational, where the therapist works in a reformatory setting in which group psychotherapy has seemed to reach the adolescents better than individual treatment. Another indication has been quoted as the economic one, as more patients can be reached simultaneously. Perhaps more appropriate would be the necessity to use a treatment procedure that will best help the child for a given age, developmental stage, and type of problem. In the younger age group, the child's social hunger and his potential need for peer acceptance help determine his suitability for group therapy. Criteria for unsuitability are controversial. Ginott suggested that accelerated sexual drives or habitual thievery makes a child unsuitable for group therapy, but others disagree with him.

EVALUATION

The results of group psychotherapy with children are difficult to evaluate. Several reports using control groups show favorable results in one study of nondirective play therapy and another of delinquents. Evaluating the results of group psychotherapy of children proves as difficult as assessing individual psychotherapy of children. Since few studies have been controlled for time as well as for other factors, including follow-up evaluations, one can say that group therapy does not supplant or replace individual therapy. It is another tool that the therapist might become familiar with by usage under supervision. If he then finds it to his liking, he can continue to use it under his own conditions of work. In crowded child psychiatric clinics, for example, various group techniques can help relieve pressures at intake, diagnosis, and treatment levels.

Impressionistically, certain results can be indicated. Group psychotherapy helps children feel unconditionally accepted by the therapist and the group members. Failures become seen as part of each child's development. Complexes of feelings and ideation gain expression. Feelings of guilt, anxiety, inferiority, and insecurity find relief. Affection and aggression are evidenced without retaliation and danger. In sum, group psychotherapy of children and adolescents still remains young and undeveloped in its full potential for study and treatment.

REFERENCES

Ackerman, N. W. Group psychotherapy with a mixed group of adolescents. Int. J. Group Psychother., 5: 249, 1955.

Asperoff, B. J., and Simon, D. Problems and approaches in child group psychotherapy in a public school milieu. Group Psychother., 16: 39, 1963.

Dubo, S. Opportunities for group therapy in pediatric service. Int. J. Group Psychother., 1: 235, 1951.

Duffy, J., and Kraft, I. Beginning and middle phase characteristics of group psychotherapy of early adolescent boys and girls. Presented at Annual Meeting, American Group Psychotherapy Association, San Francisco, January, 1965. Unpublished.

Feder, B. Limited goals in short-term group psychotherapy with institutionalized delinquent adolescent boys. Int. J. Group Psychother., 12: 503, 1962.

Gersten, C. An experimental evaluation of group therapy with juvenile delinquents. Int. J. Group Psychother., 1: 311, 1951.

Ginott, H. G. *Group Psychotherapy with Children.* McGraw-Hill, New York, 1961.

Hart, J., Kraft, I. A., Miller, M., and Williams, S. G. A preliminary study of interview group psychotherapy of boys and girls of latency age. Presented at Annual Meeting, American Group Psychotherapy Association, San Francisco, January, 1965. Unpublished.

Hulse, W. Psychiatric aspects of group counselling of adolescents. Psychiat. Quart. (Suppl.), 34: 307, 1960.

Kraft, I. A. Some special considerations in adolescent group psychotherapy. Int. J. Group Psychother., 11: 196, 1961.

Lebovici, S. Psychodrama as applied to adolescents. J. Child Psychol. Psychiat., 1: 298, 1961.

MacGregor, R. *Multiple Impact Therapy with Families.* McGraw-Hill, New York, 1964.

Peck, H. B., and Bellsmith, V. *Treatment of the Delinquent Adolescent.* Family Service Association of America, New York, 1954.

Schulman, I. Delinquents. In *The Fields of Group Psychotherapy,* S. R. Slavson, editor, p. 196. International Universities Press, New York, 1956.

Slavson, S. R. *Analytic Group Psychotherapy with Children, Adolescents and Adults.* Columbia University Press, New York, 1950.

Speers, R. W., and Lansing, C. *Group Therapy in Childhood Psychosis.* University of North Carolina Press, Chapel Hill, 1965.

Thorpe, J. F., and Smith, B. Operational sequences in group therapy with young offenders. Int. J. Group Psychother., 2: 24, 1952.

CHAPTER EIGHTEEN

Organic Therapies

BARBARA FISH, M.D.

PSYCHOPHARMACOTHERAPY

S I N C E 1 9 4 0 amphetamines, anticonvulsants, and antihistamines have
been used to treat children with behavior disorders. The introduction of
chlorpromazine and reserpine increased the range of effective pharmacotherapy. Drugs are now as important an adjunct in the comprehensive
treatment of disturbed children as they are in the treatment of adults.

The fact that the child is a growing organism creates special problems
in evaluating the effects of drugs. However, experience has demonstrated
that drugs can control symptoms that do not readily respond to other
measures if appropriate agents are chosen and the dosage is regulated
properly. Drugs can then facilitate the educational and experiential aspects of treatment if the psychological meaning of the medication to children and their parents is treated with understanding.

RATIONALE AND INDICATIONS

With children, as with adults, one prescribes psychotropic drugs for certain target symptoms. Drugs are most effective in reducing psychomotor
excitement. Optimally, the reduction of impulsivity and irritability is accompanied by lessened anxiety, improved attention span, and more organized behavior. To a lesser extent, drugs can increase spontaneous activity
and affective responsiveness in states of apathy and inertia.

A trial of drug therapy is indicated for such symptoms if appropriate
psychotherapeutic and environmental measures do not quickly relieve the
child's subjective distress and restore optimal functioning. This judgment
differs from adult therapy to the extent that children are more dependent
on and responsive to the adults who care for them. One must evaluate the

relation of the child and his symptoms to his family before introducing drugs. Since children's symptoms usually change more rapidly than do adults', one can often evaluate a child's response to ambulatory or institutional psychiatric treatment within two to four weeks.

If symptoms disappear completely in the child's usual environment, with full resumption of social and academic activities, when social manipulation and psychotherapy are used alone, no additional treatment is indicated. However, if symptoms or a restriction in function persists after four weeks, one should not withhold drugs that may accelerate recovery because the child is responding slowly to other measures. Months or even weeks of exclusion from normal experiences at critical periods in a child's life may leave irreversible deficits. A school phobia is an outstanding example of a situation that should be treated as a medical emergency. A prompt return to school can prevent chronic disability, and drugs should be added quickly to the total treatment program if needed to accomplish this end. Even when the damage from delayed recovery is less obvious, one must weigh the slight chance of harm from drugs against the limitation in the child's function and the strain imposed on his family if drugs are withheld. If an acute crisis demands immediate medication, drugs should be withheld later on to evaluate the child's own capacity for reintegration and to determine whether medication must be continued.

RESULTS AND GOALS

Pharmacotherapy should be used as a part of the total treatment program directed toward promoting optimal development of the disturbed child. By modifying appropriate target symptoms, drugs facilitate the other aspects of therapy in children with schizophrenia and organic brain disease and with moderate to severe primary behavior disorders. Pharmacotherapy may enable severely disturbed children to participate in group activities and special classes; it helps others become amenable to psychotherapy and education that would otherwise be impossible. Drug therapy can also accelerate the treatment of less disturbed children. For example, some neurotic children with persistent anxiety, inhibitions, and phobias become more spontaneous and increase their adaptive functioning, participating more fully in psychotherapy and schooling, if they are given drugs. The younger the child, the more often is psychiatric disturbance of any type expressed in hyperexcitability, hyperactivity, and disorganized behavior that can respond to medication.

LIMITATIONS

When drug-susceptible symptoms are treated, the extent of improvement in overall psychopathology is limited by the initial severity of the disorder. The more severe, unchanging deficits in function appear to have the same prognostic significance in children as do long duration and chronicity of symptoms in adults.

Children with severe mental retardation and fragmentation of functioning associated with organic brain disease or schizophrenia are the most likely to retain residual defects. However, in the absence of effective drug treatment, they respond minimally to educational therapy, milieu therapy, and psychotherapy. In less-impaired children, hallucinations, perceptual distortions, and thought disorders may subside or disappear with drug treatment.

Drugs can modify a child's responsiveness to his experiences, but chemicals alone cannot undo learned behavior, character patterns, or neurotic attitudes. Thus, aggressive behavior responds to drugs only if it is associated with affective or motor outbursts. Less explosive negativistic children often experience little subjective discomfort and may resent the physiological changes produced by drugs, feeling these to be a threat to their autonomy. Whether drugs can improve learning and intellectual functioning and, if so, in which types of children, has still to be determined.

CHOICE AND REGULATION OF DRUGS

As with adults, pharmacotherapy with children should start with the mildest drug that may be effective. The dose should be increased regularly until symptoms disappear or until the first signs of excess dose appear (mild headache, fatigue, irritability, etc.) to make sure that the useful dose range has been fully explored. Young children rarely report such symptoms. One must ask and look for malaise, anorexia, weight loss, or sudden behavioral deterioration associated with increases in dose, which may indicate that the dose is too high for the particular child. The child's alertness, attention, and performance in school must be followed as carefully as the adult's performance on his job to determine whether the dose is insufficient or too high.

The child's response to medication may indicate that a more sedative or more stimulating mild drug is required. Otherwise, one should explore more potent drugs in the same manner and not try a haphazard succession of drugs of similar type when symptoms persist with the highest tolerated dose of a mild drug. The optimal dose is the level that maximally reduces symptoms and increases function without causing discomfort.

In mild disorders, where symptoms disappear with mild medication, drugs need be continued for only a brief period, to give the child and his family sufficient time to establish a new level of adaptation in the absence of symptoms. In severely disturbed children who do not get complete relief from symptoms even with potent medication, pharmacotherapy may need to be maintained, just as it is with chronic adult patients.

In general, more potent drugs are required for more severe disorders, but the standard diagnostic categories provide only a gross guide to severity. In children, severity within a diagnostic group increases with greater intellectual, perceptual, and neurological impairment and with greater affective and motoric disturbance. Hyperactive and hypoactive children may react differently to drugs. There are also individual differences in relative sensitivity to the sedative and stimulating properties of different drugs.

The clinician should become familiar with a few representative minor and major tranquilizers and stimulants that span the spectrum of potency and differential effects. The following discussion is limited to instances in which children's behavioral and central nervous system responses differ from those of adults. The possible systemic toxic effects require the same precautions as for adults. Young infants require special precautions.

MAJOR TRANQUILIZERS

Phenothiazines. Extensive experience has demonstrated that these compounds are highly effective in moderately to severely disturbed children with primary behavior disorders, schizophrenia, or organic brain disease.

DIMETHYLAMINE SERIES. The major difference in action from adults is that extrapyramidal reactions are rare in children and can be terminated promptly by reducing the dose. The relative potency of different members within this group is the same for children as it is for adults.

PIPERAZINE SERIES. These drugs are especially useful in hypoactive schizophrenic or severely neurotic children who require drugs as potent as the phenothiazines but who tend to be depressed by therapeutic doses of chlorpromazine. Severely apathetic schizophrenic children with I.Q.'s under 70 may require and tolerate larger doses of trifluoperazine by body weight, compared with adult patients, without any signs of dystonia. If these children are very young and respond to the drug, their motor skills, social responsiveness, and language may improve. Fish et al. demonstrated that these effects were significantly greater than placebo in mute schizophrenic children who are too impaired to respond to psychotherapy.

Less-impaired children tend to be more sensitive than adults to the stimulating effects of these drugs; small doses produce irritability, agitation, and dyskinesia. The adult dose adjusted strictly for body weight may be 2 to 5 times too high for such a child (see Tables I and II). Trifluoperazine (Stelazine) may be 20 to 100 times as potent as chlorpromazine in the same child in all but the most retarded schizophrenic children. Fluphenazine (Permitil, Prolixin) is more potent per unit dose than trifluoperazine. Prochlorperazine (Compazine), perphenazine (Trilafon), and thiopropazate (Dartal) are about 5 to 10 times as potent as chlorpromazine in the same child.

PIPERIDINE SERIES. Thioridazine (Mellaril) does not appear to have any advantage for children over chlorpromazine that outweighs its additional systemic toxicity, since chlorpromazine-induced extrapyramidal symptoms are not a problem in children. Since mepazine (Pacatal) has a relatively high incidence of toxicity in adults, its use is not advised for children.

TABLE I

Major Tranquilizers: Suggested Dosage by Weight for Children[a]

These doses are intended as a general guide to indicate the relationship of children's doses to adults'. See the text for discussion.

Name of Drug	Average Dose	Dose Range
	mg./lb./day	
Chlorpromazine (Thorazine)	1	0.5–4
Prochlorperazine (Compazine)	0.1	0.05–0.15
Trifluoperazine (Stelazine)		
Hypoactive retarded schizophrenics	0.25	0.05–0.7
All others (see text)	0.05	0.01–0.1

[a]From Fish, B. Treatment of children. In *Psychopharmacology*, N. S. Kline and H. E. Lehmann, editors. Little, Brown, Boston, 1966.

TABLE II

Major Tranquilizers: Suggested Doses for Children 6 to 12 Years[a, b]

Name of Drug	Range of Total Daily Dosage[c]	Total Dosage Divided into Number of Doses per Day
	mg./day	
Chlorpromazine (Thorazine)	50–400	1–4
Prochlorperazine (Compazine)	5–15	1–2
Trifluoperazine (Stelazine)		
Hypoactive retarded schizophrenics	2–20	1
All others (see text)	1–10	1–2

[a] From Fish, B. Treatment of children. In *Psychopharmacology*, N. S. Kline and H. E. Lehmann, editors. Little, Brown, Boston, 1966.

[b] Older children may require adult doses.

[c] Some children may require and tolerate higher doses.

Rauwolfia alkaloids. These drugs have a less reliable action than the phenothiazines and are now generally reserved for severely schizophrenic children who have not responded to phenothiazines.

MINOR TRANQUILIZERS

These drugs are primarily useful in mild to moderately severe neurotic and primary behavior disorders, comparable to their use in adults. The major difference from older patients is that children with moderately severe organic and schizophrenic reactions are frequently helped by certain of these mild medications. Prepuberty children, unlike adults and adolescents, do not tend to become addicted to medication.

Diphenylmethane derivatives. Diphenhydramine (Benadryl) is most effective in disorders associated with hyperactivity, but it also reduces anxiety in very young children who are not hyperactive. It may be helpful even in moderately severe organic or schizophrenic disorders, although it is not potent enough for the most severely disturbed children. Unlike the other drugs, diphenhydramine drops in effectiveness at puberty. Young children tolerate doses 2 to 4 times higher by body weight than do adults, and the drug reduces symptoms before producing drowsiness or lethargy. After 10 to 11 years of age, children respond like adults: The drug frequently produces malaise or drowsiness and is most helpful as a bedtime sedative (see Tables III and IV).

Substituted diols. Meprobamate (Equanil, Miltown) appears to be less effective for hyperactivity than diphenhydramine in the same children, but, unlike diphenhydramine, it continues to be effective in neurotic children into adolescence (see Tables III and IV).

Miscellaneous. Chlordiazepoxide (Librium) has a sedative action in some children comparable to the most effective minor tranquilizers. In other children it stimulates speech and thought associations, like the amphetamines, but produces a more prominent euphoria. This effect is therapeutic for some depressed, hypochondriacal, and inhibited children. In susceptible children, however, this action is associated with toxic excitation and disorganization of thought and behavior before any therapeutic effect occurs (see Tables III and IV).

To date, the large number of other minor tranquilizers have shown no special actions that differentiate them from the three drugs described above; in fact, many appear to be weaker—even totally ineffective—and more variable in their action in the same patient.

STIMULANTS AND ANTIDEPRESSANTS

Amphetamines relieve anxiety and inhibitions in neurotic children, especially those with constricted speech and affect, with learning difficulties, with school phobias, and with disturbing sexual preoccupations. Reports

TABLE III
*Mild Stimulants and Tranquilizers: Suggested Dosage by Weight
for Children*[a]

Name of Drug	Average Dose	Dose Range[b]
	mg./lb./day	
Amphetamine	0.1	0.05–0.2
Chlordiazepoxide (Librium)	0.2	0.1–0.5
Diphenhydramine (Benadryl)	2.0	1.0–5.0
Meprobamate (Equanil, Miltown)	7.5	2.0–15.0

[a] From Fish, B. Treatment of children. In *Psychopharmacology*, N. S. Kline and H. E. Lehmann, editors. Little, Brown, Boston, 1966.
[b] Some children may require and tolerate higher doses.

TABLE IV

Mild Stimulants and Tranquilizers: Suggested Doses for Children 6 to 12 Years[a, b]

Name of Drug	Range of Total Daily Dosage[c]	Total Dosage Divided into Number of Doses per Day
	mg./day	
Amphetamine	5–20	1
Chlordiazepoxide (Librium)	10–50	2–4
Diphenhydramine (Benadryl)	100–500	4
Meprobamate (Equanil, Miltown)	200–1600	2–4

[a] From Fish, B. Treatment of children. In *Psychopharmacology*, N. S. Kline and H. E. Lehmann, editors. Little, Brown, Boston, 1966.

[b] Older children frequently require adult doses.

[c] Some children may require and tolerate higher doses.

that doses up to 40 mg. a day quieted hyperactive children with organic brain disorders have not been confirmed by others who used a maximum of 20 mg. a day. Subjective discomfort, anorexia, and weight loss occur frequently in doses over 15 mg. a day (see Tables III and IV).

Antidepressants are indicated in the depressions of adolescence, comparable to their use in adults.

ANTICONVULSANTS AND HYPNOTICS

Early reports of the effectiveness of hydantoin compounds in the treatment of children whose behavior disorders were associated with nonspecific electroencephalographic abnormalities have not been confirmed by later workers.

Hypnotics have not been demonstrated to be effective in psychiatric disorders of prepuberty children. Barbiturates may actually increase anxiety and disorganization in severely disturbed children. Chloral hydrate or mild tranquilizers usually suffice as nighttime sedation, unless insomnia is associated with a severe disorder requiring major tranquilizers.

PHARMACOTHERAPY COMBINED WITH PSYCHOTHERAPY

The use of drugs in conjunction with psychotherapy presents some differences from the treatment of adults. Young children generally accept medication in a matter-of-fact fashion as something doctors give to make them better. Adolescents tend to regard medication more suspiciously as an interference with their autonomy. This attitude requires the same sensitive and skillful handling as other aspects of adolescent therapy. Since children typically tend to deny physical and psychological difficulties, they are usually all too ready to terminate medication as soon as their distress is lessened. Seriously disturbed children who need maintenance drug therapy must be helped to understand that medication is to reduce their oversensitivity at the times in their life when this becomes necessary. Rarely, an older neurotic child may use medication in the interest of his hypochondriasis or to gain attention, and this psychological problem must be resolved in psychotherapy. Parents should be told that, at best, drugs produce only quantitative changes and that the child will not be cured or made over. Discussions of all the other measures needed to help the child will emphasize this point.

The therapeutic meaning of biological measures, verbal interpretations, and environmental restrictions depends on the conscious and unconscious attitudes of all the participants. In the treatment of children, the parents' attitudes to medication and the other aspects of treatment must be dealt with as part of the therapeutic process. Drugs would destroy therapy if the doctor used them as a quick expedient to avoid responsibility for the child's complex problems in living or if he saw drugs as the ultimate weapon of authority to enforce compliance on a problem child or if he felt drugs were a measure of desperation to be used only after all other measures had failed. Children differ from adults only in that they are frequently more acutely aware of the doctor's unconscious intent and are less tolerant of his rationalizations. If drug therapy is put into its proper perspective by the physician, medication itself can then be accepted readily by parents and child as simply another way in which the doctor is trying to help the child.

CONVULSIVE THERAPY

In the United States, Lauretta Bender has had the most experience with this form of therapy in prepuberty children, having treated more than five hundred children since the early 1940's. She abandoned pentylenetetrazol (Metrazol) treatment when electroconvulsive therapy (ECT) was introduced because the latter was technically simpler to administer. She uses a standard series of twenty ECT treatments, of 100 to 110 volts and 0.1-second duration, administered with a Reiter apparatus, without premedication.

Bender considers ECT to be a valuable adjunct in a comprehensive treatment program for schizophrenic children. She believes that it acts as a nonspecific physiological stimulant "to stimulate biological maturation, to pattern primitive embryonic plasticity, to mobilize anxiety in the apathetic autistic child and to reduce anxiety in the pseudo-neurotic child." She advises against combining ECT with phenothiazines, since the latter lower the convulsive threshold. Her studies reveal no detrimental effect on development. In Sweden, Annell has used insulin shock therapy for schizophrenic children with similar results.

Psychotic adolescents who require convulsive therapy are those who resemble their adult counterparts.

LOBOTOMY

Freeman, the foremost proponent of this procedure in adults, reported on twelve psychotic children under 14 years of age and noted that some decrease in excessive motor activity was observed but that "the results in children compare unfavorably with the results of psychosurgery in adults." In principle, the irreversible destruction of tissue in the growing brain is not recommended.

REFERENCES

Annell, A. Insulin shock treatment in children with psychotic disturbances. Acta Psychother. Psychoanal. Orthopoed., 3: 193, 1955.

Bender, L. Treatment in early schizophrenia. In Progress in Psychotherapy, vol. 5, p. 177. Grune & Stratton, New York, 1960.

Bender, L., and Nichtern, S. Chemotherapy in child psychiatry. New York J. Med., 56: 2791, 1956.

Bradley, C. Benzedrine and dexedrine in the treatment of children's behavior disorders. Pediatrics, 5: 24, 1950.

Fish, B. Drug therapy in child psychiatry: psychological aspects. Compr. Psychiat., 1: 55, 1960.

Fish, B. Drug therapy in child psychiatry: pharmacological aspects. Compr. Psychiat., 1: 212, 1960.

Fish, B. Evaluation of psychiatric therapies in children. In Evaluation of Psychiatric Treatment, P. Hoch and J. Zubin, editors, p. 202. Grune & Stratton, New York, 1964.

Fish, B., and Shapiro, T. A typology of children's psychiatric disorders: I. Its application to a controlled evaluation of treatment. J. Amer. Acad. Child Psychiat., 4: 32, 1965.

Fish, B., Shapiro, T., and Campbell, M. Long-term prognosis and the response of schizophrenic children to drug therapy: a controlled study of trifluoperazine. Amer. J. Psychiat., 123: 32, 1966.

Fisher, S. Child Research in Psychopharmacology. Charles C Thomas, Springfield, Ill., 1959.

Freedman, A. M. Drug therapy in behavior disorders. Pediat. Clin. N. Amer., p. 573, August, 1958.

Lindsley, D. B., and Henry, C. E. Effect of drugs on behavior and electroencephalograms of children with behavior disorders. Psychosom. Med., 4: 140, 1942.

Nyhan, W. S. L. Toxicity of drugs in the neonatal period. J. Pediat., 59: 1, 1961.

Pasamanick, B. Anticonvulsant drug therapy of behavior problem children with abnormal encephalograms. Arch. Neurol. Psychiat., 65: 752, 1951.

Williams, J. M., and Freeman, W. Evaluation of lobotomy with special reference to children. In Psychiatric Treatment, S. B. Wortis, M. Herman, and C. C. Hare, editors, p. 311. Williams & Wilkins, Baltimore, 1953.

CHAPTER NINETEEN

Residential Treatment

MEYER SONIS, M.D.

INTRODUCTION

DURING THE PAST DECADE increasing attention has been focused on the need for more residential centers to provide a specialized program for children with behavioral symptoms not amenable to outpatient psychiatric care. Under the pressure of this need, it has been assumed that there is greater uniformity in such specialized facilities than is the case. A lack of uniformity exists not only in terms of which child is best served by which facility but also in terms of the pattern of organization, administration, staffing, and programs to be found in these institutions. Such a lack of uniformity is not a criticism of the residential treatment center but is best viewed as a symptom of the historical evolution of the facilities.

This history is intertwined with the evolution of concern about children and their care and with the evolution of clinical knowledge of the psychiatric disorders of children. Residential treatment centers are the result of attempts in Europe and America to view the child as separate from the adult and to resolve the social, medical, ethical, and educational problems of the child who has deviated in his development.

HISTORY

EARLY HISTORY

For centuries in Europe, the only consistent concern and care for the poor and neglected children and adults was manifested through the auspices of the church. In 1267, for example, English law penalized the guardian of a child for waste but did not require his accountability for any child abuse. Until the Poor Law of 1601 in England, there was no concept of governmental responsibility for the welfare of children. Children were often imprisoned, abused, and exploited; by law they had no rights. The Poor Law established public responsibility for the support of the poor—within which group were to be found many children with physical, mental, and emotional handicaps—and brought about the development of the institution called the poor house or almshouse. It was not until the amendments to this law in 1868 and 1889 that parental neglect of children became punishable as an offense, and authority was given to the State for removal of children from their parents for such an offense. Such removal, however, placed the child in a state of apprenticeship to others.

In this country the concept of public responsibility as evolved in England was carried over and modified in keeping with New World concepts and needs. Asylums and almshouses were established by the local authorities for those who could not work or who were too old, crippled, or insane. Though neglected, retarded, and emotionally disturbed children were sometimes cared for by benevolent citizens or the occasional orphanage of a church, most of these children were mixed with unfortunate adults in the almshouses.

In the 1800's the emergence of the view of children as separate and distinct from adults manifested itself in a variety of ways: the establishment of specific hospitals geared to the special needs of children; the emergence of pediatrics as a medical specialty; the initial movement to organize institutions for delinquent children; the admission of children identified as mental retardates to institutions for custodial care; the nucleus of the future juvenile court; and the prominent emergence of private, voluntary children's aid societies. In the organization and development of these private voluntary societies, aimed at providing care for dependent and neglected children, is to be found one major root of the future residential treatment center. These private agencies, many of them under the auspices of various religious denominations, sprouted throughout the country and were administered by and through humanitarian citizen interest.

Many children were indiscriminately placed in one institution or another. In most if not all of these various settings, little time or effort was spent in assessment of a child's particular needs. Behavioral symptoms as such in these children were of no interest unless such symptoms produced disciplinary problems for the institution. These children lived under rigid routines with moral and religious training predominant and without enough staff or funds or knowledge to attend to their needs. By 1900 many children, labeled as dependent and neglected or retarded but with behavioral symptoms indicative of emotional disorders, were to be found in almshouses, orphanages, state hospitals, jails, training schools, and group homes. As yet, specialized programs and facilities for the disturbed child were not available.

Twentieth Century

In the early 1900's several major developments took place, with each development playing a part in the formation of the other root of the future residential center. Social work evolved as a profession and brought with it the change of the trained layman to the professional. The contributions of psychoanalysis and psychobiology indicated the importance of early child development and the environmental influences of child-rearing practices. The mental hygiene movement emerged and prepared the public for a more positive attitude toward the mentally ill and their need for specialized facilities. The child guidance movement flourished and brought with it specialized services for the child and the use of a team approach to the diagnosis and treatment of the emotionally disturbed child. The Children's Bureau, formed in 1912 as an arm of the federal government, drew attention at the national level to the needs of children.

As social work practice in the 1900's began using principles of social diagnosis and treatment and knowledge of programmed living for children, many of the private children's aid societies refined and changed their functions from the care, placement, and management of children to placement for the treatment of children. In many orphanages, group homes, and homes for dependent and neglected children, the well-intentioned laymen who wished to help children found their programs less effective for these children and increasingly required social workers to help them move toward professionalism in their programs. Some of these institutions, through experiences of their own and in association with social work, acquired skills of their own in the group care and management of children. They found, for example, that children maintained in a somewhat controlled setting were able to benefit from the warmth of available relationships. As the field of social work continued to develop, with emphasis now on the knowledge and skill necessary for planning and directing the daily lives of groups of children, the profession of social group work rapidly gained influence in many of the institutions providing care for dependent and neglected children.

The 1930's and 1940's. Perhaps the greatest impetus toward a change in these social agencies occurred in 1935 with the Social Security Act and its Aid to Dependent Children, which enabled many children, formerly seen as dependent and neglected children, to remain with their mothers. Increasingly, many of the agencies, formerly offering a group living program for dependent and neglected children, now found themselves with an increased number of referrals of disturbed children. Such agencies moved increasingly from their administrative base of volunteers and laymen to that of a professional staff, either totally or in part, depending on their former tradition. Many of these agencies, retaining their roots in social and religious orientation, acquired staff in response to these pressures. With a new emphasis on providing children with daily care while utilizing the environment to modify behavior, other professions joined the social work staff—social group workers, educational experts, recreational and occupational therapists, and psychiatrists. With this new emphasis on longer-term growth processes for children, these agencies, through various patterns of staffing and programming, began to provide for the child's total needs in terms of living, schooling, physical well-being, and recreation.

During that same period of time, as the social agency was evolving into a form of residential treatment center, the medical community was also undergoing change as a result of the developments influencing the social agency. The public and private psychiatric hospitals, whether state hospitals or institutions for defective children, had recognized the inappropriateness of their facilities for children and had expanded their function to include specialized wards for disturbed children. Parallel to this, in 1930 the first specialized facility was established for the study, diagnosis, and treatment of seriously disturbed children and their parents and was followed by many more of these psychiatric inpatient services. These specialized services were to provide a program of treatment based on a comprehensive diagnosis and were established as part of a larger psychiatric hospital or on an independent basis.

Within these medical settings, often hospital-oriented, many problems and issues began to emerge as the routine of the hospital ward and the structure of the traditional medical service was stretched to include the flexibility needed for child living as well as for patient care. In some settings, strong orientations emerged, leading either to a physiological bias in diagnosis and treatment or to a psychoanalytic bias in emphasizing individual dynamics. It became clear that knowledge of childhood psychopathology and the treatment of such were not enough and that more knowledge was necessary about using the environment as a tool in bringing about psychotherapeutic changes. In some of these treatment hospitals, much emphasis was placed on the utilization of the nurse as a therapeutic arm of the physician, but they discovered the need for greater flexibility and knowledge of children on her part. In some settings this issue of nursing care was managed by the requirement of specific training for child psychiatric nursing; in other settings the nurse was relieved of the daily care of children by development of nursing counselors, child-care workers, or child aides.

In the early development of psychiatric hospitals for children, many children were referred to or dumped into these hospitals as a last resort, and in their acceptance by the hospital the children were literally disowned by the community. As a result, the hospital acquired a static population, and treatment programs reverted to custodial care. Some of the settings tended toward a concept of treatment biased heavily in a particular direction, depending on the orientation of its practitioners. There was a deemphasis of the original design of such centers to that of treatment based on a comprehensive diagnosis.

The 1950's. By 1950, residential treatment of emotionally disturbed children had become loosely defined; it was a descriptive term that depended greatly on the setting within which the service was offered.

In 1951 the Child Welfare League of America undertook a study of residential treatment of emotionally disturbed children. The report of their results stated:

> From the beginning it was apparent that any attempts to develop firm criteria or standards was definitely premature. Rather, it was believed that a description of differing methods of practice might serve eventually to furnish a yardstick against which deviations of sharp differences could be measured and evaluated.

In 1956, partly in response to the growing need for evolving uniform criteria regarding residential treatment centers, a Conference on Inpatient Psychiatric Treatment for Children was held under the auspices of the American Psychiatric Association and the American Academy of Child Psychiatry. Recognition was given to the fact that the inpatient treatment of children was as yet a new field of development, a field that reflected the "concepts and practices of child psychiatry, in itself a relatively new field." Recognition was also given to the many questions as yet unanswered, such as the role of the child-care worker, the need for epidemiological studies and more valid data as to judgments on the use of residential treatment and its efficacy. In this conference a definition of a children's psychiatric hospital or unit was agreed on, and uniform criteria of physical plant, location, costs, personnel, staff-patient ratio, and treatment processes were developed for such units. A children's psychiatric hospital or hospital unit was defined as "a medical facility established for the diagnosis and treatment of children suffering from psychiatric disorders in which the psychiatrist carries medical and corresponding legal responsibility for the diagnosis and treatment of the patient." It was further felt by the conference participants that "the use of the word hospital for the specific type of service under discussion will help the community recognize this service as one in a range of services, each having its own function."

Evolution to present status. The residential treatment center and its concept of residential treatment for disturbed children emerged from the roots of the social and welfare needs of children and the medical needs of children with behavioral symptoms. These roots can still be found in the residential treatment of children. In the evolution of these two main streams there can be no doubt of the various problems and issues that have positively or negatively influenced the residential treatment center and its current patterns of administration, organization, staffing, and programs.

In the residential treatment center that emerged from the orphanage, child-care institution, or group foster home, the focus on the disturbed child emerged from concern for the dependent and neglected child. In many of these institutions, the tradition of humanitarian motives—of doing good for children, making up for their deprived backgrounds, and providing moral examples for them to follow—became competitive with the principles of scientific rigor in diagnosis or professional practice and treatment. The concept that disturbed children needed more than love became difficult to accept or put into practice through an organized and designed program that was aimed at more than simply social adjustment. The issues of changing from a lay administrator, a program dependent on a voluntary staff of charitable interested citizens, and a staff who simply liked children to a professional organization were symptomatic of this evolution. In the evolution of the orphanage to a residential treatment center, much experience had been gained in the care of groups of children but little experience in utilizing the knowledge of individual children. Like Topsy, the orphanage just grew into a residential treatment center, adding staff as needs arose, changing patterns as pressures mounted, moving from tradition to knowledge—but always with the base of its operation in the root of a social or welfare agency.

On the other hand, the residential treatment center, taking root from the medical stream, grew consistently from the professional base of psychiatry as a clinical science. This growth was not without its problems— problems that arose as a result of the competition between the scientific rigor of medical tradition and structure and the needs of children as social organisms. The starched white uniform became a symbol of sterility and was changed as the hospital ward structure evolved into a home atmosphere. The knowledge of the individual children had to be balanced now with knowledge of group transactions, caring for groups of children, and professionalizing humanitarian motives. The child guidance plan, so useful in the outpatient treatment of children, had to be expanded to include the teacher, the nurse, the nurse-counselor, the child-care worker, the dietitian, the maintenance staff—but in such a way as to have the environment become a therapeutic force to support individual psychotherapy.

TYPES OF RESIDENTIAL TREATMENT CENTERS

At the present time, despite the previous attempts to develop uniformity of criteria and despite the pressing need for data comparability, it is difficult to estimate the number, types, similarities or differences in program, or efficacy of residential treatment centers with any degree of accuracy. For example, in the Child Welfare League Study of such centers in 1961 (Hylton), a list of 120 institutions offering some type of program for emotionally disturbed children was compiled, but of this number only 27 were eventually deemed suitable for study by the broad criteria established. Eliminated from this study, for example, were centers that were primarily school programs, group homes, units of mental hospitals, and research units. In this same study, "to the best of their knowledge, 4,600 children were in care at 80 residential treatment centers in 19 states."

Despite the heterogeneity of residential centers and within the limits imposed by the current reality of our knowledge, it is possible to present a profile of residential treatment and residential treatment centers as currently in practice.

KINDS OF REFERRALS

Of all referrals made to residential centers, only 15 to 20 per cent are accepted, with the majority of referrals not accepted, interestingly enough, on the basis that residential treatment is not indicated. Other reasons for nonacceptance of the referral are unavailable space, center policy, and inappropriate age. Most referrals to such centers are made by social and child welfare agencies, but this may depend on the auspices of the center; that is, the residential treatment center integral to a child psychiatric program may accept most of its referrals from within its own program. In a study of 1,000 children referred for residential treatment in New York State, "less than 25 per cent of the children have lived only in their natural homes, while 40 per cent of the children have lived in four or more homes or institutions, and three-fifths of the children did not have a continuous relationship with both natural parents."

KINDS OF CHILDREN

The majority of children served in residential centers are between the ages of 9 and 14, with the range between 5 and 17 years of age and with a ratio of more boys than girls. There are only a few centers available for adolescents at the present time.

The children served range from the child diagnosed as psychotic to the child with an adjustment reaction of childhood or adolescence; very few are diagnosed as having a chronic brain syndrome or as suffering from mental retardation. Studies have suggested that the spread of diagnostic categories in various residential centers indicates a random selection. It seems that this selection may be based on the nature of behavioral symptoms, the age of the child, the degree of parental alienation from the child, and the capacity of the institution to cope reasonably with the child. For example, in residential centers the child who is more aggressive, less difficult to reach, but more disoriented is often the younger child; the older child is less aggressive, more difficult to reach, and less disoriented. In other words, the residential center can cope more reasonably with the younger child who is severely disturbed and with the quieter adolescent. The average length of time that children remain in residence is about two years.

KINDS OF INSTITUTIONS

Currently, if a profile were drawn of institutions within which the emotionally disturbed child is found and within which residential treatment is the service offered, the following patterns would emerge.

Placement units. These institutions, the numbers of which are impossible to ascertain, are under private auspices and indirectly supported financially through contract for service with city, county, or state welfare departments. The institutions are thought of as providing treatment for emotionally disturbed children, but they are really providing group care management, or custody of a substandard nature to the children in residence. These institutions are inadequately staffed, with an insufficient number of staff to provide a constructive program, and with most, if not all, of the staff untrained and ill-equipped for the task. Many of the children in these institutions are there for placement purposes as a result of behavioral symptoms that have made them unmanageable in the community and have brought them to the attention of the courts and child welfare services. These children have seldom had the benefit of psychiatric examination and, if examined, would reveal extreme social pathology in addition to whatever psychopathology is present.

Residential center units. These institutions, the numbers of which are greater than the psychiatric inpatient units, are primarily under private auspices and financially supported through federated (Community Chest and various religious charities) and public (city, county, state, or welfare department contract-for-service) sources. These institutions are primarily under social work administration, direction, and practice. For emotionally disturbed children they offer a program of therapeutic care, complemented or supplemented by individual or group psychotherapy. In most of these institutions, the physical plant and program provide for almost all the child's needs, such as living, schooling, routine medical care, recreation, and socialization. An adequate staff-child ratio is maintained to carry out the program. Some of these institutions utilize the community resources, if possible, for the education, recreation, and socialization of their children or for treating a child who requires hospitalization.

In these institutions, procedures and daily living are established in such a way as to involve staff members in meaningful opportunities for constructive interaction with the child. The professional and nonprofessional staff in such an institution covers the spectrum of social work, social group work, clinical psychology, activity group therapy, educational specialists, recreation staff, child-care supervisor, child-care worker, maintenance and kitchen staff, pediatrician, psychiatrist, art-drama teacher, dentist, and neurologist. In many of these institutions, the psychiatrist is utilized as a consultant—serving as a member of an admissions committee, supervising others in their psychotherapy of children and parents, or providing in-service training—or else he is employed as a staff member to provide psychiatric treatment for selected children.

Many of the children in these institutions are probably the least disturbed—severity of symptoms, intensity of behavior, diagnosis, chronicity—of all the children in residential treatment centers. Most of these children are children of disturbed parents who have not been able to cope with the child.

Psychiatric inpatient units. These institutions are under psychiatric administration, direction, and practice. By design, organization, and procedures, they offer a program of psychiatric diagnosis and treatment of the emotionally disturbed child and a treatment regime that includes the daily care of the child. These institutions are under private, public, or university auspices and, on the whole, are integral to other child psychiatric services. They are utilized many times as a clinical facility for purposes of training in psychiatry and child psychiatry. Financial support of the institution depends on its auspices, with a source of funds similar to that of the residential treatment center.

As with the other residential treatment centers, these are self-sufficient in physical plant and program and provide for almost all the needs of children. In addition, they can provide more totally for the medical needs of the children within residence.

There are many similarities between these psychiatric inpatient units and the residential centers, but the differences are accentuated by the former's deliberate focus on a design of psychiatric diagnosis and treatment. This focus permeates the organization, program, staff philosophy, and goals. The nature of the organization as a psychiatric facility provides for the integration of all staff purposes under the leadership of the psychiatrist and with the basis of decisions about the child integral to therapeutic goals.

The children in these institutions are more disturbed than children ordinarily found in the residential centers. Their behavioral symptoms are more extreme, but they are manageable in such a setting. Since the psychiatric focus is basic, there is more opportunity for individual psychotherapy. For example, the Child Welfare League Study of 1961 stated, "The lowest child-psychiatrist ratios occur in the large psychiatric training centers, with ratios from almost two children per psychiatrist to seven; these same centers have the largest number of children in therapy with psychiatrists."

Since the ideal of involving all parents in active treatment cannot be carried out in practice, various patterns are developed to manage this issue, such as periodic two- or three-day visits of the parents, psychiatric or casework treatment of parents in their own community, and a policy of accepting only children whose parents are able to be involved in their regular treatment regime.

State hospital units. These institutions, under the auspices of a state mental health or hospital system, are under psychiatric administration and direction. Many offer programs of long-term care and treatment of children with chronic psychiatric disabilities. The patient population of these institutions reflects this chronic disability in terms of diagnosis (chronic brain syndrome, childhood schizophrenia, severe behavior disorders, mental retardation), age (more adolescents), social pathology, nature of behavioral symptoms (intense, severe, aggressive, chronic), and unavailability of community resources to these children previous to admission.

These institutions are also self-sufficient and provide for the total needs of children insofar as physical plant is concerned, but not in terms of total program. Most of these institutions have insufficient professional staff to carry out a program of total long-term care and rehabilitation.

PROBLEMS

Of all the children descriptively diagnosed as emotionally disturbed and mentally ill, the children whose behavioral symptoms produce a guarded prognosis—controversial in terms of cause and mode of treatment and yet severely in need of a comprehensive program of care and treatment—are also the children who face the problems produced by the evolutionary history of the residential treatment center. Problems for the child, mental health professionals, and community are not simply those of insufficient community facilities but also those of heterogeneity of definitions, approaches, ideologies, programs, methods, practices, and results. Problems have also been compounded by the community attitude toward the disturbed child.

A comprehensive exposition on the subject of residential treatment of children does not as yet exist, but fragments exist in the professional literature, studies published and unpublished, programs and conferences held, and the collective experiences of the various residential treatment centers. If an exposition were to present the relevant issues, it would of necessity have to include the problems of cause, diagnosis, and treatment of the psychotic child; the differences and similarities between the child diagnosed as symbiotic, autistic, atypical, and schizophrenic; and the knowledge available for the diagnosis and treatment of the brain-damaged child. It should contain discussion of minimal brain damage, soft neurological signs, perceptual motor deficits, body image, developmental arrest, learning disability, and special sensory deprivation. Such a study should discuss the issues in the diagnosis and in the treatment regimen prescribed for children whose behavioral symptoms reflect child-rearing practices as well as neuronal disorders, genetic abnormalities, developmental phase, social pathology, psychopathology, nutritional imbalance, or parental disorder, or any combination of these.

In addition, such an exposition would include the various theories of child development as this knowledge can be applied to the daily care of children; the difference between the practice of psychotherapy and social case work, care, and treatment; the education, training, and experience of the child-care worker, counselor, and therapist and their role differentiation; a discussion of medical-legal responsibility and its implication for the mental health and illness of children; the need for new laws governing child welfare practices and commitment procedures; and more answers to the many questions posed in 1956 by the Conference on Psychiatric Inpatient Treatment of Children.

Though such an exposition must await the further developments of the behavioral clinician and scientist, the past history of the residential treatment center does suggest the lessons to be learned from this history.

USE OF RESIDENTIAL TREATMENT

Residential treatment has become a term synonymous with a therapeutic prescription for a child with behavioral symptoms that are indicative of serious pathology and prognosis, supported, maintained, or aggravated by the environment within which the child lives and an environment already suspect as a causative agent. It is also a prescription for a child with symptoms not amenable to therapeutic intervention ordinarily available to the child while living in the environment but believed to be amenable to a treatment program offering: (1) separation of the child from this environment, (2) a corrective emotional experience through daily care, (3) an opportunity for the child to maximize his ability to make use of individual psychotherapy, and (4) an opportunity for the parents, now temporarily relieved of the child, to maximize their capacity to make use of psychological help.

The separation of the disturbed child from his environment can produce anxiety in the child that can be constructively used in his behalf if a physical environment can be made available for him to explore, manipulate, experiment with, and exploit. This environment should be one in which routines can be supplied as orientation for the child, not as imperatives of nature; one in which controls can be instituted to signal the limits of the environment and the limits of safety and to act as a comfort to the child when he fears abandonment while he probes the unknown.

This prescription can be an effective one to the extent that: (1) A comprehensive diagnosis is the basis of fitting the prescription to the child; (2) such a diagnosis also establishes the determinants of whether the child with behavioral symptoms can make use of separation as the therapeutic agent (placement), of separation and therapeutic care as the vehicle for change (residential center), of separation and therapeutic care as the entree for treatment (psychiatric inpatient unit), or of separation and controlled therapeutic care as the vehicle for psychiatric rehabilitation (state hospital); (3) residential treatment is integrated with the total range of clinical and nonclinical services available for the child with behavioral symptoms—that is, outpatient child psychiatric clinics, day care centers, acute service, specialized educational classes, foster and group homes with professional and semiprofessional staff, half-way houses, summer camps; and (4) the recommendation for residential treatment includes responsible plans for maintaining the relationship of the community to the child while the child is in residence.

REFERENCES

Aichhorn, A. *Wayward Youth*. Viking Press, New York, 1952.

Beskind, H. Psychiatric inpatient treatment of adolescents: a review of clinical experience. Compr. Psychiat., 3: 354, 1962.

Bettelheim, B., and Sylvester, E. Milieu therapy: indications and illustrations. Psychoanal. Rev., 36: 54, 1949.

Bloch, D. A. *A Study of Children Referred for Residential Treatment in New York State*. New York State Health Resources Board, Albany, 1959.

Cohen, R. L. The influence of child guidance practices on children's inpatient units. J. Amer. Acad. Child Psychiat., 3: 151, 1964.

Hylton, L. F. *The Residential Treatment Center*. Child Welfare League of America, New York, 1964.

Krug, O. The application of principles of child psychotherapy in residential treatment. Amer. J. Orthopsychiat., 108: 695, 1950.

Maier, H. W., editor. *Group Work as Part of Residential Treatment*. National Association of Social Workers, New York, 1965.

Reid, J. H., and Hagan, H. R. *Residential Treatment of Emotionally Disturbed Children*. Child Welfare League of America, New York, 1952.

Robinson, J. F., editor. *Psychiatric Inpatient Treatment of Children*. American Psychiatric Association, Washington, 1957.

Stanton, A. H., and Schwartz, M. S. *The Mental Hospital: A Study of Institutional Participations in Psychiatric Illness and Treatment*. Basic Books, New York, 1954.

CHAPTER TWENTY

Day Treatment

RUTH L. LAVIETES, M.D.

DEFINITION

DAY TREATMENT, sometimes termed day care or partial hospitalization, is that form of treatment in which the child spends the major part of the day in the treatment center, returning to his home for evenings and weekends. This method of therapy is relatively new, having been introduced in the early 1950's. It is designed to serve children who require more therapeutic intervention than is offered by a child guidance clinic but who need not be removed from their homes for residential therapy. Many day treatment centers are connected with hospitals, constituting one part of the range of services provided.

THERAPEUTIC FACTORS

MILIEU

Since the child spends a great part of his waking hours in the day treatment center, the establishment of a therapeutic climate is necessary to aid his rehabilitation, to enhance treatment, and to avoid antitherapeutic developments. Milieu embraces such factors as the degree and form of structure, the consistency of experience to which the child is exposed, the measures used to reduce anxiety and provide satisfactions, the management of undesirable behavior, the apportionment of the therapeutic responsibility among various staff members, and the staff attitudes toward one another.

THERAPY

The emphasis that psychotherapy is given varies. Some centers see the operation as a framework for intensive psychotherapy; others view the milieu, opportunity for relationships, and removal from the home for a large part of the day, as the therapy itself. Psychotherapy within a center where the child necessarily relates to many adults in addition to his therapist—teachers, social workers, psychologists, aides, nurses, household and clerical staff—differs from psychotherapy that is temporally and geographically separated from the balance of the child's activities.

Therapists usually spend less time with the child than do other staff members, and therapists may not be present when significant situations occur. Therapy hours often compete with other scheduled events. Since the population in day centers is composed of quite severely disturbed youngsters—largely psychotic, severe personality disorders, and chronic brain disorders—the ego-supporting therapies and pharmacotherapy are widely used. Therapeutic methods—such as the application of group techniques to the classroom, the use of individual teachers for corrective object relations, and emphasis on the life space interview—evolve from the special features of the day treatment center.

EDUCATION

In a day treatment program, school takes up most of the child's day. Hence, there has been a close association between day treatment and special education of the emotionally disturbed child. Almost all day centers have an intramural school, since the regular school environment is one of the critical areas of failure for which children are referred. Because school can serve as a vital therapeutic instrument, the educational experience should be integrated into the total treatment plan.

The therapeutic value of coordinating education and therapy lies in the provision of a controlled environmental experience in which therapeutic gains can be reinforced, self-esteem and peer identification can be promoted, and techniques for coping with the environment and for developing useful defenses against impulses and anxiety can be provided. The school teacher—with her educational understanding of behavior, methods, and goals—should participate in the overall treatment plan in order to utilize the therapeutic potential of the classroom and to avoid aggravation of the child's problems.

TREATMENT OF PARENTS

Since day treatment is predicated on the idea of children remaining in their homes, treatment of the parents is indispensable to obtaining optimum results. Parents of children disturbed enough to require day treatment have a high incidence of psychopathology, much of which interlocks with that of the child. The goal of therapy is the improvement of parental function and the reduction of the parental contribution to the child's illness so that the child can remain in the home and sustain the gains achieved by treatment. Various forms of therapy are used—individual, group, joint, family.

RATIONALE

Day treatment is based on the assumption that children who would ordinarily be referred to residential centers are capable of achieving comparable gains while remaining in their homes. Helping a child within the home and community has the advantage of permitting simultaneous change in child and parents so that readaptation is facilitated. It avoids the anxiety and loss of self-esteem attendant on separation from the parents, the geographical distance that works against effective parental treatment, and the disadvantages of institutional living. The burden of management of the child is shared by the family, and the cost is lower than in residential institutions.

INDICATIONS AND CONTRAINDICATIONS

Day treatment is indicated for those children requiring long-term treatment for an emotional disorder that has seriously impaired their social and academic adjustments. It is also useful as a transition between hospitalization or residential treatment and a complete return to the community. It is contraindicated for children who are homicidal or suicidal or who come from homes where responsible parental functions are not provided or where parental psychopathology fosters the continuance of the child's illness or is too massive to permit the child's improvement within the home.

GOALS AND RESULTS

The goals of day treatment are the return of the child to community facilities and the maintenance of gains. Only one study comparing the results of this mode of treatment with others dealing with similar groups of children has appeared. According to this report, concerning schizophrenic children, those showing concomitant evidence of brain damage who came from normal families showed improvement comparable to that of controls in residential treatment. Nonorganic schizophrenic children, presumably having a larger reactive factor in their illness, did better in residential treatment.

REFERENCES

Goldfarb, W., Goldfarb, N., and Pollack, R. Treatment of childhood schizophrenia. Arch. Gen. Psychiat., *14*: 119, 1966.

LaVietes R., Cohen, R., Reens, R., and Ronall, R. Day treatment center and school: seven years' experience. Amer. J. Orthopsychiat., *35*: 160, 1965.

Vaughan, W. T., Jr., and Davis, F. E. Day hospital programming in a psychiatric hospital for children. Amer. J. Orthopsychiat., *33*: 542, 1963.

CHAPTER TWENTY-ONE

Psychiatry and the School

RUTH L. LAVIETES, M.D.

INTRODUCTION

E DUCATION IS the process by which a culture prepares its young to assume an appropriate role in the social structure. Although this process begins at birth, in Western culture it begins to be transferred from the parents and the home environment into the formalized social institution of the school when the child is about six years of age. Readiness for formal education, as determined by law, is based on theories of neurological maturation and psychological development—that is, resolution of infantile family conflicts and achievement of latency.

Going to school is the child's first systematic separation from home and his first exposure to the administrative structure of society. The child must attempt to adjust to a strange adult and to a large peer group. He needs to perform tasks from which escape is difficult. His attitudes toward teachers, children, and work bridge the gap between his early experiences with parents and siblings and later experiences in adult life. The years a child spends in school influence his total personality—affecting the values he ascribes to himself, his relations to others, his potential for work productivity, and his life adaptation. School, therefore, offers a rich opportunity for the enhancement of mental health. School affects the total child population, cutting across all socioeconomic groups, with a captive attendance throughout childhood and adolescence and with both a legal and a social hold on the child. School is committed to the welfare of children, providing the only compulsory professional contact between society and the child. Early detection of emotional disturbance and application of preventive measures are possible within this habitat of all children, and therapeutic measures can be undertaken in situ.

HISTORY

Problems of learning and manifestations of cerebral pathology have interested physicians for many years. Itard and Séguin studied mental retardation, and Montessori devised educational procedures for retarded and normal children, stressing sensory and cognitive development. However, the advent of psychoanalysis marks the real beginning of widespread clinical focus on education. Freud's concept that anxiety results in repression and symptom formation and that neuroses were caused by excessive control of impulses led to the idea that psychopathology could be prevented by giving children freedom to develop without the traditional repressive techniques employed both by authoritarian parents and by schools. These ideas coincided with those of John Dewey, who stressed the value of learning through individual experimentation, with limited interference from books or teachers.

Progressive education—predicated on the idea that children, if left free to use their own powers of exploration, would learn about the world through natural curiosity and warm interpersonal relationships—developed from the ideas of Freud and Dewey. Their considerable impact on American education began in the 1930's, but the initial optimism about progressive education waned as it was found that it resulted in no diminution of neurotic disturbance. Apparently innate factors and crucial life situations influence the child's psychic development despite modifications of school attitudes. Extremes of educational practice, either traditional or progressive, are not common today, most educational systems occupying a middle ground.

After World War II, there was a shift in emphasis from theoretical contributions to the therapeutic alleviation of the specific educational problems of disturbed children. Along with this change, there was considerable discussion of the prevention of mental illness through the cooperative efforts of clinicians and educators, but the systematic implementation of this concept has been limited.

ROLE OF THE PSYCHIATRIST IN THE SCHOOL

In the past, psychiatrists functioned largely as theoreticians for experimental educational models and occasionally as consultants, usually for special or private schools. Child psychiatrists, in their practices, have had to deal with school as an important aspect of the child patient's life. Actually, most referrals of children for psychiatric evaluation originate with school problems. In the past few years the role of the psychiatrist has expanded in connection with the tendency to develop special classes, with emphasis on community psychiatry, and with increasing acceptance by educators of the value of the psychiatric contribution. A 1963 survey indicated that 174 child psychiatrists work with schools in some capacity. This number has probably increased considerably since then, but, as there are over 40 million children in the public schools, the proportion is a very small one.

As a consultant to the school, the psychiatrist acts as a specialist in the understanding of human behavior and its developmental derivatives, both innate and environmental; of motivation; and of interpersonal intervention techniques.

ROLE IN RELATION TO EDUCATOR

Because clinicians and educators do not share a common frame of reference or language and because status problems arise when one professional enters another's domain, the psychiatrist has many obstacles to overcome in translating his abilities and knowledge into a form useful to the educator. Their understanding of the source of disturbance, methods of intervention, and goals may differ widely. The psychiatrist preparing for school consultation should, therefore, be exposed to educational viewpoints, operational problems, and teaching methodologies; in so doing, he will find himself much more aware of the social forces operating on mental illness and of the extent of clinical and subclinical disturbance in the population.

CONSULTATION

Psychiatric school consultation functions primarily in the areas of consultation to related mental health personnel working in the school (psychologists, social workers, guidance teachers, etc.), consultation to special programs for deviant children, and direct consultation to teachers in class and case management. In the last role, the psychiatrist is in the position of dealing with teacher-class-administration or with teacher-pupil-administration. This has some resemblance to the parent-child-society unit in therapy; but, since there is much less acceptance by educators of this interactional viewpoint, circumspection on the part of the psychiatrist is required. Errors in this area have probably been responsible for most of the difficulties in school consultation.

Teachers come with supposedly external problems—difficult pupils or restrictive administrative regulations—that may actually reflect internalized conflicts about achievement, identification, regression, rebelliousness, etc. The psychiatrist attempts to reduce the defenses of denial, intellectualization, projection, and avoidance and to bring feelings into the open without directly introducing the concept of the educator's role in the problem. The consultant conveys his identification with and respect for the teacher's role by relating his own experiences, especially those that counteract his omnipotent image; by demonstrating methods of coping with problems; by communicating general mental health principles; by talking to the teacher as colleague and not as patient; and by recognizing the realistic limitations of both his and the teacher's roles.

Extending Role

School consultants usually go through a process of role evolution in which, after they are considered omnipotent, they are then tested as to whether they can identify with the educator. With successful completion of this phase, the next step is to be helpful on the level of applied psychiatry. Extension of consultative functions into matters of policy-setting on an administrative level is the final stage. It is in this last capacity that the most effective preventive mental health measures can be introduced. Pertinent psychodynamic principles can be incorporated into the total educational experience of the child, embracing such areas as teacher-child relations, group and developmental dynamics, school morale, curriculum selection, and teacher training and supervision.

PSYCHIATRIC DISORDERS RELATED TO SCHOOL

Learning Disorders

Learning disabilities are one of the commonest causes for which children in latency and adolescence are referred for psychiatric evaluation and treatment. About 10 per cent of school-age children are reported to have learning difficulties of sufficient degree to require special services outside of the regular classroom. The incidence in boys is greater than in girls by a ratio of 8 or 10 to 1. Although there is no absolute correlation between emotional disturbance and learning disorders and although some children with severe pathology learn very well, there is, on the whole, a close relationship between the factors, regardless of the origin of the learning disability.

Causes. The majority of children suffering from difficulties in learning appear to do so on the basis of a constitutional, neurological deficiency. Maturation lags in the sensorimotor, perceptual, and integrative systems appear to be responsible for difficulties in auditory and visual discrimination, laterality, memory, symbolization, and expressive language. Even in these cases, however, the effects of poor learning experience often lead to emotional disturbance, which complicates the diagnostic and therapeutic procedures.

Besides those children with a biological basis for disability, some children with intact neurological equipment present a picture of psychogenic learning impediment. They have received considerable attention in psychiatric literature. Although any aspect of learning may be affected by psychological factors, reading disabilities are by far the most common and most disabling of the learning disorders.

Psychologically, intellectual activity is considered a function of the ego (perception, cognition, integration, reality-testing), and inhibition of intellectual activity represents a restriction of ego function as a result of conflict between impulses and the superego or the outside world. The child's early experiences within the family, especially in the areas of intake of food (which is symbolically equated with intake of knowledge) and curiosity (in efforts to understand birth, growth, death, sex, and bodily functions), influence the child's freedom and interest to learn.

In addition to attitudes toward the intake of knowledge, early attitudes toward the parents affect the learning process. The teacher is identified by the child with the parents, and children learn initially in order to please the teacher and gain his praise and rewards. The teacher-child relationship is, thus, the major tool for learning. Only later, toward adolescence, does the ego-ideal develop and take over as the chief motivator. If the development of relations between parents and child has miscarried in the pre-school period, with inadequate resolution of infantile conflicts in aggressive and sexual spheres, the child is not ready to learn within the teacher-child relationship, and learning disorders may result.

Psychogenic learning disabilities. Some examples of psychogenic learning disabilities are the following:

EARLY NEGATIVE CONDITIONING. Early unpleasant school situations—such as a harsh teacher; a temporary handicap, like undetected poor vision; excessive competition; poor health, leading to excessive absence; being ridiculed; and fear of aggressive peers—can lead to negative associations to school and consequent avoidance of learning.

OPPOSITIONALISM. A power struggle with the parents, derived from earlier periods of psychosexual development, may be carried over to the teacher-child relationship, causing the child to use his energies to defeat the teacher and parents in their efforts to make him learn.

INTOLERANCE OF ANXIETY. Children who have been excessively shielded from frustration, challenge, or unpleasant emotions may find intolerable the tension necessitated by initial experiences and expectations outside the home with a strange adult or peer group. They may react with regression or avoidance.

THREAT TO OMNIPOTENCE. Children who have developed a defense of omnipotence against perceived threats from the environment have difficulty in putting themselves in the vulnerable position of learner with the teacher and the other children and may react by attempts to divert the class's attention to something in which they excel—often mischief.

FEAR OF LEARNING. The act of learning may be equated with aggression or sexual curiosity. To look, to see, to know, or to display mastery of knowledge may produce a conflict with the superego or with the environment relating to earlier unresolved competition with parent or sibling. Fear of retaliation may lead to inhibition of one or several of the ego functions necessary to learning. Carried further, the child may assuage guilt over drives by punishing himself by not learning—for example, by appearing stupid.

NEGATIVE SYMBOLIC ASSOCIATIONS TO SPECIFIC LEARNING ITEMS. Occasionally, a child forms a unique, personalized association of a negatively charged nature to a minute item or limited area of learning, such as the sexualization of a letter or the castration or deprivation implication of subtraction, which interferes with learning in that circumscribed area.

DEFLECTION OF ATTENTION BY INTRAPSYCHIC CON-FLICT. Some children may be so preoccupied with intrapsychic conflicts on a conscious or unconscious level that the ego is not free to direct enough attention to the learning process to be effective. The ritualistic obsessive-compulsive child is an example of this.

RETARDATION OF SECONDARY PROCESS THINKING. Since most learning experiences are oriented toward symbolic materials, the child must have the capacity for logical, abstractional, cause-and-effect, time-sequenced thinking. In psychotic children, primary process thinking may predominate and impair comprehension of symbolic material.

LACK OF MOTIVATION. Because of special familial circumstances or because of alienation from the cultural mainstream, a child may attach no importance to learning. He is unable to identify with the teacher and derives no satisfaction from mastery of process because the goals of school are meaningless.

Prognosis. Prognosis of the conditions just described varies considerably, depending on the source of the disability, the underlying diagnosis, its severity, and the type and duration of treatment. On the whole, prognosis with emotional disorders of learning is considered more favorable than with those disorders having a neurological basis. Certainly complete restitution of function is possible in the former; in the latter, follow-up studies indicate a persistence of difficulty into adulthood.

Treatment. Therapeutic intervention in emotional disorders of learning must be two-fold. Where there are continuing blocks to the absorption and integration of knowledge, therapy must be devoted to the amelioration of these blocks. However, children with such disorders are almost always markedly deficient in the necessary skills and requisite knowledge commensurate with their ages, and they will not automatically catch up as a result of treatment. This necessitates the addition of remediation procedures, either concomitant with or after psychotherapy. Although remediation usually requires two professional persons, a therapist and a teacher, efforts to combine this role in the form of therapeutic tutoring have recently been reported. In this process, the learning block and its origin are dealt with simultaneously.

SCHOOL PHOBIA

"School phobia" is a term used to describe the condition in which a child refuses to attend school because of an irrational fear. The term "phobia" is used in the general meaning of aversion rather than with the implication of the phobic mechanisms of displacement, projection, and externalization, which are not present in all cases.

This syndrome appeared comparatively recently, within the past three decades, as a result of compulsory education laws, which made school attendance mandatory up to a certain age, and the syndrome has since been steadily increasing. It accounts for about 2 to 8 per cent of referrals to child guidance clinics. The incidence is about the same for boys as for girls. Occurrence is highest up to the fourth grade, decreasing thereafter. School phobics seem to come from homes in which middle-class child-rearing practices are employed.

Diagnostic groupings. The diagnostic groupings underlying the symptom fall into three main categories. Most cases are psychoneuroses, with anxious, obsessional, hysterical, or depressed features. The ego strengths of this group are generally good, as evidenced by adequate or even superior performance in social and intellectual spheres outside the circumscribed symptom.

A second group suffers from personality disorders. They may represent a more insidious, severe, or chronic stage, and they appear more commonly in older children. In these cases the ability of the ego to integrate the demands of drives, superego, and reality is impaired, and defenses of withdrawal, regression, and projection are present, which result in a constricted personality with little energy beyond that used to cling to the mother.

The third group is a psychotic one, in which the inability to attend school is only one manifestation of the severe underlying illness.

Causes. School phobia is thought to be rooted in the mother-child relationship. Early dependency ties to the mother have not been resolved because of the mother's need for the attachment. The mother is usually indulgent and devotes herself to gratifying the child's infantile needs, with considerable underlying hostility and guilt. School, the first enforced separation of the symbiotic unit, produces a climate for separation anxiety. The episode is precipitated when imbalance in the mother's emotional equilibrium, due to marital or family-of-origin factors, coincides with an exacerbation of anxiety in the child. Because the child is overvalued at home, school is a challenge to his omnipotence. He may, therefore, be very sensitive to any narcissistic threat. There is often great repressed hostility toward the mother for preventing the child's developing autonomy, and with this symptom the child both satisfies and frustrates the love object. He may also satisfy his need to avoid growing up into a sexual being by remaining a dependent, presexual baby. The father usually plays a role supporting or enhancing the psychopathology of mother and child.

Clinical features. The typical pattern in school phobia is that of an early latency child who, without apparent reason or as an ostensible consequence of some minor event, expresses great fear of school and wishes to remain at home with his mother. He often has above-average intelligence and has previously done well in school. The onset usually follows a weekend or holiday. The child may complain of a stomach ache or other pains and may vomit. Bribes, threats, and pressures produce panic and great resistance to returning to school.

School phobia differs from truancy primarily in that anxiety, somatic symptoms, overattachment to family, high valuation of school, and internalized conflicts are present, but acting out and antisocial behavior are absent.

Prognosis.   School phobia has been referred to as one of the emergencies of child psychiatry, since the prognosis varies inversely with the length of absence from school. Prolonged absence aggravates the psychodynamic conflicts and adds secondary gains to remaining away from school. The prognosis for return to school is generally good, especially in the psychoneurotic group. Those cases in which there is no return or where absences occur throughout the school career fall into the severe characterological or psychotic group. However, about half of all children continue to manifest subclinical symptoms, such as chronic anxiety and vague somatic complaints, throughout their school careers. The prognosis is less favorable in boys than in girls. This may be due to differences in social expectations of independence directed toward the two sexes, as reflected in a syndrome that is primarily a result of faulty development of autonomy. Prognosis also correlates with the degree of parental pathology.

Treatment.   Because school phobia involves child, parent, and school in an interlocking relationship, therapeutic efforts must be directed to all three aspects from the outset. The child should be engineered back to school as quickly as possible, utilizing whatever manipulations of class placement, hours, and the like are necessary. Simultaneously, both parents and child should enter psychotherapy for clarification of the dynamics that have resulted in the pathological interrelationships. The return to school cannot be considered to have any therapeutic significance without resolution of the underlying dynamics, as recurrence of refusal to attend is certain.

Because of the primarily familial origin, family therapy has been used successfully. Attempts have been made to treat school phobia within the school, where therapeutic support for attendance can be provided and where school personnel can aid in therapeutic efforts. It is also possible to administer therapy in the home, where the therapist aids parent and child in the physical return to school. For more severe cases, hospital therapy, which provides separation from family pathology, is used. Deconditioning of the negative associations to school has also been attempted.

CULTURALLY DEPRIVED CHILDREN IN SCHOOL

Interest has focused recently on a large group of children from the lowest socioeconomic class, who show a disproportionately high incidence of learning disability and behavior disturbance and who have a high rate of school failure. In this group degree of retardation in learning is considerable, and only a small proportion of these children complete high school or enter college as compared with the rest of the population. These children have been referred to as "culturally deprived," "culturally alienated," and socially or culturally "disadvantaged."

Members of this group come from poverty-stricken families alienated from the mainstream of culture who can provide only minimal sustained parental stimulation and opportunities for the children to learn and explore the world. The culturally deprived child enters school with lags in cognitive and verbal skills that incapacitate him. As a result of this, the child gradually falls behind academically, and behavior problems increase.

Among specific handicaps are: (1) limitations in the ability to use abstract symbols, abstract cognitive processes, and complex language for interpretation and communication, with compensatory overemphasis on motoric modes of problem-solving; (2) low motivation for academic learning, with inability for sustained application to tasks and goals selected by others; (3) deviance from the perceptual modes commonly employed in schools, such as short auditory attention span and predominance of understanding in spatial rather than in temporal terms; (4) low level of identification with the teacher, whose intellectual pursuits are considered feminine, and, conversely, a high level of identification with peers displaying physical prowess and resistance to authority.

On the other hand, culturally deprived children may possess certain skills and competencies that are superior to those of their middle-class peers but that are not fully utilized in school. Among these are accuracy of certain social perceptions, resourcefulness in the pursuit of self-selected goals, sustained involvement in a self-selected task, capacity for independence in self-care, and high capacity for spontaneity of response.

The possibilities for culturally deprived children to obtain optimal benefits from educational experiences without special help are limited. The long-range social implications of their school failure are considerable, as it is this group of children who, in mid-adolescence, enter the labor market with insufficient skills for current industrial technology and from whom the ranks of the unemployed, the petty criminals, and the drug addicts are formed.

REHABILITATION PROGRAMS

In an effort to combat the handicaps and utilize the strengths of these children, various special school programs have been instituted throughout the country. These programs have as goals the prevention of initial or continuing failure and the remediation of social, cultural, and academic gaps in the education of the child. Innovations in curriculum have been introduced, with special focus on reading and language, including the use of new teaching techniques and new materials, such as reading primers featuring urban, racially integrated, and realistic characters. Team teaching, which employs specialists in the various curricular areas, and ungraded classes to reduce the onus of retardation are being used. Extracurricular stimulation, such as trips and clubs during and after school and on weekends and vacations, attempt to fill gaps left by the home. Efforts to bring parents closer to the school, to increase guidance programs, to reduce the size of classes, and to recruit better teachers to schools in disadvantaged areas are in operation.

PREVENTIVE PROGRAMS

On the preventive side are the preschool programs. Proceeding on the assumption that the culturally deprived child is, at 5 or 6 years, already handicapped in educational readiness, these programs begin when the child is 3 years old and attempt to provide in school the stimulation heretofore left to the home. All these efforts attempt to bring the lower-class child into consonance with the middle-class school on the assumption that, despite the continuing differences in lower socioeconomic group concerns and interests, all or most lower-class children can enter the middle class through education. Another view would assume that, until the school modifies its goals and concerns to meet the cultural needs of different groups, these children will continue to be at a disadvantage.

EDUCATION OF EMOTIONALLY DISTURBED CHILDREN

It is estimated that 5 to 10 per cent of school children are sufficiently disturbed to require clinical help. Although private institutions have provided education for disturbed children for a number of decades, special classes for emotionally disturbed children under the auspices of public education are of relatively recent origin. Pressures for these classes came from teachers who were experiencing difficulty in containing and educating certain children and from parents concerned with their children's educational failures or exclusion from school because of emotional illness. Additional influencing factors have been the emphasis on reaching the non-patient population, such as those who do not seek treatment, and the realization that treatment facilities are too limited and individual treatment too lengthy and costly for the number of children requiring it. Psychiatrists and other clinicians have recently shown an interest in education as a treatment of choice as a result of disappointment with the effectiveness of psychotherapy with certain groups of children, such as schizophrenics and lower-class urban children with conduct disturbances.

Along the continuum are programs emphasizing therapy, others emphasizing academic achievement, and still others based on personality or learning theory. Mention may be made of (1) the use af audiovisual or teaching machines to instruct children, usually psychotic, for whom human interaction is anxiety-producing; (2) use of behavioral conditioning with simple immediate reward-and-punishment systems to induce desired behavior in primitive children; (3) emphasis on sensory, perceptual, or kinesthetic procedures as a basic remediation measure for major learning disorders; and (4) use of curricula designed jointly by clinicians and educators to reduce anxiety, emphasize mastery, support ego functions, and the like.

Special classes, ranging in size from two to fifteen children, exist within public schools, clinics, hospitals, residential treatment centers and as separate special schools, the last usually under private auspices. Although many existing classes are a desperate holding action for children excluded from regular classes, some attempt to provide active treatment programs. Programs range along a continuum with regard to theory and methodology.

THERAPEUTICALLY ORIENTED PROGRAMS

Therapeutically oriented programs are based on the assumption that a therapeutic milieu or technique is the most effective route to therapeutic and educational goals. Such programs are most often attached to hospitals or clinics, where clinical personnel are available and influential in planning and carrying out the program.

ACADEMIC ACHIEVEMENT PROGRAMS

Programs that focus on academic achievement are based on the assumption that maximum exploitation of the educational potential of the disturbed child is the shortest route to his rehabilitation. These facilities are usually designed and implemented by educators. Clinical consultation may be minimal.

TYPES OF DISORDERS

Although the diagnostic range of children requiring special education is wide—covering severe neurosis, chronic brain syndrome, adjustment reactions of childhood, and psychosis—most of these children from the educator's point of view fall into two behavioral categories: (1) the acting out or disturbing child and (2) the fearful, withdrawn, or disturbed child. The former constitutes the majority, with prevalence throughout elementary and secondary schools. Most pressure for special education is, for obvious reasons, for this group of children, but less work on special programming for them has been done. The fearful or withdrawn child, although in the minority and with greatest prevalence in preschool and elementary school, has received more clinical attention, and there has been a greater development of special programs for such children.

Actually, all school behavior disturbances are determined by anxiety, although this may not be externally apparent. The child who acts out instead of internalizing is either showing a symptomatic variation of conflict resolution or, because he comes from a subculture whose standards differ from those of the school, is made anxious by being forced to accommodate to alien standards and thus resorts to the adaptive modes to which he is accustomed. These adaptive modes are intolerable in the usual school setting.

Differences among the types of children who cannot seem to profit from regular classroom experiences are of great significance in educational programming, although overt symptoms may not always give the clue to the differences. For example, a highly anxious, neurotic child with inhibition of aggression may require a flexible approach allowing him the freedom to exercise autonomy and self-assertion. A schizophrenic child, anxious as a result of chaotic boundaries between self and nonself, may require a highly structured classroom milieu to aid in reducing ego disorganization. A child who acts out as an expectation of deprivation may require programming to reduce his constant search for gratification. A child who acts out as an expression of unresolved infantile omnipotence may need the experience of a firm teacher to aid in his adaptation to reality, an experience denied him at home.

The implications of psychodynamic understanding of behavioral symptoms affect not only classroom milieu and teacher attitudes but also educational methodology. Such aspects of programming as timing, routines, level of sensory input, use of materials, and choice of disciplinary measures or such aspects of curriculum as the ratio of fantasy to reality and the relationship of content areas to instinctual drives are influenced by one's understanding of psychodynamics and psychopathology.

GROUPING

Because of the wide range of individual differences in children, the problem of grouping is significant. Where selective grouping is possible, homogeneity with regard to required milieu and teaching methodology is, on the whole, preferable. However, this concept must often be modified by peer relationships among the children. A child with a conduct disturbance whose behavior is aggravated by similar classmates may be better able to control impulsive behavior when he is with nonaggressive children. A group of schizophrenic children may become better focused on reality if they are influenced by peers with greater ego strengths.

EVALUATION

There is considerable controversy about the trend toward establishing special classes for emotionally disturbed children. The tendency to subdivide children into special groups, according to deviation from the norm, has been marked in recent educational practice, but research evaluations have not, up to now, lent support to the greater value of special classes in terms of academic achievement, although social adjustment may be improved.

In addition, special classes obscure the concept that some children's deviation may be less symptomatic of psychic distress than of a reaction to the frustrations resulting from conflicting needs of child and school. Clinicians have voiced objection to special classes because they decrease the clinical-educational investment in seeking modes of adaptation and deprive the deviant child of the benefits of normal peer groups. The ecological view of therapeutic intervention—that it is designed not to reconstruct the deviant child but to bring him into balance with his environment—recommends use of special costly resources, such as special classes and hospitalization, minimally, at times of crisis, with the goal of return to the regular facility as quickly as possible.

Long-range evaluation of the effects on disturbed children and their peers of education in special versus regular classes is needed.

HIGH SCHOOL AND COLLEGE PSYCHIATRY

High school and college coincide with the periods of early, middle, and late adolescence, with their physiological, social, and interpersonal stresses. The ego, which works at maintaining psychological homeostasis, is subjected to special stresses in this transitional period, and the results of these stresses are responsible for many of the emotional problems seen in high school and college students. School often becomes the arena to which the many conflicts are brought.

HIGH SCHOOL

The major psychiatric problems encountered in high schools, in addition to those of adolescence per se, are learning disabilities carried over from elementary school, low motivation, underachievement, behavioral problems, and the phenomenon of the early dropout.

The experience of entering high school—with its increased size, departmentalization, many teachers to relate to, and pressure for achievement—constitutes a stress for the 13- or 14-year-old. He may react by loss of impulse control, inability to concentrate, and somatization—all resulting in underachievement and its secondary disadvantages. The adolescent with delinquent trends is resistant, hostile, and suspicious of school; it is here that the greatest conformity to authority and control is expected of him. His failures will be exposed to his peers, before whom he must maintain a strong façade. His adolescent narcissism is threatened by failure, and he avoids the danger by the acting out of rebelliousness. Since high school attendance is mandatory in this country and there are few alternatives available for the adolescent who is poorly equipped or motivated for it, the high schools and a good proportion of their students are deadlocked in a struggle in which there are few avenues for resolution.

Therapeutic programs. Therapeutic and other intervention programs to aid in these problems include individual and group counseling and therapy, modifications in curriculum in the direction of greater activity and practicality and less formality, work-study programs, vocational training, smaller classes, remedial programs, and extracurricular enrichment. Results have been equivocal. Since there is a high correlation between family pathology and cultural deprivation and high school difficulties, preventive efforts in earlier years may be more effective. There is also room for experimental programs, particularly those based on the concept of practical alternatives to mandatory high school attendance.

COLLEGE

There has been a steady increase in the number and size of college psychiatric services offered in the last two decades. Many institutions offer comprehensive diagnostic, counseling, and psychotherapy services. Where such services exist, they are used by about 10 per cent of the student body.

The 17- or 18-year-olds entering college are a selected group. They have performed well in previous schools, have higher-than-average intelligence, are highly motivated, and come from families with a high investment in them. Despite all this, insecurities abound. This is a period of transition to adulthood. For many it represents the first complete separation from home, with its consequent exposure to different standards and values and increased autonomy, responsibility, and freedom. The need to succeed competitively in academic, social, sexual, and possibly athletic spheres is very great. Problems in the areas of dependency, sexuality, self-esteem, and achievement of identity require resolution.

Causes of problems. Emotional problems in college students correlate highly with disturbed home environments. Divorce, discord, and mental illness are common. Family attitudes of inconsistent discipline, inadequate role differentiation, rigidity, overly high or unreal expectations, and unfavorable comparison of the child with other siblings seem to play a causative role in the student's adaptive breakdown in college.

Diagnosis. Depression, early schizophrenia, and all forms of neurosis and personality disorders with impulsive behavior predominate. Conflicts are expressed not only as psychic symptoms, especially anxiety and depression, but in the form of poor grades, inability to concentrate, somatization, overactivity, antisocial behavior, and a variety of sexual behaviors, including compulsive sexuality, homosexuality, and illegitimate pregnancy. Minority students attempting to achieve social mobility in college, students supporting themselves, students under pressure to achieve high grades, students from highly protected environments, and students moving from rural areas to cosmopolitan centers are all high-risk groups. There is a seasonal incidence of difficulties at examination times, when the defenses of avoidance, evasion, rationalization, and projection break down. One of the greatest problems is the high drop-out rate; 35 to 40 per cent of students do not graduate. This cannot be explained on the basis of lack of intellectual capacity, as there is no significant difference in I.Q. or extent of academic difficulty between those who remain and those who leave.

Treatment. Brief psychotherapy is very common in college services, partly because of policy and scarcity of staff but also because students are particularly suited to this form of therapy. They tend to make rapid emotional contact, are labile, act out transference feelings and unconscious conflicts, and exhibit a wide range of regressive and progressive swings. Their youth, physical attractiveness, intelligence, and verbal ability are also therapeutic assets but are risks for countertransference phenomena, such as overidentification and overprotectiveness. Counseling programs, using faculty members as advisers in educational matters, are in wide use. Ideally, these programs should be integrated with psychiatric services, with the counselor handling minor emotional problems with consultation and referring more serious ones to the mental health service.

The practice of psychiatry within an institution dedicated to higher education is considerably influenced by the attitude of the administration and the faculty toward it. Colleges have traditionally espoused a policy of survival of the fittest, not of those less fit. The emphasis on the part of the college community on intellectualism, scientific objectivity, and the accumulation of knowledge is subtly opposed to the emphasis by the psychiatrist on affectivity, interpersonal relationships, and the importance of the unconscious. In practice, the college psychiatrist is often confronted with conflicts between students and administration in which his dual role as physician and college official requires delicate balancing. In order to function with any effectiveness, the practice of psychiatry at any college must have sanction and approval on the highest administrative level.

REFERENCES

American Psychiatric Association, Committee on Preventive Psychiatry. *The Psychiatrist as a Consultant to the School.* American Psychiatric Association, Washington, 1964.

Ekstein, R., and Motto, R. L. Psychoanalysis and education: an historical account. Reiss-Davis Clin. Bull., 1: 7, 1964.

Farnsworth, D. *Mental Health in College and University.* Harvard University Press, Cambridge, 1957.

Gordon, E. A review of programs of compensatory education. Amer. J. Orthopsychiat., 35: 640, 1965.

Kahn, J. H., and Nursten, J. P. School refusal: a comprehensive view of school phobia and other failures of school attendance. Amer. J. Orthopsychiat., 32: 707, 1962.

Klein, E. Psychoanalytic aspects of school problems. Psychoanal. Stud. Child, 3–4: 391, 1949.

Morse, W. C., and Cutler, R. L. Public school classes for the emotionally handicapped: a research analysis, pre-publication draft. Council for Exceptional Children, Washington, 1964.

Pearson, G. H. J. A survey of learning difficulties in children. Psychoanal. Stud. Child, 7: 322, 1952.

Pearson, G. H. J. *Psychoanalysis and the Education of the Child.* W. W. Norton, New York, 1954.

Prentice, N. M., and Sperry, B. M. Therapeutically oriented tutoring of children with primary neurotic learning inhibitions. Amer. J. Orthopsychiat., 35: 521, 1965.

Rabinovitch, R. D. Reading and learning disabilities. In *American Handbook of Psychiatry*, S. Arieti, editor, vol. 1, p. 857. Basic Books, New York, 1959.

Reissman, F. *The Culturally Deprived Child*. Harper & Bros., New York, 1962.

Silverman, J. S., Fite, M. W., and Mosher, M. M. Clinical findings in reading disability children: special cases of intellectual inhibition. Amer. J. Orthopsychiat., 29: 298, 1959.

Waldfogel, S., Coolidge, J., and Hahn, P. The development, meaning, and management of school phobia. Amer. J. Orthopsychiat., 27: 754, 1957.

Whittington, H. G. *Psychiatry on the College Campus*. International Universities Press, New York, 1963.

CHAPTER TWENTY-TWO

Psychiatric Treatment of Adolescents

JAMES F. MASTERSON, JR., M.D.

INTRODUCTION

THIS CHAPTER describes some special characteristics of the initial phase of the therapeutic encounter with adolescents.

THE PARTICIPANTS

The adolescent does not have the final decision about treatment and may feel disillusioned with and suspicious of all adults. The parents, on the other hand, do have the final decision and are often burdened with both guilt and anger. Furthermore, the adolescent is usually in a state of regression when first seen, and he usually expresses his emotions indirectly, through his behavior, rather than verbally. In addition, he has certain emotional needs that have to be met in treatment.

The most useful qualities in the therapist who treats adolescents are directness and flexibility—a willingness and ability to handle issues directly as they arise, a capacity to follow the trends in the patient's behavior without dogmatic theoretic bias, and an ability to alternate his therapeutic role quickly as the situation demands.

CONSULTATION

Treatment can be viewed as a continuous process from the initial consultation until the termination of psychotherapy. With the first phone call, the therapeutic process begins, as the therapist gathers information on the problem, formulates his approach, senses the focus of the parents' anxiety, and often advises them how to explain the consultation to the adolescent, thereby minimizing such difficulties as the adolescent's regarding the consultation as punishment or an effort to force him to conform. The independence of the adolescent is indicated immediately by seeing *him* first, requesting his permission to see the parents, and stressing the confidential nature of the contract.

Unlike therapy with adults, therapy with adolescents places the burden of contact on the therapist; therefore, he must attempt as soon as possible to get an adequate appraisal not only of the patient's problems but also of anticipated transference reactions and resistances. Interviews with parents often help the therapist to this goal by providing evidence of their unconscious attitudes toward the patient. These attitudes will form the basis for later transference manifestations. Projective tests, such as the Rorschach, are also helpful.

Since the adolescent does not have final control and since the parents are often embroiled with anger, guilt, and denial, the therapist truly carries a parentlike responsibility. He must decide what treatment is necessary, whether or not the parents can afford it, and whether or not he is the appropriate person to conduct it. Few therapists can treat all adolescents. The way in which the therapist resolved his own developmental problems often makes him suited to one adolescent and unable to treat another. He then must formulate the situation in such a way as to maximize motivation for treatment. In order to deal with the parents' resistance, he may need to emphasize the gloomy outlook if the adolescent does not receive treatment.

The parents' guilt about their role in the patient's problems should not be assuaged but should be used to motivate *them* to seek help. Conjoint treatment of the parents by a social worker gives added emphasis to the therapeutic impact, especially if the social worker is supervised by the psychiatrist treating the adolescent. The need to involve the parents varies with the developmental stage of the adolescent; the closer to early adolescence he is, the more necessary it is to involve the parents; the closer to late adolescence he is, the less necessary is parental involvement.

INITIAL PHASE

If the consultation has been handled properly, the stage has been well prepared for treatment. It should be made clear to both parents and adolescent that the goals of treatment are the independence, health, and reality-orientation of the adolescent. This is of great help in handling therapeutic issues when they arise later.

With the formal beginning of therapy, the therapist attempts to establish a therapeutic contact and contract by first understanding the patient's initial defensive maneuvers. Then he interprets these maneuvers in terms of their current interpersonal unconscious meaning rather than their historical context. More simply, the therapist attempts to understand the emotional message the patient is trying to convey by his behavior; then he reads it back to him. This technique establishes the therapist's interest and competence and tends to overcome the adolescent's suspiciousness and testing. The cornerstone of all therapy with adolescents is telling them what they feel, rather than expecting them to tell you, and then responding appropriately to the indicated therapeutic needs. Since the messages expressed are as varied as the number of patients one sees, the therapeutic responses also vary and include interpretation of the unconscious, direction, support, limit-setting, interference with parents' destructive behavior, and interested silence. A case described below illustrates one response.

Dave, a 17-year-old boy, the third of three children, had a three-year history of depression, culminating in a serious suicide attempt. He suffered from a severe character disorder of the deprived affect type, which was masked by a rigid obsessive-compulsive facade.

The patient's past history was that of a compliant, eager-to-please, subservient child; he was able to adjust fairly well throughout childhood until onset of adolescence, when his submissive relationship with his brother raised unconscious homosexual conflicts. He became depressed, left home for prep school in search of relief, went on to college, and finally made a suicidal attempt after a series of interviews with a psychiatrist.

Underneath his compulsive facade, the patient felt (1) utter futility at the possibility of anyone caring for him, (2) sadistic and masochistic fantasies and impulses, (3) homosexual impulses, and (4) great anxiety about control. Interviews with the parents revealed that, despite their verbal protestations to the contrary, they had little interest in or responsiveness to Dave. The father, constantly out of the home, atoned for his guilt by overindulging the patient materially and never attempting to set limits for him. The mother used the patient for emotional support and infantilized him.

In the interview with the patient, he presented a bizarre and rigid smiling face, which masked his underlying depression. He showed contempt for the father, a doctor, and all authority figures, and he caricatured psychiatry. In addition, he gave a history of putting people on, putting up a façade to see if they would discover his feelings behind it. He also hinted at several abortive and dismally unsuccessful attempts at heterosexual intercourse.

The consultation interviews suggested that the patient's initial transference reaction would be a feeling that the doctor, like all authority figures, was incompetent, was not deserving of respect or trust, and did not care about him. Therefore, the therapist should deal with the patient's initial testing maneuvers by (1) confronting the patient with the feelings beneath his façade, (2) setting limits to help give the patient control, and (3) providing him with alternate ways of dealing with these feelings.

The therapy began with the patient's joking about the fact that he expected no help from anyone, didn't care about himself, planned more suicidal attempts, but "was giving the therapist a chance." The therapist responded that the patient was trying to put him in a bind so that, if things did not go well, the therapist would be responsible for a suicidal attempt. The doctor then stressed that he could not accept this bargain, that, though the patient needed help, the therapist could not do the job alone; he required the patient's cooperation. The therapist then said that, if the patient wanted to commit suicide, he would not be able to stop him but that this was a miscarried effort to deal with his problems. Next, the therapist interpreted the patient's joking behavior as an effort to put him on. He pointed out that the patient had a long history of similar efforts with all people, efforts that were followed by a feeling of delight when the people were able to perceive his underlying feelings. Then the therapist noted that the patient's family was not interested enough to try to penetrate this façade.

When the therapist scheduled him for an early morning hour, the patient joked at great length about getting up early. The therapist brushed this aside with a simple comment that the patient was angry. The patient revealed that he had fantasies of throwing bricks through windows and of punching people in the nose. The therapist then tried to indicate alternate ways of handling these feelings by saying that, rather than smiling and making a joke about it, the patient should verbalize his anger.

During a reluctant but frank admission of sexual difficulties, the patient dramatized his regressive behavior by eating lollipops, playing with children's toys, refusing to get a job. The therapist, feeling that the relationship could sustain the challenge, told the patient directly that the regressive activity was a running away from his problem, probably because he felt he couldn't handle it; that he wanted to be a child to escape his sexual feelings and yet he also wanted help; that he was working at cross-purposes with himself, since it is not possible to have both—either he had to involve himself and use the help offered to deal with and master his problems, or there was truly little hope.

This example shows how the therapist, basing his approach on the dynamic constellation revealed in the consultation, actively attempts to establish a relationship by clarifying the current interpersonal unconscious meaning of the patient's testing behavior and then responding appropriately to the indicated therapeutic needs.

REFERENCES

Berman, S. Psychotherapeutic techniques with adolescents. Amer. J. Orthopsychiat., 24: 238, 1954.

Blos, P. *On Adolescence.* Free Press of Glencoe (Macmillan), New York, 1962.

Eissler, K. R. Notes on problems of technique in the psychoanalytic treatment of adolescents: with some remarks on perversions. Psychoanal. Stud. Child, 13: 223, 1958.

Geleerd, E. R. Some aspects of psychoanalytic techniques in adolescence. Psychoanal. Stud. Child, 12: 263, 1957.

Gitelson, M. Character synthesis: the psychotherapeutic problem of adolescence. Amer. J. Orthopsychiat., 18: 422, 1948.

Holmes, D. *The Adolescent in Psychotherapy.* Little, Brown, Boston, 1964.

Johnson, A. M., and Fishback, D. Analysis of disturbed adolescent girl and collaborative psychiatric treatment of the mother. Amer. J. Orthopsychiat., 14: 195, 1944.

Lorand, S., and Schneer, H. *Psychoanalytic Approach to Problems and Therapy.* Hoeber Medical Division, Harper & Row, New York, 1961.

Masterson, J. F. Psychotherapy of the adolescent: a comparison with psychotherapy of the adult. J. Nerv. Ment. Dis., 127: 511, 1958.

Contributors

E. JAMES ANTHONY, M.D.

Ittleson Professor of Child Psychiatry and Director, Division of Child Psychiatry, Washington University School of Medicine; Training, Teaching, and Supervising Psychoanalyst, Chicago Institute for Psychoanalysis; Professorial Lecturer, University of Chicago School of Medicine, Chicago, Illinois; Fellow, Center for Advanced Study in the Behavioral Sciences, Stanford University, La Jolla, California; Physician, Barnes and Allied Hospitals, St. Louis, Missouri

LEON CYTRYN, M.D.

Assistant Professor of Pediatric Psychiatry, George Washington University School of Medicine; Research Associate, Children's Hospital of the District of Columbia; Consulting Psychiatrist, Jewish Foundation for Retarded Children, Washington, D.C.

LEON EISENBERG, M.D.

Professor of Psychiatry, Harvard Medical School; Psychiatrist-in-Chief, Massachusetts General Hospital, Boston, Massachusetts

STUART M. FINCH, M.D.

Professor of Psychiatry, University of Michigan Medical School; Chief, Children's Psychiatric Service, Children's Psychiatric Hospital, University of Michigan Medical Center, Ann Arbor, Michigan

BARBARA FISH, M.D.

Professor of Child Psychiatry, New York University School of Medicine; Director of Child Psychiatry, Bellevue Hospital Center, New York, New York

ALFRED M. FREEDMAN, M.D.

Professor of Psychiatry and Chairman of the Department of Psychiatry, New York Medical College; Director of Psychiatric Services, Flower and Fifth Avenue Hospitals, Metropolitan Hospital, and Bird S. Coler Memorial Hospital and Home, New York, New York

MARCIA K. FREEDMAN, Ph.D.

Senior Research Associate, Conservation of Human Resources, Columbia University, New York, New York

SAUL I. HARRISON, M.D.

Professor of Psychiatry, University of Michigan Medical School; Director of Training, Children's Psychiatric Hospital, University of Michigan Medical Center; Supervising Psychoanalyst, Michigan Psychoanalytic Institute, Ann Arbor, Michigan

LEO KANNER, M.D.

Professor Emeritus of Child Psychiatry, Johns Hopkins University School of Medicine; Honorary Consultant, Johns Hopkins Hospital, Baltimore, Maryland

HAROLD I. KAPLAN, M.D.

Professor of Psychiatry and Director of Psychiatric Education and Training, New York Medical College; Attending Psychiatrist, Flower and Fifth Avenue Hospitals; Visiting Psychiatrist, Metropolitan Hospital and Bird S. Coler Memorial Hospital and Home, New York, New York

IRVIN A. KRAFT, M.D.

Associate Professor of Psychiatry and Pediatrics, Baylor College of Medicine; Medical Director, Texas Institute of Child Psychiatry; Chief of Psychiatry, Texas Children's Hospital, Houston, Texas

MAURICE W. LAUFER, M.D.

Member, Institute for the Health Sciences, Brown University; Adjunct Professor of Education, Rhode Island College, Providence, Rhode Island; Director, Emma Pendleton Bradley Hospital, Riverside, Rhode Island

RUTH L. LaVIETES, M.D.

Assistant Clinical Professor of Psychiatry, and Director of Child Psychiatry, New York Medical College; Associate Attending Psychiatrist, Flower & Fifth Avenue Hospitals; Associate Visiting Psychiatrist, Metropolitan Hospital and Bird S. Coler Memorial Hospital and Home, New York, New York

REGINALD S. LOURIE, M.D.

Professor of Pediatric Psychiatry, George Washington University School of Medicine; Director, Department of Psychiatry, Children's Hospital of the District of Columbia, and Hillcrest Children's Center, Washington, D.C.

JAMES F. MASTERSON, JR., M.D.

Professor of Clinical Psychiatry, Cornell University Medical College; Attending Psychiatrist and Head of Adolescent Program, New York Hospital (Payne Whitney Psychiatric Clinic), New York Hospital, New York, New York

MEYER SONIS, M.D.

Professor and Chief, Division of Child Psychiatry, Department of Anatomy and Psychiatry, University of Pittsburgh School of Medicine, Pittsburgh, Pennsylvania

ROBERT L. STUBBLEFELD, M.D.

Professor and Chairman, Department of Psychiatry, University of Texas Southwestern Medical School, Dallas, Texas

JOSEPH D. TEICHER, M.D.

Professor of Psychiatry, University of Southern California School of Medicine; Director, Children's and Adolescents' Psychiatric Services, Los Angeles County General Hospital; Faculty, Southern California Psychoanalytic Institute, Los Angeles, California

ETHEL A. WILSON (deceased)

Late Special Assistant to the General Director, Beth Israel Medical Center, New York, New York

HENRY H. WORK, M.D.

Professor of Psychiatry and Head of Division of Child Psychiatry, University of California at Los Angeles School of Medicine, Los Angeles, California

Index

Alfred M. Freedman

Alfred M. Freedman received his A.B. from Cornell University and his M.D. from the University of Minnesota Medical School. After Army Service in World War II, he engaged in neurophysiological and neurochemical research, and trained in general and child psychiatry at Bellevue Hospital. He received his certificate in psychoanalysis from the William Alanson White Institute for Psychoanalysis, and is a Diplomate of the American Board of Psychiatry and Neurology. Since 1960 he has been Professor and Chairman of the Department of Psychiatry at the New York Medical College. Dr. Freedman is Director of the Metropolitan Community Mental Health Center, and Director of Psychiatry at Flower and Fifth Avenue Hospitals, Metropolitan Hospital, and Bird S. Coler Hospital; in addition, he is President of the American Psychopathological Association and President-elect of the American College of Neuropsychopharmacology. He has published over a hundred scientific papers, and is co-editor of the *Comprehensive Textbook of Psychiatry* (1967) and of *Psychopathology of Adolescence* (1970).

Harold I. Kaplan

Harold I. Kaplan received an undergraduate degree from Columbia University and an M.D. from the New York Medical College in 1949. He trained in psychiatry at the Kingsbridge Veterans Hospital and Mount Sinai Hospital in New York and became a Diplomate of the American Board of Psychiatry and Neurology in 1957; presently he is an Associate Examiner of the American Board. He began the practice and teaching of psychiatry and was certified in psychoanalytic medicine at the New York Medical College in 1954. He became Professor of Psychiatry and Director of Psychiatric Training and Education at the New York Medical College in 1961. He is Attending Psychiatrist at Metropolitan Hospital Center, Flower and Fifth Avenue Hospitals and Bird S. Coler Hospital. He is the Principal Investigator of ten National Institute of Mental Health training programs, specializing in the areas of undergraduate and graduate psychiatric education as well as the training of women in medicine. He is the author of over seventy scientific papers and co-editor of the *Comprehensive Textbook of Psychiatry* (1967) and of *Comprehensive Group Psychotherapy* (1971).